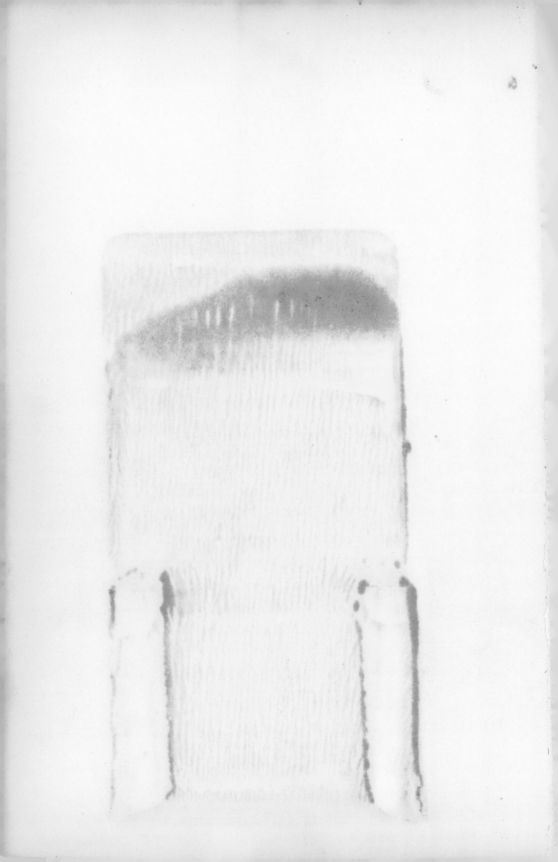

A Pilot's Meteorology

* *
* *
*

CHARLES GREHAM HALPINE, M.S. (AERO),

Captain, United States Navy (Ret.)

*Formerly Assistant to the Director of Engineering and
Head of the Technical Data Branch,
U. S. Navy Department, Bureau of Aeronautics.*

SECOND EDITION

D. VAN NOSTRAND COMPANY, INC.

PRINCETON, NEW JERSEY

TORONTO

LONDON

NEY YORK

D. VAN NOSTRAND COMPANY, INC.

120 Alexander St., Princeton, New Jersey (*Principal office*)
257 Fourth Avenue, New York 10, New York

D. VAN NOSTRAND COMPANY, LTD.
358, Kensington High Street, London, W.14, England

D. VAN NOSTRAND COMPANY (Canada), LTD.
25 Hollinger Road, Toronto 16, Canada

To the late CAPTAIN EDWARD JOHN DORN *of the United States Navy, graduate of the United States Naval Academy, Class of 1874—a grand old salt of the days of "wooden ships and iron men," yet one who remained always so young that, at three-score-and-ten, he enthusiastically took to the air; the man whose kindness gave me my career; one whose life was an inspiring example, and whose memory lives on, undimmed by time.*

PREFACE

Since the first edition of this book was published, great advances have been made both in the science of meteorology and in its practical application to flight, navigation, and weather forecasting. The second edition, by careful revision and extension of content, reflects the present concepts of the science.

It is the aim of this book to present in simple, concise language those meteorological concepts which especially concern the airman, and to provide the groundwork for further study of the science of meteorology. It is hoped that this book will enable the student—either with supervised training or by self-instruction—to interpret intelligently for himself the various weather reports, weather maps, and actual weather phenomena so that he may become a better and safer airman.

Special mention should be made of Chapter XII, "Pressure-Pattern Flight or Aerologation," written by Robert M. Mansfield, Navigator, Trans World Airlines, and expert in transoceanic aerial navigation. It presents the practical result of recent meteorological research in an attempt to develop a true air navigation technique in which the shortest time route rather than the shortest distance route is used in flight. Although this chapter represents an advanced type of meteorological application, it has been added to the new edition for the emphasis it places upon the future which meteorology holds for the student. The information given should also prove invaluable to transoceanic pilots and navigators.

The author wishes to express his sincere appreciation to the individuals and organizations listed below for their kind and generous assistance in the large amount of detailed work entailed in order to bring out the second edition:

To the Friez Instrument Division and the Eclipse Pioneer Division of Bendix Aviation, Inc., for new cuts of modern instruments.

To the Navy Department Bureau of Aeronautics for new material on aircraft icing.

To the U. S. Weather Bureau and the Civil Aeronautics Administration for material from their meteorological pamphlets and bulletins.

To Lieutenant Commander George L. Hammond, U.S. N.R., for his most excellent assistance in revising and bringing up to date the chapters on "Weather Reports" and "Weather Maps."

To my very good friend, Mr. Charles A. Zweng, of the Pan American Navigation Service, of North Hollywood, California, for his generous permission to use the valuable material of his most comprehensive "Aviation Dictionary."

And last, but no means least, to his wife, Helen Bullard Halpine, for her loving encouragement and help for many months in preparing and proofreading the entire volume.

CHARLES GREHAM HALPINE

Annapolis, Maryland,
July, 1952.

CONTENTS

CHAPTER   PAGE

PREFACE V

I. INTRODUCTION I

II. THE ATMOSPHERE: ITS CHARACTERISTICS, COM-
POSITION, AND STRUCTURE 4

III. THE ELEMENTS OF METEOROLOGY AND THEIR
MEASUREMENT 11

IV. CLOUD TYPES AND OBSTRUCTIONS TO VISION . 41

V. VARIATIONS OF TEMPERATURE AND THEIR EF-
FECTS 74

VI. CIRCULATION OF AIR: CURRENTS AND WINDS 96

VII. AIR MASSES, FRONTS AND DISTURBANCES—
THEIR DEVELOPMENT AND EFFECT . . . 118

VIII. WEATHER REPORTS 169

IX. WEATHER MAPS 193

X. WEATHER FORECASTS 219

XI. ICE FORMATION OF AIRCRAFT 245

XII. PRESSURE-PATTERN FLIGHT OR AEROLOGATION 269
By Robert M. Mansfield

GLOSSARY 297

APPENDICES 319

Explanation of Teletype Symbol Weather
Reports 320
Winds Aloft Maps 322
Highest and Lowest Temperatures . . . 328
Precipitation Areas and Amounts . . . 329
700-Millibar Constant Pressure Chart . . 330
Continental Weather Map 331
Airport Weather Maps (1–5) 332
Beaufort Scale 337
INDEX 339

vii

Chapter I

INTRODUCTION

Meteorology is the science which treats of the atmosphere, of its various conditions and changes, their causes and effects.

Applied meteorology is the application of the basic science to meet the problems of wind and weather encountered in our daily living.

Dynamic meteorology explains meteorological phenomena on the basis of, and by the use of, known laws of physics and thermodynamics.

Synoptic meteorology is that branch of meteorology in which "synoptic charts" are used to present a visual synopsis of the weather as observed and recorded over a large area at a given time. By studying a series of these charts, combined with his knowledge of the basic science, the meteorologist is enabled to predict weather changes and movement in the form of *weather forecasts.*

Since the early days of aviation, great changes have taken place in general opinions of the relation of weather conditions to flight. In the early days of flying, it was believed that winds and rain would always be a source of danger to those who ventured aloft. The author still remembers vividly a day with Mr. Wilbur Wright at Governors Island, New York, in the fall of 1909. The whole day was spent in waiting, while Mr. Wright's plane remained poised on its monorail. Finally, at sundown, the plane was rolled back into its hangar, because the wind had refused to drop below twelve miles an hour!

Now, however, expectation is growing that, with continued progress in aircraft design, in the use of instruments and electronic devices, and improvement in piloting technique, flight will tend to become more and more independent of weather conditions. To be practical, however, we must remember that, at best, aviation is many years away from that state of perfection which would allow us to regard the weather lightly. If flying is to be a dependable, efficient means of transportation, we must assume that weather conditions will always constitute a major factor.

The mariner, when confronted with a thick fog, a blinding snowstorm, or a gale, can reduce speed or can even drop anchor and await more favorable conditions. The predicament of the airplane pilot is more serious. Suppose that, after battling head winds which have greatly retarded his progress, he approaches his destination with his reserve of fuel running low. He has no choice but to bring his craft to earth; and in fog, icing, or other storm conditions he can only pray for a safe landing. The pilot who is well versed in meteorology, however, and who consequently recognizes timely warnings, can avoid these dangers either by altering his route in the proper manner or by landing his plane in safety while there is still time.

Further, the pilot who understands the behavior of air currents and other conditions is often able to alter, at need, his altitude and course so as to be aided by tail winds, thus decreasing his flight time and cost of operation, and so increasing his chances of landing safely by reaching his destination with reserve fuel still available for use if some emergency keeps him aloft to await favorable landing conditions at the airport.

In training for their mission, military pilots must necessarily take certain risks which the average civilian pilot would not consider. Yet one of the first rules which a student naval aviator learns is that "obtaining information of weather conditions on a cross-country flight ranks in importance with the inspection of the engine and plane. . . . In peace times, except in emergencies, no cross-country flight should be undertaken until all available information of conditions on the way has been obtained." *

In planning a flight, the pilot is particularly interested in:

(*a*) Direction and velocity of wind at various levels.

(*b*) Height and thickness of clouds.

(*c*) Danger of low clouds extending far enough down to hinder visibility of the earth's surface.

(*d*) Weather to be expected along the route.

(*e*) Areas and altitudes of icing, severe turbulence, etc.

(*f*) Limited visibility—fog, smoke, precipitation, etc.

These six items cover most of the meteorological factors of safety. It is nowadays possible for expert meteorologists to forecast much of this information with a fair degree of reliability. From a study of weather maps, cloud types and movements, air masses, fronts, and pressure tendencies, the pilot himself can learn to recognize (with surprising ease) the most important indications of the weather to be expected along his route, at least for several hours in advance.

The basic principles of meteorology are simple. The student himself need not widely explore great reaches of physics and higher mathematics; this preliminary work has been done for him by the research scientists who brought these simple principles to light. Today so much can be learned so easily that there is no excuse for any pilot's lacking good practical knowledge of meteorology and short-time forecasting. His safety and, even more important, the safety of the passengers who place themselves in his care, or the success of his military mission, depends upon it.

QUESTIONS

1. Define meteorology.
2. How can a pilot avoid dangers in flying?
3. In planning a cross country flight what are the six most important meteorological items of interest to a pilot?

* U. S. Navy, *Aviation Ground School Manual.*

Chapter II

THE ATMOSPHERE: ITS CHARACTERISTICS, COMPOSITION, AND STRUCTURE

CHARACTERISTICS OF THE ATMOSPHERE

That mass of air which surrounds our planet, covering land and sea alike in an unbroken envelope, is called the **atmosphere.** In some ways, it shares the characteristics of an ocean. Although we cannot see it, it is as real, as material, as the aqueous oceans which cover some three-quarters of the surface of the globe. It has its currents, which we call winds. Some of these flow with the regularity of the great currents of the seas, while others are as changeable as the flight of a butterfly. Near the surface of the earth, these currents are retarded or deflected by irregularities of the terrain. We find *airfalls* flowing over the tops of ridges and buildings just as waterfalls plunge over precipices. We find just the reverse, also, for air striking an obstacle may be deflected upward for a considerable distance. (Of this phenomenon and of its importance to the aviator, we shall learn more in Chapter VI.) The atmosphere becomes less dense, on the average, as we proceed upward, and colder (up to present-day flying altitudes).

Air, the material of the atmosphere, is a mechanical mixture of several gases. Yet it conforms to the general laws of gases as if it were composed of one gas only. It is highly compressible and perfectly elastic. Though very light, it has a definite weight, which, at ordinary temperature and pressure, is about 1/770 of the weight of water, or about 1.22 ounces per cubic foot.

By its weight, air exerts pressure upon everything it touches. At sea level, the average pressure is about 14.7

pounds per square inch.   This pressure is exerted equally in
all directions.   Although, at sea level, the total pressure on a
human body amounts to approximately 30 tons, we do not
notice it, for it is balanced by an equal pressure from within.
Yet it is the same as that exerted by a column of water 33 feet
high or by a column of mercury 29.92 inches high.

Just as the pressure at any point in a column of water or
mercury depends upon the weight of the column above that

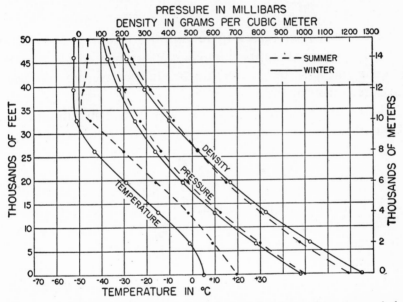

FIG. 2–1.   Average variation of temperature, density, and pressure of the
atmosphere with respect to altitude above the earth's surface.

point, so the pressure of the air depends upon the weight of
the air column above the given point.   Atmospheric pressure
decreases with altitude, slowly approaching zero.   (There is
no sharp limit at which the atmosphere meets empty space; a
gradual merging occurs.)   With a normal distribution of temperature, the pressure on a mountain-top is less than that at the
bottom of an adjacent valley.

It follows that the air in the valley, being under greater
pressure, is denser than that on the mountain-top.   A cubic

foot of air at sea level weighs more than a cubic foot of air at any higher level. Further, because it is easily compressible, a pound of air at sea level occupies less space than a pound of air at any higher point.

At ordinary pressure and temperature, a pound of air has a volume of 13.1 cubic feet.

In general, as we rise above the surface of the earth we find that the air grows colder with fair regularity up to an altitude of about 6 to 8 miles. Above that level the air temperature remains fairly constant up to about 25 miles altitude. From there upward it increases again rapidly, reaching a temperature of 350° F at approximately the 40-mile level. Above that, the increase becomes more gradual as we move toward the outer limits of the atmosphere.

The normal variation of pressure, density, and temperature, at the most usual flying levels, is shown in Figure 2–1.

COMPOSITION OF THE ATMOSPHERE

As stated before, air is a mechanical mixture of gases. At sea level, dry pure air contains about 21 per cent of oxygen and 78 per cent of nitrogen. Small quantities of other gases, such as carbon dioxide, hydrogen, helium, argon, krypton, and neon, are also found present. None of these latter has any practical bearing on the study of weather.

There is one component of air, however, which, though found in variable and relatively small quantities, is of major importance in meteorology—i.e., water vapor. A molecule of water vapor weighs about ⅝ as much as a molecule of dry air. Without water vapor in the air, we should have few of the phenomena which comprise what we call weather. There would be no clouds to protect us from the heat of the sun, no rain to water the plant life upon which animals and men depend for food. Life in its present form could not exist upon the earth.

It is interesting that, on the average, the water-vapor content of the atmosphere varies with the altitude and the latitude; it is lowest at high altitudes and high latitudes. Although practically all of the water-vapor content is concentrated below the 25,000-foot level, no air with a water-vapor content of zero has been found in nature.

The table below illustrates the change in concentration of the principal atmospheric gases as the water-vapor content is changed.

PRINCIPAL CONSTITUENTS OF THE ATMOSPHERE *
(Per cent, by volume)

Water-Vapor Content	Nitrogen	Oxygen	Argon
0.0	78.08	20.95	0.93
0.2	77.90	20.90	0.93
0.9	77.40	20.80	0.92
2.6	76.05	20.40	0.91

* Excluding impurities.

STRUCTURE OF THE ATMOSPHERE

Science divides the atmosphere into three main structural divisions. From lowest to highest they are known, respectively, as the **troposphere,** the **stratosphere** and the **ionosphere.** Since the atmosphere gradually becomes more and more rarefied with increased altitude, there is no definite altitude at which it may be said to end and outer space to begin. In practice, however, the 500-mile point may be taken as the outer limit of our atmospheric envelope. At that point there are only 4 molecules per cubic *mile,* as compared to about 2700×10^{16} molecules per cubic *centimeter* at sea level.

The Troposphere

About one-half of the atmosphere lies below an altitude of 18,000 feet; most of the remainder is concentrated within 6 to 8 miles above the earth's surface. Practically all weather phenomena occur within this range. There is considerable motion of winds and convectional currents, which often carry heat and water vapor to considerable altitudes. The mixing of the air thus effected tends to produce a fairly rapid rate of temperature decrease with altitude. This part of our atmosphere is called the *troposphere*. Its upper limit, where convective currents cease, is called the *tropopause*.

The Stratosphere

Above the tropopause lies the *stratosphere*. It is characterized by the absence of vertical currents. Motion is mainly horizontal in stratified flow, as the name implies.

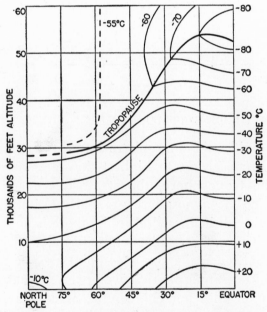

FIG. 2–2. Mean temperature of the atmosphere, Northern Hemisphere, showing the variation with latitude in temperature distribution, and variation in the altitude of the tropopause.

The base of the stratosphere (the tropopause) does not remain fixed, however. It varies in altitude with the latitude, the season, and the local weather below it. It is lower over the poles than over the equator, lower in winter than in summer, and lower over areas of low pressure than over areas of high pressure.   Figure 2–2 shows that the base of the stratosphere averages about 28,000 feet over the pole and rises with fair regularity to about 54,000 feet over the equator.

The cloudless state of the stratosphere is of great advantage to air travel since it is free from the tropospheric storms of the lower altitudes.   Recent high-altitude research indicates that the early conception of the stratosphere as a region of constant temperature does not hold good in the fall months, but appears to be so in the spring.   The temperature sometimes varies quite rapidly, with time, but follows no cycle of diurnal variation, nor can these changes be attributed primarly to sky conditions since tropospheric clouds do not reach these altitudes. From late (though not entirely complete) data the temperature in the region of 70,000 feet appears to be fairly uniform, from about $-45°$ C to $-65°$ C.   In the upper reaches of the stratosphere, however, actual temperature *increases* of 225° C have been indicated, i.e., from $-50°$ C at 25 miles to $+175°$ C at 40 miles.

Wind velocities at all altitudes are exceedingly variable, having been recorded from zero to over 220 mph.   In general, the winds above 30,000 feet appear to decrease with altitude up to about 50–70,000 feet, and then increase again.

As a result of intensive research at high altitudes now being carried on in many parts of the world the figures given above may become subject to considerable correction.   There is still a vast field to be explored and a wealth of new information to be gained which may be revolutionary indeed!

The Ionosphere

The upper limit of the stratosphere is considered to be about 60 miles above the earth's surface.   A range of about 500 miles above this level is known as the *ionosphere*.   This region is so named because there the number of free ions in the atmosphere increases and important electrical phenomena occur.   In the winter season, auroras occur throughout the entire region, sometimes extending downward into the upper stratosphere.   Ionized layers of the ionosphere have the property of reflecting radio waves, thus greatly affecting their transmission and propagation.

QUESTIONS

1. Define atmosphere.
2. In what ways does the atmosphere resemble the ocean?
3. What are airfalls?
4. What is "air"?   Describe its physical characteristics.
5. Describe how the temperature, pressure and density of the atmosphere vary with the altitude.
6. Describe the composition of the atmosphere.
7. What small component of air is of major importance in meteorology? Explain the importance of this.
8. Name the three main structural divisions of the atmosphere.
9. What is the troposphere?
10. What is the tropopause?
11. What lies above the tropopause?   How does it differ from the troposphere?
12. Does the base of the stratosphere (the tropopause) remain fixed?   Explain how it varies in height.
13. What characteristic of the stratosphere is of great advantage to air travel?
14. Describe briefly temperature and wind velocity in the stratosphere.
15. What is the ionosphere?

Chapter III

THE ELEMENTS OF METEOROLOGY AND THEIR MEASUREMENT

In order to make an intelligent appraisal of any weather situation, we must first observe the various meteorological elements. These, when combined, make up a picture of the weather situation.

It is of the greatest importance that observations of these elements be accurate. Under doubtful weather conditions, the safety of flight depends entirely upon the reliability of weather observations and predictions. The data obtained must, therefore, be trustworthy and correct.

At ordinary land stations of the U. S. Weather Bureau, the following meteorological elements are observed at or near the surface:

(*a*) Pressure
(*b*) Pressure tendency (barometric changes)
(*c*) Temperature, humidity, and dew point
(*d*) Wind direction and velocity
(*e*) Cloud forms
(*f*) Cloudiness
(*g*) Ceiling
(*h*) Weather
(*i*) Visibility
(*j*) Precipitation

In addition to these surface observations, many stations also observe conditions existing at higher levels. There wind direction and velocity, and temperature, pressure, and humidity are regularly observed at altitudes well into the stratosphere.

By arrangement with the Weather Bureau, ships at sea transmit radio reports of weather conditions. Each ship gives its position and as many of these data as may be available. Transoceanic aircraft also transmit, in their hourly position reports, weather data pertinent to their location and altitude.

These reports do much to increase the accuracy of forecasts along the air lanes, thus improving the safety of ocean air travel and reducing the problems of the air navigator.

We shall discuss each of the meteorological elements briefly.*

Pressure

Atmospheric pressure is usually measured by a mercurial barometer constructed in the following manner.

A glass tube of uniform internal diameter, somewhat more than 30 inches in length, and closed at one end, is completely filled with pure mercury. It is then placed, open end down, in a vessel, or "cistern," which also contains mercury (the open end having been temporarily sealed during the inverting process to prevent spilling of the liquid). The mercury in the tube falls until the top of the column is about 30 inches above the level of that in the cistern, leaving a vacuum in the upper part of the tube. Since the weight of the column thus left standing in the tube is exactly balanced by the pressure which holds it up—namely, the atmospheric pressure—it follows that the height of the column will vary as the supporting pressure varies. As the atmospheric pressure decreases, the height of the supported mercury column will be decreased; as the pressure increases, the mercury column will rise higher. Each change in height of the column will be directly proportional to the change in pressure. Since the mean pressure is nearly 15 pounds per square inch, and the mean barometric height

* More detailed information may be found in the instruction pamphlets issued by the U. S. Weather Bureau and by the Meteorological Office, London, England, and also in Publication No. 9 of the Secrétariat de l'Organisation Météorologique International, Lausanne, Switzerland.

(at sea level) is about 30 inches, a change of 1 pound per square inch in pressure is, therefore, represented by a 2-inch change in the height of the mercury column.

In practical barometer construction, the glass tube containing the mercury is encased in an outer tube of brass. This outer tube is suspended by a ring at the top. At its lower end is a flange to which the several parts forming the cistern are attached. The upper part of the brass tube is partly cut away to expose the mercury column for observation. A scale for measuring the height of the mercury is fitted over this opening, and along the scale travels a *vernier* for extract reading. Fixed in the middle of the brass tube is a thermometer, the bulb of which is covered toward the outside but open toward the mercury, and nearly in contact with the glass tube, so that the thermometer indicates the temperature of the mercury rather than that of the external air. In every reading of the barometer, the temperature of the mercury column must be taken into account.

It is evident that, as the mercury in the tube rises with an increase in atmospheric pressure, the mercury in the cistern must fall, and vice versa. As the height of the mercury column above the existing level in the cistern must be known, some means must be adopted to ascertain this height under varying conditions. In the Standard Barometer, a vertical screw presses against the bottom of the cistern, which is a flexible cell. By means of this screw, the head of which projects from the bottom of the instrument, the surface of the mercury in the cistern (which is visible through a glass casing) may be raised or lowered until it exactly coincides with the level marked as zero on the scale.

Other things being equal, the mercury will stand higher in the tube when it is warm than when it is cold, because of expansion. For purposes of comparison, all barometric observations are reduced to a standard which assumes the mercury column to be 32° F (0° C).

Since the weight of the air column at any place also depends on the local gravity, another correction must be applied to barometric pressures to reduce them to the pressure observed under conditions of normal gravity at Latitude 45° North.

With the application of these two corrections, the correct air pressure at the level of the barometer is obtained.

Pressure also varies, however, with height above sea level. It is necessary, therefore, to apply a third correction to reduce the reading to that pressure which would be observed if the barometer were at sea level.

The pressures recorded in weather reports are, therefore, not the actual readings taken, but are those which **would have been** recorded at sea level by a correct barometer, with a temperature of 32° F, subject to local gravity equal to normal gravity at 45° North Latitude.

Besides the mercury barometer, the aneroid barometer also is in general use. It depends for its action upon partly exhausted sealed metallic bellows which contract or expand with the increase or decrease, respectively, of the surrounding air pressure. The movement of the bellows is transmitted mechanically to a pointer which moves across the face of a graduated scale to indicate the pressure. Although liable to certain types of minor errors, this type of instrument, if properly designed and constructed and carefully maintained, may be depended upon for accuracy quite adequate for practical meteorological purposes. It possesses distinct advantages, being light in weight, compact, and readily adaptable to continuous recording. The recording type of barometer is generally known as a barograph. Various types of barometric instruments are shown in Figures 3–1 and 3–2. The *microbarograph,* a very sensitive instrument, is used to record small and rapid changes of atmospheric pressure. The Aircraft Flight Analyzer shown (one of many types) is carried in the aircraft and records barometric altitude (curved line) and periods during which the gyropilot and radio were in use (jagged lines along edges of card).

C

Courtesy Bendix-Friez.

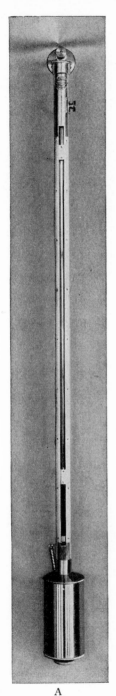

A   B

FIG. 3–1.   (A) Mercurial and (B) Aneroid Barometers.
(c) Altimeter (sensitive type).

B

Courtesy Bendix-Friez.

A

FIG. 3–2. (A) Microbarograph and (B) aircraft flight analyzer.

Until about the year 1916, barometric pressure was reported as the length of the mercury column, either in "inches of mercury" or in "millimeters of mercury." Since that time a new unit called the "bar," representing the normal pressure near sea level, has come into use. Pressures are given in thousandths of this unit, called *millibars* (abbreviated "mb"). This system, first used in European countries, was adopted as standard by the U. S. Weather Bureau and the U. S. Navy on July 1, 1939; it has since been adopted by all member-countries of the International Meteorological Organization, and all pressures are now reported in millibars. Because it would entail considerable time and expense to convert the scales of present instruments, readings of pressure are still taken at some observing stations in inches (or millimeters), and are then converted into millibars by means of simple tables or converting scales. Some more recent instruments have scales in both "inches" and "millimeters."

A "bar" is a unit of pressure equal to 1,000,000 dynes per square centimeter, the equivalent pressure at the base of a column of 29.53 in. or 750 mm of mercury.

1 millibar (mb) = $\frac{1}{1000}$ of a bar, or 1000 dynes per sq cm

The following table shows the relation between inches and millimeters of mercury, and millibars:

1 in. Hg	= 25.4 mm Hg	= 33.9 mb
1 mm Hg	= 0.039 in. Hg	= 1.33 mb
1 mb	= 0.0295 in. Hg	= 0.75 mm Hg

A "standard atmosphere" is one in which the sea-level atmospheric pressure is 1013.2 mb (29.92 in. Hg, 760 mm Hg), the sea-level temperature is 59° F (15° C), and the lapse rate is 3.5° F per 1000 ft (6.5° C per 1000 meters) up to 7 mi (11 km).

Since pressure varies with height above sea level, an ordinary aneroid barometer, carried aloft, may be used to indicate change in altitude by the change in indicated pressure; hence the instrument may be calibrated to read directly in altitude above (or below) sea level. Instruments, so constructed and calibrated, are called "altimeters." They are carried in aircraft to indicate the altitude at which the aircraft is flying. Calibrated to "standard atmosphere," these instruments are adjustable to allow for changes in the actual sea level pressure. The latest types also automatically compensate for changes in the air temperature. (See Figure 3–1 (C).)

The relation between pressure of "standard atmosphere" and altitude above sea level is shown in the following tables:

STANDARD ATMOSPHERE PRESSURES AT 1000–FT LEVELS

Altitude (Ft)	Inches (Hg)	Millibars
18,000	14.94	505
17,000	15.56	526
16,000	16.21	548
15,000	16.88	571
14,000	17.57	594
13,000	18.29	619
12,000	19.03	644
11,000	19.79	670
10,000	20.58	696
9,000	21.38	724
8,000	22.22	752
7,000	23.09	781
6,000	23.98	811
5,000	24.89	843
4,000	25.84	875
3,000	26.81	908
2,000	27.82	941
1,000	28.86	977
SEA LEVEL	29.92	1013

VERTICAL RELATION OF 100–MILLIBAR LEVELS

Millibars	Inches (Hg)	Millimeters (Hg)	Feet	Meters
400	11.80	300	24,370	7425
500	14.75	375	18,520	5643
600	17.70	450	13,740	4186
700	20.65	525	9,700	2955
800	23.63	600	6,200	1889
900	26.58	675	3,112	948
1000	29.53	750	348	106
1013	29.92	760	SEA LEVEL	

Pressure Tendency

The *pressure tendency* (or *barometric tendency*), i.e., the character and rapidity of change in the atmospheric pressure, is also of great importance to the meteorologist and the pilot. It plays a major part in weather forecasting and is regularly reported with other observed data. The unit used is, conventionally, the total net change (in millibars and tenths) occurring in the 3-hour interval immediately preceding the reported observation.

Temperature

For single observations, air temperature is usually measured by means of the mercury thermometer. (See Figure 3–3.) To indicate extremes of temperature during any desired period, "maximum and minimum thermometers" are used. In the maximum (a mercury-type) thermometer, there is a constriction in the mercury channel, near the bulb. The mercury column breaks at that point with a falling temperature, leaving the top of the column at its highest point (until reset by mechanical means). The minimum thermometer is of the colored alcohol type which contains a small movable index in the channel. This index is carried downward by the meniscus of the fluid; but, as it expands again with rising temperature, the fluid flows past the index, leaving it at its lowest point (until reset by other means). Continuous records of temperature are obtained with the thermograph in which the unequal expansion of a solid and a liquid, or of dissimilar solids, causes movement of a pen resting on a drum revolving at a uniform speed. Of the two instruments, the mercury thermometer is the more accurate. The thermograph, however, can be made sufficiently accurate for practical purposes and does provide a continuous record, giving the temperature at any instant of time. (See Figure 3–5.)

Thermometers are housed in a louvered wooden box, which allows effective ventilation yet protects them from the direct

Courtesy Bendix-Friez.

Fig. 3–3. Maximum and minimum thermometers indicate the highest and lowest temperatures occurring during the day.

rays of the sun. The box is mounted some distance from the ground so that the instrument may be affected as little as possible by insolation during the day and radiational cooling during the night.

Two scales for temperature measurement are in common use, the Fahrenheit (F) and the centigrade (C). In the former, the boiling point of pure water is 212° and the freezing point 32°; in the latter, these points are 100° and 0° respectively. Since there are 180° F and 100° C between these two points, one degree of the centigrade scale equals 9/5 degrees of the Fahrenheit scale. Temperatures may readily be converted from one scale to the other; thus to convert a reading in centigrade degrees to the equivalent in Fahrenheit degrees, multiply by 9/5 and add 32; to convert Fahrenheit to equivalent centigrade, subtract 32 and multiply by 5/9.

Still a third scale of temperature is used, in which the boiling point of pure water is placed at 373° and the freezing point at 273°. This is called the "absolute centigrade" scale; it differs from the centigrade only by the constant 273°. This scale, used especially in calculations involving the laws of gases, has two distinct advantages: (1) negative temperature cannot occur, since there is no temperature below "absolute zero," and (2) for a given pressure the density (of air) is inversely proportional to the "absolute temperature."

For ordinary purposes, in the English-speaking countries, the Fahrenheit scale is still the more widely used. It is gradually being displaced, however, by the centigrade scale, which is more logical, being based on the decimal system. The centigrade scale is used almost universally outside of the English-speaking countries; the use of the "absolute centigrade" scale is restricted almost entirely to scientific publications and computations.

Humidity

Humidity is the term used to denote the moisture content of the air. It is acquired by the air through evaporation from the surfaces of lakes, rivers, oceans, etc., and even from snow surfaces. The *higher* the air temperature, and the *lower* the atmospheric pressure, the more moisture the air can hold in the form of water vapor. For each air temperature and pressure there is a definite limit to the possible moisture content of the atmosphere. This limit is called the *vapor capacity* of the air, at that tempearture and pressure. It is usually expressed in grams of water vapor per kilogram of dry air. For example: Air at 50° F has a vapor capacity of about 8 grams per kilogram at sea level pressure (1013 mb), while at 10,000 ft (or 696 mb) it is about 11 grams per kilogram. Similarly, at 68° F, at sea level (1013 mb), the vapor capacity is 15 grams, while at 10,000 ft (696 mb) it is about 21 grams. Thus it is seen that the decreases in pressure increased the vapor capacity by about 37 per cent and 40 per cent respectively, while the increases in temperature increased the vapor capacity by about 87 per cent and 91 per cent respectively.

Air containing all the moisture it can hold is said to be "saturated"; when it holds any lesser amount, it is "unsaturated."

Humidity may be expressed in several different ways: relative humidity, specific humidity, mixing ratio, absolute humidity, dew-point temperature, and vapor pressure.

The *relative humidity* is the ratio of the actual moisture content of the air to the amount of moisture that the air could hold, saturated, at the same temperature.   This is expressed as percentage.

The *specific humidity* is the number of grams of water vapor contained in one kilogram of air (mixture of dry air and water vapor).   It is obtained from the ratio

$$\frac{\text{density of water vapor}}{\text{density of air mixture}}$$

and is equal to

$$622 \times \frac{\text{water vapor pressure}}{\text{total air pressure}}.$$

This remains practically constant with changes of pressure or height of unsaturated air, provided no moisture is either added or subtracted.

The *mixing ratio* is the number of grams of water vapor per kilogram of *dry air* in a humid mixture.   It is obtained from the ratio

$$\frac{\text{density of water vapor}}{\text{density of } dry \ air}$$

and is equal to

$$622 \times \frac{\text{water vapor pressure}}{\text{pressure of } dry \ air}.$$

This also remains constant with pressure changes, for unsaturated air, provided moisture is neither added nor subtracted.

When the air becomes saturated both the specific humidity and the mixing ratio will vary with changes of pressure and temperature. The variation may be shown by a simple diagram. On a saturated mixing ratio curve the temperature will actually be the dew point of the air at a given pressure.

The *absolute humidity* is the number of grams of water vapor contained in one cubic meter of space.

When unsaturated air is cooled by any process, it steadily advances toward a state of saturation. The temperature to which it must be cooled at constant pressure in order to become saturated is called its *dew point*. At this point, condensation of the water vapor takes place. Dew point varies with the pressure and the water vapor content. The more closely the actual temperature of the

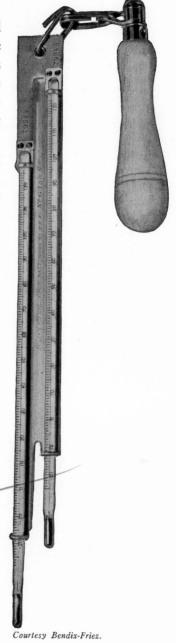

FIG. 3–4. Swivel sling psychrometer, weather bureau type. With a wet wick attached to one thermometer bulb, the instrument is whirled around by hand, producing evaporation at the wet bulb. From the wet and dry bulb reading the relative humidity is obtained from the humidity tables.

Courtesy Bendix-Friez.

air approaches the dew-point temperature, the greater is the probability of the formation of clouds or fog.

The *vapor pressure* is the *partial pressure* of the water vapor.

Humidity is usually measured with either of two common instruments, the psychrometer or the hair hygrometer. A *psychrometer* consists of two thermometers, the bulb of one

Courtesy Bendix-Friez.

FIG. 3–5. Hygro-thermograph. This instrument records both the temperature and relative humidity by tracing lines on a graduated chart fixed to a revolving drum. The temperature end is actuated by a bimetallic element. The humidity end is operated by the change in length of human hair, which is very sensitive to the moisture content of the atmosphere.

being covered by a piece of moistened wicking from which free evaporation can take place. The evaporation will cool the "wet-bulb" thermometer, causing it to indicate a temperature below that of the surrounding atmosphere, which is indicated by the "dry bulb." The dryer the air, the more rapid will be the evaporation, and, consequently, the greater the difference between the "wet-bulb" and "dry-bulb" readings.

When the air is saturated (100 per cent relative humidity), there will be no evaporation, and both thermometers will read the same. The relative humidity (per cent) is determined from humidity tables, which use as arguments the "dry-bulb temperature," and the difference in temperature between the two thermometer readings.

Free evaporation is sometimes accomplished by directing the blast of a fan on the wet bulb, or by whirling both thermometers around in the air, as in the sling type, shown in Figure 3–4.

The *hair hygrometer* operates upon the principle that hair changes in length with every change in humidity. Several human hairs are stretched within the instrument in such a manner that any change in their length moves a pointer over the face of a dial, which may be directly calibrated for relative humidity. In some such instruments the pointer carries a pen which scribes a continuous record on a graduated card mounted on a uniformly rotating cylinder, as in Figure 3–5.

Relative humidity varies with changes of temperature, while *specific humidity* remains unchanged so long as no water vapor is added to or removed from the air.

Wind Direction and Velocity

Wind direction is defined as the direction *from* which the wind blows; thus, if we say, "The wind is northwest," we mean that it is blowing *from* the northwest; an east wind blows *from* the east, and so on. Wind direction is indicated by a *wind vane*.

Frequently, by means of an electric circuit, the instrument is set up, so as to indicate the wind direction on a dial or scale at some distance away (Figures 3–6, 3–7, and 3–8).

Wind velocity is determined at or near the earth's surface, by one of three instruments, the *triple-cup rotating anemometer* (Figure 3–6), the *pitot-static type anemograph* (Figure 3–7), and the *32-cup fixed anemometer* (Figure 3–8). The triple-cut rotating anemometer is especially accurate in indicating low wind velocities. By noting the rate of rotation of the cups (i.e., the number of revolutions in a given time interval), one may read the wind velocity during that interval from the calibration curve of the anemometer. It must be borne in

Courtesy Bendix-Friez.

I   2

Fig. 3–6. (1) Wind vane and *triple-cup rotating* anemometer, with (2) wind direction and velocity indicator. The wind vane actuates the pointer of the upper dial through a selsyn motor. The anemometer, acting as a small electric generator, causes the lower pointer to move on the same principle as a voltmeter.

mind that, because of the inertia of its rotor, the cup anemometer is not adapted to the measurement of sudden fluctuations in the wind velocity, as in sharp gusts. On the other hand, it does give reliable average measurements. The pitot-static type of instrument measures the difference between the static and the dynamic pressures of the atmosphere and is calibrated to express this difference in pressures in terms of wind velocity. This type of instrument, with a recording attachment which

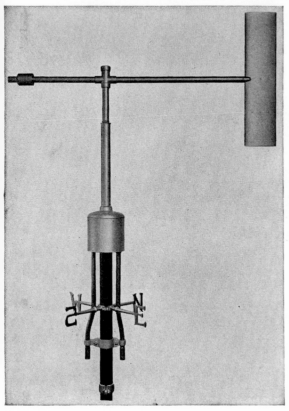
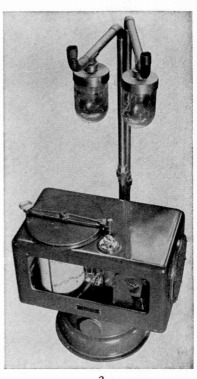

1   2

FIG. 3–7. (1) Pitot head wind vane—with (2) anemograph. Wind velocity is measured in terms of pressure, and recorded as miles-per-hour (as in an airspeed meter) on the drum of the instrument (2) connected below it. The wind direction is recorded by a second line on the same drum, a second pen being actuated by direct mechanical linkage to the wind vane. This type of instrument records all maxima and minima of gusts and lulls (instead of average velocities as recorded by the triple-cup anemometer) and depends on no outside source of power for its operation. It is, therefore, more valuable and more reliable in hurricane areas.

works on the principle of an airspeed meter, is shown in Figure 3–7. Wind speed is described in miles per hour, knots, kilometers per hour, or meters per second.

Courtesy Bendix-Friez.

FIG. 3–8.   (1) 32-cup fixed anemometer, and (2) Weather Panel, indicating wind velocity (left) and wind direction (right).   For keeping permanent records, a recording instrument (not shown) is provided.   This is one of the most recent velocity-direction combinations.

The 32-cup fixed anemometer, sometimes called the "Dines" anemometer, one of the recent improvements in this field, is illustrated in Figure 3–8.   The ring-shaped anemometer head, consisting of 32 cups, is mounted on a shaft which in turn is connected to an indicating mechanism.   Wind reaction on the cups creates a torque on the shaft.   The shaft is permitted to turn through a maximum arc of about 330°, against the action of restraining springs of such strength that the arc turned by the shaft is proportional to the wind velocity.   The wind velocity is thus indicated directly, on a suitably calibrated dial.

Even without instruments, a skilled observer may estimate the force and direction of the wind with fair accuracy by observing its effect on various local objects.   The effects are referred to what is called the Beaufort scale (see p. 202 and Appendix, p. 337).   This scale, which was devised in 1806 by Admiral Beaufort, is still in international use; on practically all weather maps, wind velocity is expressed in this manner— readings from instruments being converted into corresponding Beaufort numbers.*

The measurement of winds in the upper atmosphere is described later in this chapter.

Cloud Forms

Weather reports always include a statement of the cloud forms observed at the various levels.   The many forms of clouds, their meanings, and their relationship to each other, are described in Chapter IV.

Cloudiness—(Sky Cover)

The amount of cloudiness existing at the time of each observation is recorded and reported in terms of the number of tenths of the sky covered by clouds.   Since there is no instrument for measuring "cloudiness," the figure must be estimated.

* Numbers above 12 are an extension of the original scale.

(See Glossary, p. 301.)   An experienced observer, however, can make an estimate sufficiently accurate for practical purposes.   Because of the importance to aviation of low clouds, any significant change in the amount or height of low clouds requires a special report.

Ceiling

The ceiling is the height of the lowest cloud level about the station at which the total cloudiness covers more than one-half the entire area of the sky.   (See Glossary, p. 300.)   The ceiling, which is of great importance to aviation, is usually estimated with sufficient accuracy.   The ceiling is also frequently measured with (1) a ceiling clinometer, (2) a ceilometer, (3) by comparison with the altimeter of an aircraft in flight, or (4) by the "sounding balloons" described later in this chapter.

A *ceiling clinometer* is a device used only at night.   It consists of two parts: (a) a vertical light projector, and (b) a clinometer (angle-measuring device) mounted at a known distance from the projector.   The projector throws a spot of light on the clouds.   Placing his eye at the clinometer, the observer measures the vertical angle of inclination between the projector and the spot of light on the clouds.   From a table, the observed angle is converted direct to the ceiling height in feet.

A *ceilometer* is an instrument which does electrically what the observer does when he observes the spot on the cloud base projected by the ceiling light.   With this instrument the ceiling is measured and recorded at night and usually in the daytime.   On a bright day, however, the ceilometer may fail to detect a cloud layer.

Weather

Each weather report contains an item indicating the general state of the weather at the hour of observation, i.e., whether it be clear, rainy, showery, foggy, dusty, etc.

Visibility

Visibility is the term used to describe the horizontal transparency of the atmosphere at the surface. By agreement of the International Meteorological Organization, visibility is defined as the greatest distance at which an object, such as, for example, a boat or a haystack or a house, can be recognized as such by the average unaided eye. Each observing station maintains a chart of prominent local objects and their known distances from the observation point. Objects are chosen for their suitability for determining visibility at night as well as by day.

VISIBILITY TABLE

(Symbol "VV"—Horizontal Visibility)

Code Figure	Visibility in Statute Miles and Fractions	Code Figure	Visibility in Statute Miles and Fractions
00	Less than 1/8	32	4
01	1/8 and 3/16	40	5
02	1/4	48	6
03	3/8	56	7
04	1/2	64	8
05	5/8	72	9
06	3/4	80	10, 11, and 12
07	7/8	81	13, 14, 15, and 20
08	1	82	25, 30, and 35
10	1 1/4	83	40 and 45
12	1 1/2	84	50, 55, and 60
14	1 3/4	85	65 to 90 inclusive
16	2	86	95 to 120 inclusive
18	2 1/4	87	125 to 185 inclusive
20	2 1/2	88	190 to 310 inclusive
24	3	89	315 or more

Note that, for visibility up to 10 miles, the code figure represents the visibility expressed in eighths of a mile, e.g., 14 represents 1 3/4 miles. Above 10 miles it is necessary to refer to the table to obtain the corresponding visibility reported, i.e., for code figures above 80.

In the United States, visibility is recorded as follows:

(*a*) When greater than 15 miles, to the nearest 5 miles.

(*b*) When between 3 and 15 miles, to the nearest whole mile.

(*c*) When 3 miles or less, by the following numbers and fractions:

0, $\frac{1}{16}$, $\frac{1}{8}$, $\frac{3}{16}$, $\frac{1}{4}$, $\frac{5}{16}$, $\frac{3}{8}$, $\frac{1}{2}$, $\frac{5}{8}$, $\frac{3}{4}$, $\frac{7}{8}$, 1, $1\frac{1}{4}$, $1\frac{1}{2}$, $1\frac{3}{4}$, 2, $2\frac{1}{4}$, $2\frac{1}{2}$ and 3 miles.

Countries using the international weather code (adopted by the International Meteorological Organization, effective January 1, 1949) report visibility in their coded reports according to the table shown on previous page.

Weather greatly affects visibility—in fact, practically controls it. It is interesting to note the relation between weather and visibility in the following tabulation of the pertinent section of a *former* weather code in which "Zero" indicated "Less than 150 ft." and 9 indicated "Over 30 miles."

RELATION OF WEATHER TO VISIBILITY

Visibility Number	Type of Weather			
	Fog or haze	Rain	Snow or sleet	Drizzle
0	Dense		Very heavy	
1	Thick	Tropical	Very heavy	
2	Medium	Tropical	Heavy	
3	Moderate	Very heavy	Moderate	Thick
4	Mist	Heavy	Light	Moderate
5	Light mist	Heavy	Very light	Light
6	Light mist	Moderate	Very light	Light
7	(or haze)	Light		
8		Very light		
9				

Precipitation

The item of precipitation included in the weather report is of interest to the aviator for several reasons. First, when entered with other data upon a weather map, it defines the general rain or snow areas; second, by its amount, it gives the pilot an idea of what degree of firmness of ground he may expect, if forced to land elsewhere than on a well-drained airfield.

Precipitation of moisture is measured by means of a *rain gauge,* or *snow gauge,* which indicates the amount in inches of depth. In principle, the rain gauge is merely a vertical tube, closed at the bottom and open at the top. Over the top is a funnel-shaped mouth, the largest diameter of which is several times the diameter of the tube. This magnifies the readings and renders them more accurate. For example, if the tube diameter is 2 inches and the "collecting surface" of the top is 4 inches in diameter, the depth of water draining into the tube will be four times the actual rainfall. The most usual proportion of funnel and tube diameters is $8:2.53$; in this case the actual rainfall is multiplied tenfold by the gauge. A typical rain gauge is shown in Figure 3–9. An ordinary rule, yardstick, or other type of measuring rod, is frequently used to measure the depth of snow.

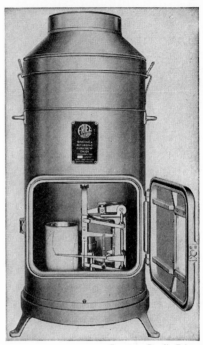

Courtesy Bendix-Friez.

Fig. 3–9. Rain and snow gauge. (Ferguson weighing and recording type.)

Proper Use of Observations

For a correct analysis of any weather situation over a large area, observations must be taken simultaneously at various points throughout the area. These data, when plotted on a synoptic chart, will provide a picture of the state of the atmosphere throughout the area at that moment. From his picure, the meteorologist can make an adequate analysis as a basis for general weather forecasting, storm warnings, or flying-weather information.

Compilation of observed data over long periods of time establishes mean or normal values for the year and for the various seasons. Such data provide a description of the *climate* of the area, or of the individual observing station involved. Frequency tables of cloud heights, storms, visibility, wind forces and directions, fogs, etc., though of little value in forecasting the weather, are of great value in planning the location and layout of airports and landing fields. The information to be assembled in the form of frequency tables has been outlined by the International Commission of Air Navigation. Such tables are published by the official meteorological bureaus or departments of the member countries.

Aerological Soundings

Observations of the meteorological elements at various levels in the upper air are made by means of aerological soundings, which may be made in any of several ways, according to the data desired and the facilities available. The force and direction of the wind are ascertained by means of *pilot balloons*. Pressure, temperature, and humidity are measured by means of instruments called *meteorographs,* of which there are two types: the aerometeorograph, which is carried aloft by an aircraft, and the radiometeorograph or "radiosonde," carried aloft by a small free balloon and operated by radio.

(*a*) *Pilot Balloons.* For obtaining data on the winds aloft, small balloons of known weight are inflated, with hydrogen or helium, to a definite free and total lift (depending on actual balloon weight) to secure a pre-determined average ascensional rate. (See Glossary, p. 309.) Thus, if the effect of vertical wind components be disregarded, the height of the balloon can be known, within practical limits of accuracy at any instant after its release. Its ascensional flight is followed by

Official photo, Bureau of Aeronautics, U. S. Navy.

FIG. 3–10. Aboard the aircraft-carrier, U.S.S. WASP. The start of a "pilot-balloon sounding," employing the theodolite (instrument in foreground) to determine the velocity and direction of "winds aloft." The pilot-balloon, of known ascensional rate, has just been released by the observer. Assistant (at right) holds stop-watch and recording-pad. Through the theodolite at regular intervals the observer sights the balloon, the assistant recording its bearing (i.e., direction) and angular altitude. From the data recorded, the winds aloft, at various levels, are then obtained by plotting the path of the balloon on a special plotting-board.

means of a theodolite (see Figure 3–10), and, at predetermined times, measurements of the angular altitude and azimuth of the balloon are recorded, until the balloon passes into the clouds or out of sight, or bursts.   The data so obtained, plotted on a diagram, reproduce the horizontal projection of the flight path of the balloon.   From this, the velocity and direction of the wind at the various levels are charted.

(*b*) *Aerometeorograph.*   The aerometeorograph is a compound instrument of the recording type for measuring atmos-

Courtesy Bendix-Friez.

Fig. 3–11.   Aerometeorograph (cover removed).   Aerological soundings are made by this instrument, carried aloft in an airplane, attached in a shock-proof mounting.   On the revolving drum shown, three separate instruments record temperature, pressure, and humidity at the various altitudes, while a fourth (at bottom) marks time intervals on the edge of the sheet.

pheric pressure, temperature, and humidity (Figure 3–11). Pressure is measured by an aneroid barometer, temperature by a bimetallic thermometer, and humidity by a hair hygrometer. Pens or styluses trace the readings of the several elements on a scaled record sheet, which is wrapped around a rotating drum turned by clockwork.   For reliable readings, this instrument must be calibrated frequently under standard conditions.

To make an aerological sounding, the aerometeorograph is attached to an aircraft in a vibration-absorbing mount, and in such a position as to be free from the local effect of the engine and fuselage—usually near a wing -tip. To overcome

Courtesy Bendix-Friez.

A   B

FIG. 3–12. (A) Radiometeorograph (radiosonde) in flight, showing balloon and parachute with transmitting instrument suspended below. (B) Radio receiving and automatic recording instrument.

the effect of lag in the instrument, the pilot ascends slowly in "steps," leveling off at various altitudes in order to allow the recording elements to reach equilibrium with surrounding conditions.

(*c*) *Radiometeorograph or "radiosonde."* At more than 200 stations over the world upper-air observations are made also by means of *radiosondes* or *radiometeorographs* attached to balloons (Figure 3–12). (The number of radiosonde stations is expected to be considerably increased in the near future.) These instruments are miniature radio transmitters which give records of free-air temperature, pressure, and humidity from the earth's surface to heights well up into the stratosphere, between 50,000 and 100,000 feet. The Weather Bureau and the Air Force have recently replaced airplane observations made with the aerometeorograph by radiosonde observations, but the Navy still continues to use both methods.

Radiosonde observations are made at 4:00 and 10:00 A.M. and at 4:00 and 10:00 P.M., E.S.T.; the data are evaluated and the reports transmitted over the teletype circuits to the various forecast centers by 1:00 P.M. and 1:00 A.M. E.S.T., respectively.

The radiosonde's three great advantages over the aircraft-carried aerometeorograph are: (1) the great heights at which observations may be obtained; (2) the fact that it may be used in all weather conditions, thus providing the meteorologist with greatly desired data even in severe storms and fog, at times when all aircraft are grounded; and (3) analysis can be made as the data are received from the instrument while in flight (not having to wait for the airplane to return with it).

The use of upper-air data (aerological soundings) will be described in Chapter IX, on "Weather Maps."

QUESTIONS

1. Name the ten meteorological elements which are observed by the Weather Bureau at or near the earth's surface.
2. How do ships and transoceanic aircraft assist the Weather Bureau in preparing its forecasts?
3. Name the instruments used to measure atmospheric pressure.
4. Describe briefly how each one operates.
5. In what units is atmospheric pressure measured? (a) Define Standard Atmosphere. (b) How is pressure tendency indicated?
6. How is temperature measured?

7. What temperature scales are used, and what are their salient points?
8. What is: (a) Humidity? (b) Relative humidity? (c) Specific humidity? (d) Mixing Ratio? (e) Absolute humidity?
9. Explain what is meant by saturated and unsaturated air.
10. What is meant by dew-point?
11. What is vapor pressure?
12. What instruments are used to measure humidity?
13. Describe briefly how each works.
14. Define wind direction and velocity.
15. Briefly describe the instruments employed in their measurement and the units used.
16. Describe the "Beaufort Scale" of wind velocities.
17. What is meant by the term "cloudiness," and how is it reported?
18. Define ceiling, and tell how it is measured.
19. What is meant by "visibility," and how is it reported?
20. Define precipitation.
21. How is it measured?
22. What is the purpose of "aerological soundings"? In what three ways are they made?
23. What data are obtained by each of the above methods?
24. What are the particular advantages of the radiosonde over the aircraft-carried aerometeorograph?

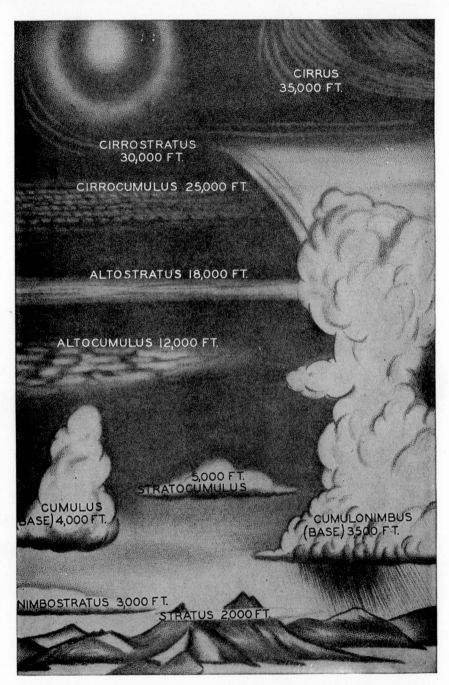

Basic clouds at average altitude levels.

Chapter IV

CLOUD TYPES AND OBSTRUCTIONS TO VISION

CAUSES OF CLOUDS

When air can no longer hold all of its water-vapor content in invisible form, a cloud is formed by the condensation of a part of the water vapor into visible droplets, snow, or ice crystals. Cloud droplets average about $\frac{1}{1000}$ of an inch in diameter. The visible water contained in a cloud may vary from $1\frac{1}{2}$ to 8 grains per cubic foot ($\frac{1}{10}$ to 5 grams per cubic meter). The condensation occurs as the result of the cooling of air below its dew point by any of the following processes:

(*a*) Cooling by expansion in rising convective currents.
(*b*) Cooling by expansion of mechanically lifted air.
(*c*) Cooling by mixture with colder air.
(*d*) Cooling by contact with a colder surface.
(*e*) Cooling by rain falling through air already at or close to its dew point.
(*f*) Cooling by radiation of heat from the air into the outer atmosphere (particularly at night).

In connection with forecasts based entirely upon local indications, clouds assume a most important role. By observation of their motions, information may be obtained regarding velocity and direction of winds aloft. Through the study of their development, changes in the weather may often be forecast with a fair degree of accuracy.

Nuclei

For precipitation, some form of nuclei around which condensation can begin is usually necessary. The most active hygroscopic nuclei are: salt particles, which float in the atmosphere in great quantities; tiny ice crystals formed by the freezing of water vapor; and smoke particles produced by ordinary (incomplete) combustion.

Types of Clouds

Although clouds may be observed in an infinite variety of shapes and sizes, they may be classified readily into ten general types, given in the following table:

Family	Type	Approximate Average Altitude of Base (ft)	Approximate Altitude Range of Base (ft)	Approximate Thickness (ft)
A *High Clouds*	Cirrus (Ci)	32,000	18,000–52,000	(very thin)
	Cirro-stratus (Cs)	28,000	16,000–50,000	(thin)
	Cirro-cumulus (Cc)	22,000	12,000–50,000	(thin)
B *Medium Clouds*	Alto-stratus (As)	17,000	6,000–20,000	1,000– 2,700
	Alto-cumulus (Ac)	15,000	7,000–25,000	300– 800
C *Low Clouds*	Strato-cumulus (Sc)	6,000	1,000– 8,000	1,000– 8,000
	Nimbo-stratus (Ns)	3,000	500– 6,000	3,000– 6,000
	Stratus (St)	2,100	500– 6,000	5– 200
D *Clouds with vertical development*	Cumulus (Cu)	4,000	1,500– 5,000	500– 5,000
	Cumulo-nimbus (Cb)	3,000	1,500– 5,000	5,000–15,000

There follows a brief description of the main cloud types. Some of the photographs of clouds are taken from a chart prepared by the U. S. Weather Bureau for the purpose of helping observers to identify the several cloud forms according to the International System of Classification. The International abbreviations are given in parentheses after the cloud names. An edition containing a larger number of photographs and more detailed descriptions may be obtained from the Superintendent of Documents, Washington, D. C.*

HIGH CLOUDS

Cirrus (Ci)—Figures 4–1, 4–2, 4–3, 4–4, and 4–5

This is a detached cloud of delicate and fibrous texture, usually without shading, generally white in color, and often of a silky appearance.

This is the highest and thinnest of all clouds, occurring generally at altitudes above 25,000 feet where the extremely low temperature ($-30°$ F to $-40°$ F) causes the formation of ice crystals instead of water droplets. Because of its extreme thinness, and because of the various processes operating to produce it, this cloud appears in a greater variety of forms than any other. The amount of water vapor at this elevation varies in the same way as at all other altitudes. When the amount of water vapor is small, the cirri appear as delicate threads. As the quantity of moisture increases, they appear as tufts and tangled masses, or even as sheets and streams.

When detached, light and silky in appearance, without connection with cirro-stratus or alto-stratus, cirrus is considered a sign of fair and settled weather. This type is illustrated in Figures 4–1 and 4–2.

Certain other types can be used to advantage when weather maps are not available. These are usually associated with "depressions" (i.e., low-pressure atmospheric disturbances) of the most energetic type. Though of rather rare occurrence, they are so characteristic in form that one with any

* Circular S, 2nd Edition; January, 1949. "Manual of Cloud Forms and Codes for States of the Sky," U. S. Government Printing Office, Washington, D. C. (Price 25 cents.)

F. Ellerman.

FIG. 4–1.   Cirrus in parallel trails and small patches.

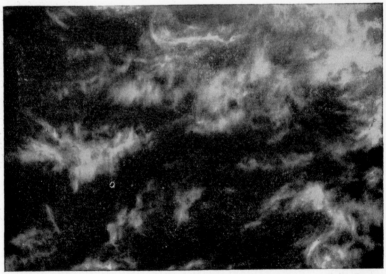

H. T. Floreen.

FIG. 4–2.   Cirrus with an irregular arrangement of filaments.

knowledge of cloud forms will seldom fail to read them correctly.

Cirri arranged in long parallel bands, which because of perspective seem to radiate from a definite point over the horizon, are the first messengers of a severe storm. (See Figures 4–3, 4–4.) This type is known as "banded cirrus"

From "Cloud Studies," A. W. Clayden. Permission E. P. Dutton & Co., Inc.

Fig. 4–3. Band cirrus (cirrus-vittatus).

(cirrus-vitatus). Cirri composed of drawnout filaments with tufts or tangled masses at their ends (called "mares' tails") warn of an approaching depression, though perhaps not one of such violence as that indicated by the banded type. Filaments with no balls or tufts at the ends are considered a "doubtful" type (see Figure 4–5). When the mares' tails are followed very shortly by cirro-strati and then by the lowering alto-strati they indicate definitely the approach of a storm within from twenty-four to forty-eight hours.

Closely allied to the "mares' tail" in structure and appearance but considerably lower, and *much* lower than the fair-weather cirrus, is the "windy cirrus" (cirrus-ventosus). This cloud is almost a positive indication of a coming depression

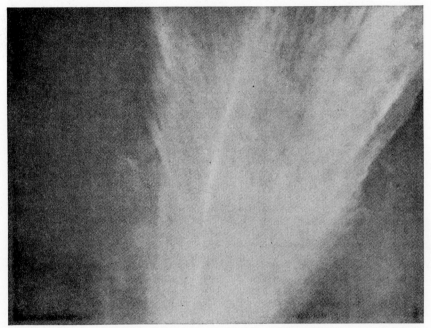

From "Cloud Studies," A. W. Clayden. Permission E. P. Dutton & Co., Inc.

FIG. 4–4. Band cirrus (cirrus-vittatus).

with considerable wind. It is characterized by curving branches leaning forward in the direction of movement and by other long curving branches lagging behind and below. Fluffy parts are usually present, marking the origins of the long curving fibers. Undoubtedly this cloud, like others of a similar order, is formed by direct change of water from the vapor to the solid, and the fibers are made of minute snow-

flakes. The condensation is evidently attended by rapid movements which draw out the cloud, as fast as it is formed, into
long, curving lines which mark lines of motion. This variety
is always, therefore, an indication of strong winds and rapid
eddying movements in the region in which it occurs. Such
strong disturbances overhead are sometimes followed, but

H. T. Floreen.

FIG. 4–5. Cirrus and cirro-stratus clouds, merging toward the horizon.

more usually accompanied, by similar movements of lesser
intensity at the ground level.

In squally or thundery weather, a special kind of cirrus
called "false cirrus" or "cirrus densus" often emanates from
the "anvils" of a cumulo-nimbus (Fig. 4–21, p. 63). This
is not a true cirrus cloud; it is much lower and more dense.

Cirro-stratus (Cs)—Figures 4–5, 4–6, and 4–7

Cirro-stratus appears in patches as a thin whitish sheet. At times it completely covers the sky, producing a general whitish appearance, while at other times it takes a more or less distinct form resembling a web. Such a sheet often produces halos around the sun and moon, as shown in Figure 4–6. This cloud is similar to the cirrus but is lower, thicker, and

G. A. Clarke.

FIG. 4–6. Cirro-stratus in a thin, fibrous sheet with halo.

forms a more uniform sheet. It is composed of ice crystals, and its average altitude is about 28,000 feet.

Like cirrus, cirro-stratus sometimes forms as a result of the evaporation and subsequent re-condensation at a higher level of cumulus and cumulo-nimbus. It has no connection with approaching cyclonic disturbance, but since all energetic depressions produce this type of cloud, its appearance is a good indication of rain. When cirro-stratus appears within a few hours after cirrus, the probability of rain during the next twenty-four hours is about 80 per cent. A halo in the sky has long been considered as a sign of coming rain, although it merely shows the presence of cirro-stratus. The character and appearance of cirro-stratus which follows cirrus will usually give an idea of the intensity of the depression, and therefore of the danger of gales.

Cirro-stratus following cirrus is illustrated in Figure 4–5.

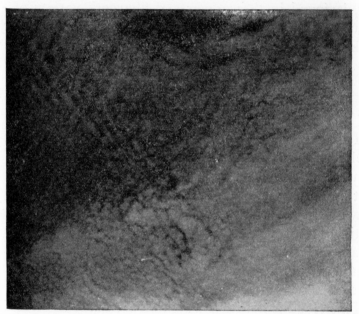

H. T. Floreen.

FIG. 4–7. Cirro-cumulus. There is some cirro-stratus in lower right portion of the picture.

Cirro-cumulus (Cc)—Figure 4–7

Cirro-cumuli are small globular masses, or white flakes either without shadows or with very slight shadows, arranged in groups and often in lines. The average altitude is about 22,000 feet.

Cirro-cumulus is pre-eminently the cloud of beauty. It forms from a single or double undulation of cirrus or cirro-stratus sheet which is to a certain degree unstable at its altitude. This instability, however, is frequently of very limited duration; cirri and cirro-strati often are observed to pass quickly into cirro-cumuli and then to reappear shortly after in their original form, with no evidence of cirro-cumulus structure.

This type of cloud occurs frequently in its soft "flocculent" form, as shown in Figure 4–7, and is usually an indication of fair weather. An indication of coming rain and wind, however, is found in that grayer and "harder" variety of cirro-cumulus which resembles the scaly pattern on the backs of mackerel, and produces what is known as "mackerel sky."

MEDIUM CLOUDS

Alto-stratus (As)—Figures 4–8 and 4–9

This is a striated, fibrous, or smooth veil, more or less gray or bluish in color like thick cirro-stratus, but without halo phenomena. The sun or moon usually shows vaguely with a faint gleam, as through ground glass. This is popularly known as a "watery sky." Differences of thickness may cause relatively light patches between very dark parts but the under-surface never shows sharp relief, although there is usually a striated or fibrous structure in places, and occasionally a mammillated appearance.

This cloud is not itself a rain cloud, but is associated with the coming wet weather. It usually precedes a general rain by a few hours; in the northern part of the United States, this period is about six hours.

When cirro-stratus follows cirrus within a few hours and is in turn followed by alto-stratus, the probability of rain within the succeeding 6 to 12 hours is about 90 per cent, which is as great an accuracy as can be derived from a knowledge of the conditions prevailing over the country as gained from the weather map.

The approximate height of alto-stratus is about 17,000 feet, and its thickness is considerably greater than one would

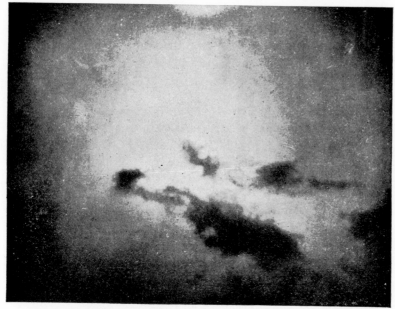

G. A. Clarke.

FIG. 4–8. Thin alto-stratus with fracto-stratus (or fracto-cumulus) below.

U. S. Weather Bureau.

FIG. 4–9. Alto-stratus, with thin alto-cumulus at a lower level.

ordinarily imagine, being from 1,000 to 2,700 feet thick at different times of the year.

Alto-cumulus (Ac) —Figures 4–10, 4–11, 4–12, 4–13

Alto-cumuli are rather large globular masses, white or grayish, partially shaded, arranged in groups or lines, and often so closely packed that their edges appear confused. The smaller elements of the regularly arranged units may be fairly

F. Ellerman.

FIG. 4–10. Turreted alto-cumulus (*castellatus*) above and tall cumulus (*castellatus*) below (at left).

small and thin, with or without shading appearing around the margin of a group whose center is generally larger and more compact. This is shown in Figure 4–12.

A cloud sheet that is continuous, at least over the greater part of the layer, and consists of dark and more or less irregular elements, with sharp relief on the under-surface of the

C. F. Brooks.

Fig. 4–11. Lenticular alto-cumulus.

C. F. Brooks.

Fig. 4–12. Alto-cumulus, active form.

sheet, is classed as alto-cumulus. This is illustrated in Figure 4–13.

Figure 4–11 shows the lenticular form of alto-cumulus, most frequently seen above mountains and high plateaus, where they are constantly blown by wind, and often molded into rolls. Small cloud flakes break off from the leeward edges and evaporate. Again, they may assume an ovoid

A. C. Lapsley.

FIG. 4–13. Alto-cumulus, laminated form, resulting from degeneration of cloud sheet.

shape, as shown in the illustration, through the arching up of a humid layer.

An indication of a change to a chaotic and thundery sky is the variety *alto-cumulus castellatus*. In its lower parts it resembles the ordinary alto-cumulus arranged in a line and resting on a common base, but in its upper parts its shows development with turreted and castellated tops rising through the unstable layer about them. (See Figure 4–10.)

LOW CLOUDS

Strato-cumulus (Sc)—Figures 4–14 and 4–15

Strato-cumulus develops patches, or a layer, of laminae, globular masses, or rolls, the smallest of the regularly arranged elements being fairly large, soft, and gray with darker parts. It shows a low, continuous sheet also which may be thick or thin with distinct irregularities of large size.   The elements

F. Ellerman.

Fig. 4–14.   Strato-cumulus, photographed from an altitude of 5,700 feet. To an observer at sea level these would appear to be higher and smaller and might be called alto-cumulus.

are arranged in groups, lines, or waves, aligned in one or two directions.   Very often the rolls are so close together that the edges join.   They may cover the whole sky with a wavy appearance.   Strato-cumulus is distinguished from alto-cumulus by this criterion: if the smallest well-defined and regularly arranged elements (not the detached elements which are generally seen on the edges) are no greater in their smallest

diameters than 10 solar diameters, approximately the width
of three fingers when the arm is held extended, the cloud is
alto-cumulus.

Strato-cumulus may be formed from stratus as general convective activity increases and vice versa.　A typical case of this
is shown in Figure 4–15.　The wavy or rolled appearance of
the strato-cumulus is a principal characteristic which serves
to distinguish it from stratus with its flat bases and tops.

W. J. Humphreys.

FIG. 4–15.　Strato-cumulus, irregular rolls.

Strato-cumulus is most frequent in the winter; in this season its altitude is much below the average—often 1,000 feet
or even less.　This is a comparatively thin cloud (the average
thickness is about 1,400 feet) but when well developed it
makes the day dull and dreary.　It will sometimes "burn off"
after the sun breaks through the thin portions and heats the
earth below.　At other times it may cover the sky for several
days without breaking.　Generally there are updrafts under

the thicker portions, which cause considerable bumpiness above and below the cloud, as well as within it. When it appears in rolls, as in Figure 4–15, it is a good indication of wind, for the rolls really mark the crests of atmospheric waves. The rolls lie nearly at right angles to the wind producing them. If there is not much wind at the surface, it should be looked for just *above* the cloud layer.

J. C. Hagen.

FIG. 4–16.   Nimbo-stratus, with fracto-cumulus roll near the horizon.

Nimbo-stratus (Ns)—Figure 4–16

This is a low, amorphous layer, usually nearly uniform, and of a dark-gray color. It seems feebly illuminated, seemingly from the inside.

Nimbo-stratus usually evolves from a layer of alto-stratus which has thickened and developed downward, sometimes with a ragged appearance, and has sunk lower in the atmosphere. Beneath this layer there is generally a progressive development of very low, ragged clouds, separated at first, but later fused into an almost continuous layer. Broken, irregular fragments often drift below the layer, particularly as the storm is breaking up; these are called "scud."

This is the ordinary rain cloud, though not the type which gives the heaviest rainfall. Rain or snow precipitated from nimbo-stratus is usually steady. The base of this cloud is seldom higher than 6,500 feet above the earth; its altitude varies considerably, the most usual level being about 2,000 feet. The duration of the cloud depends upon its size and development, and upon the rate of progression of the general storm conditions with which it is associated. It may last only a few hours, but, especially in winter, it may cover the sky for two or three days. A rising barometer and a change in wind are the usual indications of clearing.

Stratus (St)—Figure 4-17

This is a low, uniform layer of cloud resembling fog, but not resting on the ground.

When thin, stratus gives the sky a characteristic hazy appearance. At other times, there may be a solid sheet of cloud; stratus may reach a thickness of several hundred feet. When broken, it is called fracto-stratus. It may occur with any other type of cloud. During or after precipitation, it frequently forms as "scud" beneath nimbo-stratus.

Stratus may be typical fog which has actually been lifted from the ground; it may also be formed by condensation between cool and warm currents.

Rain from stratus always takes the form of a light drizzle —that is, small droplets very close together. When there is no precipitation, stratus shows some contrasts of dark and light patches, the lighter parts being nearly transparent. Pure stratus (that is, stratus formed as such) usually does not "burn off" as easily as does typical land fog, and may persist for several days before being dissipated.

The aviator may gain valuable information while flying over stratus: under favorable conditions, when the cloud sheet is not too thick, its upper surface indicates the contours of the ground beneath. Rivers and valleys appear as depressions, hills and mountains as elevations. This is a practical point worth remembering; many aviators, doubtful of their location, have been able to get their bearings in just this way.

G. A. Clarke.

FIG. 4–17. Stratus, in a uniform sheet below the level of the hilltop, with shreds of fracto-stratus along the hillside.

A condition of "inversion" (i.e., an *increase* of temperature with increase of altitude) often accompanies stratus; in such a case, the layer of cloud floats just below the stable warm layer of the inversion.

CLOUDS WITH VERTICAL DEVELOPMENT

Cumulus (Cu)—Figures 4–10, 4–18, 4–19

Cumulus is a thick cloud with vertical development; the upper surface is dome-shaped, exhibiting rounded protuberances, while the base is nearly horizontal.

When the cloud is opposite the sun the surfaces toward the observer are brighter than the edges of the protuberances. When the light comes from the side the cloud shows strong contrasts of light and shade. Seen against the sun the cloud is dark with bright edges, like the top of the cumulo-nimbus in Fig. 4–20. True cumulus is sharply defined above and below; its surface often appears hard and clear-cut. There

H. T. Floreen.

Fig. 4–18. Cumulus of fair weather (cumulus humilis).

is a ragged type of cumulus, however, called fracto-cumulus (Fc), which shows continual change. Cumulus has a uniform structure; that is, it is composed of rounded parts right up to its summit with no fibrous structure. The base is usually gray. Even when large, cumulus produces only light precipitation.

This type of cloud is always formed by the action of convective currents in the following manner:

Air warmed by contact with the earth's surface under sunshine, becoming lighter, rises as a cork rises through water; thus an ascending current is created. This effect is most pronounced over the sunny slopes of mountains and unwooded areas, over plowed fields and sandy beaches; it is less pronounced over cool forest-lands, fields covered with grassy

F. Ellerman.

FIG. 4–19. Cumulus and cumulo-nimbus. The large cloud has just grown into cumulo-nimbus.

crops, and over lakes. The current cools the warm air by expansion as it rises, finally reaching its dew point; a cloud begins to form at what is called the condensation level, which marks the flat base of the cloud. By its own inertia, sometimes with the aid of unstable conditions, the air rises beyond this level, and so the cloud grows vertically until halted by a layer of stable air.

Because they are the visible tops of invisible ascending currents, cumuli are of great interest to the aviator. Since rising warm air is replaced by descending colder air, downward currents also are to be expected. Cumuli indicate areas of turbulence, or "bumpiness," of which the pilot should beware, especially when flying a heavily loaded plane, or when flying at low altitudes. On the average, these turbulent areas extend between the altitudes of 4,000 feet and 6,000 feet, though they may reach as high as 10,000 feet.

Research shows that the rate of ascent of warm air currents often reaches 10 to 12 feet per second. In thunderstorms, the rate is much more rapid.

Although the most active ascending currents are practically certain to produce clouds, turbulence frequently does occur on cloudless days, when the air is dry. In such a case, the air is not cooled to its dew point until it reaches very high altitudes. We see now why those fine, warm, summer skies, which appear ideal for flying, turn out to be uncomfortably bumpy.

A type of cumulus which is flat and only slightly rounded on top, with little vertical development, and which shows only faint shadows, or none, on the under side, is called *cumulus humilis*. This is an indication of fine, fair weather. Cumulus humilis is illustrated in Figure 4–18, ordinary cumulus in Figure 4–19.

Cumulus clouds which grow to great heights with typical "cauliflower" structure indicating great turbulence, internal motion, and congestion within, are called *cumulus congestus*. This type usually develops very rapidly into the cumulonimbus or thunderstorm cloud described in the next section.

Cumulo-nimbus (Cb)—Figures 4–19, 4–20, 4–21, and 4–22

This is a heavy mass of cloud with great vertical development. The upper part rises like a tower or mountain, often

U. S. Navy.

Fig. 4–20.   An isolated cumulo-nimbus, showing a rain shower from its base.

A. F. McQuarrie.

Fig. 4–21.   Cumulo-nimbus with anvil.

spreading out in the form of an anvil, and has a fibrous texture.

Cumulo-nimbus generally produces showers of rain or snow, sometimes of hail, and often thunderstorms as well. A mass of cumulus, however heavy it may be and however great its vertical development, should not be classed as cumulo-nimbus unless at least part of its top is in the process of transformation into a cirrus mass. When a quick, heavy shower occurs, it may be assumed that the cloud is cumulo-nimbus even though lower clouds may hide the fibrous crown. Figure 4–19 shows a typical cumulo-nimbus not yet completely developed but already showing the fibrous texture along the upper right edge of the "tower."

Figure 4–20 shows a fully developed cumulo-nimbus with rain already falling from it. Note the false cirrus (cirrus densus) or "scarf cloud" floating out from the right edge of the cloud about half way to the summit.

Figure 4–21 shows a typical cumulo-nimbus with its great anvil head spreading out over it. Note the ragged edge to the anvil and the wisps of cirrus about it. The anvil is composed chiefly of ice crystals which are extremely active nuclei for raindrops. Often such an anvil or tower may be seen in the sunlight from many miles away long before the base of the cloud becomes visible. This signpost in the sky marks an area of most turbulent air with probable hail and torrential rain of the "cloudburst" variety. *The sensible flyer never attempts to fly through or under such a storm but always goes around it.*

A mammillated formation often appears on the lower surface of the lateral parts of the anvil or under the low storm collar. In the first area this formation is quiescent; in the second it "boils." The boiling type appears at the beginning of a squall or just before. This cloud is called *cumulo-nimbus mammatus;* an example is shown in Figure 4–22.

The author has seen thin sheets of pure stratus, also, with just such a mammillated structure. These formed in humid air at about 4,000 feet. Such a formation usually appears below an inversion, whose stable layer prevents further upward development.

The *line squall* is a type of storm which advances across the country along a broad front. It extends across the sky in the form of a long line of an arch and is called *cumulo-nimbus arcus*. Except for the tornado and hurricane it is the

W. J. Humphreys.

FIG. 4–22. Cumulo-nimbus mammatus.

most violent of all storms. It will be discussed further in Chapter V.

The Tornado Cloud

A characteristic black, funnel-shaped cloud always announces the tornado. It is associated with general thunderstorm conditions and with a pronunced cold front with possible line squalls. The tornado is the briefest of storms, living but an hour or two, but is also one of the most destructive.

Its diameter may be only a few feet or a mile. Since the pressure at the center is much lower than that of the surroundings, violent whirling winds are produced, often with speeds exceeding 200 miles per hour.

Wide World Photo

FIG. 4–23. This towering funnel-shaped tornado swept towards Rockwall, Texas, April 30, 1947, disrupting communication lines and damaging nearby farm houses. This picture was made by Maxine Buhler, a nurse, enroute to Rowlett, Texas.

The Waterspout

The waterspout is similar in nature to the tornado, though usually far less violent.

The author has personally observed waterspouts off the west coast of Mexico. On that occasion, 10 were observed within one hour, seven being visible at one time. Gray patches of strato-cumulus were floating lazily at an altitude of about 2,000 feet. In each case, a whirl started at the base of one of these patches. Then from the center of the whirling area, the cloud extended downward in an irregular funnel shape to about the 1,500-foot level. From this point, an unsteady, whirling, tube-shaped cloud 20 to 40 feet in diameter descended toward the surface of the ocean.

Directly under the end of the tube, the water became violently disturbed and began to whirl in a counterclockwise direction. (This was observed through powerful field glasses, from a distance of about 800 yards.) From the whirling area, which had a diameter of about 75 feet, light clouds of vapor, known as "cascade," rose to meet the snout of the descending tube. The cloud tube and the rising vapor were distinctly seen rotating around a hollow core.

Of the 10 waterspouts, only 3 or 4 made a complete junction with the surface of the water; the tubes of the others descended to between 500 and 1,000 feet of the water, and then appeared to be drawn back up into the clouds above. The complete waterspouts remained whole for from 5 to 10 minutes, and then broke at an altitude of about 250 feet, the upper sections of the tubes being drawn upward, while the lower sections dissipated in the surrounding air.

According to old legends of the sea, waterspouts have been broken by shells or cannonballs fired into them. A shell can hardly break up a cloud; these waterspouts may have broken naturally just when the shells were fired. Although the author, being a lover of the sea in all its moods, is reluctant to destroy any of its romance, he believes that this particular legend should be dissipated like the broken waterspouts.

Fog

Fogs are stratus clouds formed at or near the surface of the ground or water. They are classified under five main types, according to the manner in which they were formed, as follows:

(a) Radiation fogs.
(b) Advection fogs.
(c) Upslope fogs.

(d) Frontal fogs.

(e) Convergent fogs.

Radiation fogs. After sunset, the surface of the earth radiates the heat received from the sun's rays during the day and is cooled; the surface temperature may fall well below that of the lower layers of the air. If calm conditions prevail, these lower layers are cooled by contact, and if surface temperatures fall below the dew point, condensation takes place close to the ground. Thus radiation fog is formed. Being colder and heavier than the overlying air, it first fills up the valleys and low places and so is often called "ground fog." When there is little or no wind the fog is shallow. Light winds cause the air to be chilled to a greater height, through gentle mixing; in this case the fog is deeper. Winds with a speed greater than 5 or 6 miles per hour usually cause such thorough mixing of the warm and cool air that the temperature inversion is destroyed and no fog forms. As the sun rises the earth's surface and the air in contact with it are warmed; then fog of this type "burns off," usually within an hour or two. The rising vapor then, frequently, recondenses at a higher altitude as a layer of stratus.

Advection fogs. This type of fog is usually caused by the passage of warm moist air over a colder surface. The simplest form of this type is produced from comparatively warm sea air which drifts in over colder land surfaces in winter. Such fog is usually quite shallow and, like radiation fog, burns off quickly under the influence of the sun. Another type of advection fog forms in summer when air from the heated land surfaces flows out over the cooler surface of the ocean. In midafternoon, because of the increased heat over the land surfaces, a light sea breeze springs up and the dense fog which formed over the sea is carried inland. Later at night when the land breeze again prevails the fog moves back over the sea. Sometimes when winds are light, fog formed in this way persists for a day or more. In the same manner although on a smaller scale, advection fogs form over and around inland lakes and rivers. Since many of the airports in the Middle West of the United States are located near the shores of lakes and rivers, pilots should be particularly watchful for such fogs especially after dark.

Advection fogs also form at sea when air heated by a warm current moves over a colder current, or over the colder inshore waters emptying from large rivers. If the temperature differences are slight, conditions are not greatly different from those producing radiation fog; only a shallow fog is formed which soon burns off under the action of the sun. When temperature differences are large fog may form even in the face of high winds, and may become very dense and very deep; under these conditions the fog may even lift somewhat above the surface, becoming, in effect, a low-lying stratus cloud.

A less frequent type of advection fog is caused by the passage of very cold, dry air over a warmer water surface. The heating of the lower contact layer causes rapid evaporation from the water surface but condensation occurs just above. This type is seen most frequently in the Arctic regions and is called "arctic smoke." However, the author has observed it as far south as Washington, D. C., during the freakish cold snap in February, 1940. The phenomenon occurred over the unfrozen surface of the Anacostia River when cold, dry, polar air with a temperature of only 6° F settled down to the ground from the upper atmosphere.

Upslope fogs form chiefly on the great plains of the West which rise gradually from about 1,000 feet of elevation at the Missouri River to 5,000 feet at the eastern foot of the Rockies. An easterly wind in this area results in mechanical lifting of the air. The adiabatic cooling caused by expansion under decreasing pressure reduces the temperature of the air about 5.5° F for each 1,000 feet of ascent. (Note: The "adiabatic" process of heating and cooling of air is explained in Chapter V.) Air moving westward from the eastern boundary of Nebraska and cooling adiabatically should, therefore, be about

22° colder when it reaches the western boundary of the state. The greater the wind velocity, the more rapid is the cooling. Dense fogs often form in these regions even with fairly strong winds. Of course, conditions which would of themselves produce radiation fogs often are contributing factors.

Frontal fogs may form at any stage of the passing of a "front." (Fronts are discussed in Chapter VII.) When rain falls into the cool air just ahead of a warm front, the moisture content of the air is increased and its dew point raised, so that fog forms sometimes almost instantaneously. Surface cooling by a heavy shower also contributes to the formation of such fog. The mixing of warmer air with the air of a cold front may produce temporary fog as the front passes.

Convergent fogs are one of the most important types of fog and one which is directly related to frontal activity. They are caused by convergence in the cold air beneath either a cold front, a warm front, or an occlusion. Any condition which causes a convergence of the cold air beneath a front toward the frontal surface will cause a forced ascent of the cold air beneath the front. If the humidity of the cold air is close to the saturation point before this ascent starts, it is clear that condensation will occur within a short time after the cold air commences rising. Since convergence caused in this way may cause the ascent of cold air over a very wide region under a frontal surface, and since the rate of ascent is frequently relatively uniform over a wide area, this type of fog may affect simultaneously a widespread region.

There are other sub-classifications of fog, modified more or less by local conditions in each case. This section is not intended as a complete treatment of the subject; to the student who wishes to go more deeply into the subject, the author recommends Dr. George F. Taylor's treatment of it in his excellent *Aeronautical Meteorology* (Pitman, 1938).

Until flying by instruments has been perfected, the pilot should make every effort to avoid being caught in the air by fog. It has been said, "Anyone can be taught in a month to fly blind, and then it takes the rest of his lifetime to teach him when *not* to fly."

Hydrometeors

Bodies of solid or liquid water falling through the air are called "hydrometeors." The following classifications are some of the more common:

Rain: The falling from clouds of drops of water (in the liquid state) in which most drops are larger—or, if not larger, sparser—than the drops in drizzle.

Drizzle: Very small and uniformly dispersed droplets that appear to float in the air and to follow very slight air currents.

Freezing Rain: Rain that falls in liquid form but freezes to the exposed surface of the ground or to unheated objects on the ground.

Freezing Drizzle: Drizzle that freezes similarly to rain as described above.

Snow: White or translucent ice crystals chiefly in complex branched hexagonal form (six-pointed "stars"), often mixed with simple crystals.

Granular Snow (or Frozen Drizzle): The solid equivalent of drizzle.

Sleet: Transparent, more or less globular, hard grains of ice, about the size of raindrops, that rebound when striking hard surfaces.

Hail: Ice balls or stones, ranging in diameter from that of medium-sized raindrops to an inch or more.

Soft Hail: White, opaque, round or sometimes conical, kernels of snow-like consistency, 1/16 to 1/4 inch in diameter. It occurs mostly during showers.

Obstructions to Vision

Haze. Extremely fine particles of matter from the earth and tiny salt particles from ocean spray form haze. Haze gives the effect of a fine veil over distant objects; the veil appears pale yellow if the object observed is nearly white, pale blue if the object is dark. The distance at which details can be distinguished is reduced in proportion to the density of the haze. In fair weather, ordinary haze reduces visibility by about two-thirds, and in dull, overcast weather, by about five-sixths.

Dust. Dust consists of extremely fine particles of clay, loam, etc. These may be picked up and held suspended in the air by ascending currents. They are coarser than haze particles and not so evenly distributed in the air, and do not remain in suspension so easily. Seen through dust, the sun appears pale and colorless, or perhaps yellowish, while distant objects take on a light tan or grayish hue. Except in the great dust storms of the midwestern United States, dust is usually local in origin. It affects the appearance of objects according to its own particular color.

Sandstorms. In dry areas, strong winds may pick up coarse particles of sand and carry them a considerable distance, thus producing a sandstorm. Breathing becomes difficult if the particles are inhaled. Considerable damage may be done to aircraft engines and propellers, and in severe sandstorms, visibility may be reduced to zero.

Because of their weight, the coarser particles do not rise more than a few hundred feet. Very fine particles, however, may be carried to great heights and over great distances in the upper atmosphere. An approaching sandstorm appears as a great, dark, billowing wall, and should be avoided, if possible.

Smoke. Smoke is composed of fine particles resulting from incomplete combustion. It is easily confused with dust or haze, or, from a distance, even with fog; sometimes it can be distinguished only by its odor. It is an obstruction to vision, especially in industrial areas and in the vicinity of forest or brush fires. Unlike fog, haze, and dust, it gives the sun a reddish tinge in the daytime and a deeper red color at sunrise and sunset.   Smoke and fog together form a dense mixture commonly called "smog."

QUESTIONS

1. What atmospheric condition causes the formation of clouds?
2. What processes cause formation of clouds by cooling of air?
3. Why should the development and motion of clouds be studied?
4. What are the most active nuclei around which condensation begins?
5. Name the ten main cloud types.   State the approximate average altitude of their bases and their approximate thickness.
6. Describe different forms of cirrus clouds and briefly state their indications.
7. Describe cirro-stratus.   What are its usual indications?
8. Describe cirro-cumulus clouds in their two main forms and state the indications of each.
9. Describe alto-stratus.   With what is it usually associated?
10. Describe alto-cumulus clouds in their most usual forms.
11. Describe strato-cumulus clouds.   (a) What are their distinguishing characteristics?   (b) When are they most frequently seen?   (c) With what atmospheric condition are they associated?
12. Describe nimbo-stratus clouds.   (a) From what are they usually evolved?   (b) What kind of precipitation do they usually produce?
13. Describe stratus. (a) What is fracto-stratus or "scud"?   (b) In what two particular forms may stratus appear?   (c) What form of precipitation does it produce?   (d) What valuable information may be gained while flying above stratus?
14. Name the two types of clouds with vertical development.   (a) What causes their vertical development?   (b) What kind of precipitation do they produce?
15. Describe the following forms of cumulus clouds and state with what each is associated.   (a) Cumulus humilis.   (b) Cumulus congestus.
16. Describe a typical cumulo-nimbus cloud.   (a) From what does it usually develop?   (b) What is an "anvil," and of what is it composed?
17. Why are cumulo-nimbus clouds avoided by sensible fliers?
18. What is a "line squall"?
19. Discuss the tornado cloud from the following points: (a) Appearance.   (b) With what associated.   (c) Extent.   (d) Pressure distribution and wind velocity.
20. What is a waterspout?   Describe its formation.
21. Define fog.   What are the five main types of fog?
22. Discuss briefly the formation of each of the five types of fog.
23. What are hydrometeors?   Name the more common forms of hydrometeors.
24. Define the following: (a) Haze.   (b) Dust.   (c) Sandstorms.   (d) Smoke.   (e) Smog.

Chapter V

VARIATIONS OF TEMPERATURE AND THEIR EFFECTS

Atmospheric Equilibrium

If an air particle, when displaced upward or downward for a short distance, tends to return to its original level, then the atmosphere is said to be in a state of *stability* (or equilibrium). If, on the other hand, the displaced particle tends to continue to move away from its original level, the atmosphere is said to be in a state of *instability*. If the particle, when displaced, tends neither to return to its former level nor to keep moving but rather to remain at its new level, the atmosphere is said to be in a state of *neutral stability*. A fourth, and frequently occurring, state of the atmosphere is found as a combination of the stable and unstable states above. If an air particle is stable during displacement only within certain limits and becomes unstable if displaced beyond those limits, it is said to be in a state of *conditional instability*.

A pendulum suspended with the weighted end down is in a state of stability; if displaced slightly, it will return to its former position. If the same pendulum is exactly balanced on its pivot with the weighted end *up,* it is in a state of instability; any small displacement will cause it to move farther and farther away from the vertical position until it swings to the weight-down position and achieves a state of stability. Similarly, unstable air constantly seeks to reach a state of stability.

An example of neutral stability is found in a perfect ball on a perfectly smooth and perfectly level surface. The ball may be moved readily from one position on the surface to another; yet, when placed in a new position, it has no tendency either to move farther on or to return to its former position. If the ball be started rolling, it will tend to continue its motion, because of its own inertia, until acted upon by some retarding force. Air, likewise, when set in motion, tends to keep moving, because of inertia. The effect of this inertia is superimposed upon that of the displacing force, whether the equilibrium of the air be stable, unstable, or neutral.

Although the principles governing the stratification of the atmosphere are the same as those governing the equilibrium of a pendulum or ball, their operation in regard to the atmosphere is far more complex, since the density of air is greatly affected by both pressure and temperature. Saturation is another complicating factor: when condensation takes place, the latent heat of vaporization (the heat which was stored in the process of evaporation) is released to increase the temperature of the air.

When heat is added, air expands. In expanding, it becomes lighter, and consequently rises, being replaced by descending cooler air. The warm air carries its heat with it to a higher level. This transfer of heat by ascending and descending currents is called *convection*.

As the warm air rises, it meets with continually decreasing pressure, and so continues to expand. Conversely, the cold air, as it descends, is compressed by the increasing pressure. In both cases, no heat is contributed or taken away by the surroundings. Any process in which there is no gain or loss of heat through outside factors is called an "adiabatic" process.

Unsaturated warm air, expanding adiabatically as it rises, is cooled by its own expansion at the rate of 1° F for each 180 feet (or 5½° F for each 1,000 feet) of ascent. Similarly, unsaturated cool air is warmed by adiabatic compression at the rate of 1° F for each 180 feet of descent. This rate of temperature change of ascending or descending unsaturated air is called the *dry-adiabatic lapse rate*.

When *saturated* air is cooled by expansion, condensation of moisture occurs, and latent heat of vaporization is released. Consequently, the rate of cooling is only about half that of unsaturated air. We call this the *saturation-adiabatic* or *moist-adiabatic lapse rate.* The actual figure depends upon the temperature and pressure, and the weight of water being condensed. For practical purposes, we use the average figure, which is approximately 1° F for each 360 feet of change in altitude.

When saturated air is cooled by expansion so that not only condensation but *precipitation also* occurs, the rate of cooling becomes more rapid than the moist-adiabatic due to the heat lost by the rain falling out of the cloud as soon as it condenses. As heat is lost, the process is no longer truly adiabatic and is called a *pseudo-adiabatic process,* with its corresponding *pseudo-adiabatic lapse rate.*

In Chapter II we learned that below the tropopause, the atmosphere grows colder, on the average, with increasing altitude. The left-hand curves in Figure 2–1 (average temperature-height curves) show the "lapse rate" of temperature with altitude which is about 1.7° C or 3° F per thousand feet. Remember that Figure 2–1 shows the *average* temperature-height curves for summer and winter. The actual curve for any particular locality on any given day may vary considerably from the average, particularly in the lower altitudes. It may also change quite radically in the course of the day under various influences explained later in this chapter.

With these principles in mind let us now examine in detail the reactions of an air particle under different conditions of stability and instability.

Let us take for an example a body of unsaturated air at the surface of the earth with a temperature of 65° F and a dew point of 49° F at sea level. Now the following points should be noted: (1) in the dry-adiabatic cooling of unsaturated air, the dew point decreases about 1° F for each 1,000 feet as the air rises and expands, or increases by the same amount as it sinks and is compressed.   (2) In moist-adiabatic cooling, the dew point decreases (or increases) at the same rate as the temperature of the air.   In Figure 5–1 we see what happens when the distribution of temperature in relation to height (as shown by the temperature-height curve) is such that there is (1) a slow lapse rate, (2) a rapid lapse rate, and (3) a medium lapse rate.   For the sake of simplicity the temperature-height curves and the "adiabats" (curves of adiabatic lapse rate) are drawn as straight lines approximating the actual curves.

Stability.   Temperature-height curve No. 1 illustrates a slow lapse rate of about $2\frac{1}{2}°$ F per thousand feet.   An air particle lifted from the surface of A and carried through the surrounding atmosphere would cool dry-adiabatically until it reached its saturation temperature or dew point, at 49° F, in this case at 3,555 feet, since $\dfrac{65-49}{5\frac{1}{2}-1}=\dfrac{16}{4.5}=3.555$.   This point, where condensation begins, is known as the *"condensation level."*   Thereafter it would cool moist-adiabatically as shown by the moist-adiabat.   From the figure, we see that the particle would arrive at each level with a temperature lower than that of the surrounding atmosphere.   Being colder, it would be denser than the surrounding air at any level above point A; it would therefore resist being lifted and, if left to itself, would return to its original level.   In such a case in which the adiabats are always on the "cold side" of the temperature-height curve, the atmosphere is said to be *totally stable.*

Instability.   Now let us consider temperature-height curve No. 2 which shows a rapid lapse rate of about $7\frac{1}{2}°$ F per thousand feet.   Here, also, the lifted air particle would cool dry-adiabatically up to point C and then follow the moist-adiabat. In this case, however, the particle would arrive at each level above point A with a temperature *higher* than that of the surrounding atmosphere.   Being, therefore, less dense and lighter than the surrounding air it would tend to assist the lifting force and, if left to itself, would continue to move upward.   Above point C, its upward motion would become greatly accelerated since the difference in temperatures of the particle and the surrounding atmosphere would increase rapidly. In such a case in which the adiabats are always on the "warm side" of the temperature-height curve, the air is said to be *totally unstable*.

Conditional Instability. Between the two states of atmospheric equilibrium which we already have discussed, there is a state in which the temperature-height curve shows the atmos-

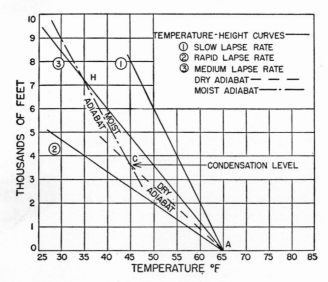

FIG. 5–1. Illustrating (1) stability, (2) instability, and (3) conditional instability.

pheric lapse rate to lie *between* the dry-adiabatic and moist-adiabatic lapse rates. In this case the lifted air particle being colder than the surrounding atmosphere would resist being lifted. At an altitude of 7,200 feet, at which level the particle would have neutral stability, resistance would cease. Above that point the particle, being warmer than the surrounding air, would assist the lifting force. We see that the particle is stable from the ground up to 7,200 feet and is unstable above that level. Since in such a case the instability of a body of air is conditional upon its being lifted to a certain level, the air is said to be *conditionally unstable*.

The cases discussed in the preceding paragraphs and illustrated in Figure 5–1 show only the behavior of an air particle which begins its ascent from the earth's surface.   These principles hold at any level.   It should be remembered, however, that the temperature-height curve for any great change of altitude is seldom, if ever, a straight line.   The curve varies in shape and slope under different conditions.   This point will be illustrated in Figures 5–2 to 5–7, inclusive.   From a study of the actual temperature-height curve the depth of the stable and unstable layers of air may be determined.

Diurnal Temperature Changes of the Atmosphere

Of the high-frequency (short-wave) radiation emitted by the sun as light rays, only about 15 per cent is absorbed by the atmosphere, which permits practically free passage of this type of radiation.   About 42 per cent of this radiation is immediately returned to space, partly by the "scattering" produced by gas molecules and dust particles, but chiefly by reflection from clouds and from the surface of the earth.   Only about 43 per cent reaches the earth, 8 per cent being reflected directly into space.   The remaining 35 per cent is absorbed by the earth's surface and, like that portion absorbed by the air, is converted into low-frequency, long-wave radiation (heat waves).

A part of the long-wave energy emitted by the earth is radiated directly into the air, and of this, a small part is returned to the earth once more by convective currents.   The major portion is absorbed by water vapor and by the water of the clouds; it is transmitted to the atmosphere through the process of evaporation.   Eventually, all the long-wave radiation of the earth and the atmosphere is given up to space, but at a slower rate than that at which short-wave radiation is received.   We find that the daily average total of atmospheric energy is nearly constant.

Air close to the ground is heated chiefly by direct contact with the earth's surface. This heating by contact occurs only in the surface layer; the effects decrease with increasing altitude. Above a certain level, the atmosphere is heated entirely by solar radiation. The air near the surface is heated in one manner over land, in another over oceans. For this reason, we shall consider these phenomena separately.

Diurnal Temperature Changes of Air over Land Areas. Let us refer to Figure 5-2:

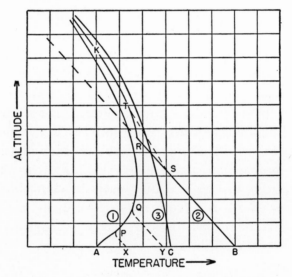

Fig. 5-2. Diurnal variation of temperature with altitude, over LAND areas.

At night, the surface of the ground, radiating its heat, becomes cooler than the air immediately above it. By contact, the lower layers of the atmosphere are cooled in turn to a temperature lower than that of the layers just above. The temperature-height curve resembles Curve No. 1 in the diagram. The air near the surface, instead of growing colder with increased altitude (as illustrated by the *average* curve in Figure 2-1), actually grows warmer. This phenomenon is called an *inversion*. (Inversions will be discussed later in this chapter.)

After sunrise, the surface of the earth becomes warmed and heats the air in contact with it.   At the same time the upper air is heated slightly by direct radiation.   The lapse rate close to the ground changes from negative (as at A) to positive (as at X).   When it equals the dry-adiabatic lapse rate, warmed air rises and cools at that rate until it reaches altitude P where it meets with an "inverted" condition.   There it has a tendency to rest, being colder and heavier than the air above.

As heating continues, however, and as warmed air continues to rise from below, the inversion is gradually lessened and may even be entirely overcome.   This process is ilustrated by the dotted section of curve Y-Q.   The heated air, carrying moisture with it, then mounts to higher and higher levels as the depth of the unstable layer increases.   At about midday the surface temperature reaches point B; the temperature-height curve now resembles Curve No. 2.   If the water vapor content is low, so that the air has not yet been cooled to its dew point, the curve follows the dry-adiabat (broken line) to altitude R, then follows curve R-T-K.   On the other hand, if evaporation at the ground has produced such humidity that at altitude S the dew point has been reached, the rising air follows the moist-adiabat (dotted line) S-T, and then the curve T-K.   In this case S is the condensation level and clouds form between altitudes S and T.

The outgoing radiation increases until about two hours after the sun has passed the meridian when a balance is reached between heat being received at the earth's surface and being radiated.   After this the radiation of heat is greater and the temperature of the surface decreases.

Again the lower layers of air are cooled, the temperature lapse rate decreases, and the atmosphere becomes stable.   By evening, it reaches a condition illustrated by Curve No. 3.

The diurnal heating of the air causes a steep lapse rate in the lower atmosphere, with consequent rising currents, which stir and mix the air of the lower levels, and often of much higher levels. These currents, which convey heat and moisture to the higher levels, are called *convectional currents*.

The annual variations of temperature have the same effect, on a larger scale, as the diurnal variations: they tend to maintain a steep lapse rate of temperature in the lower atmosphere, with consequent mixing of the air by convectional currents.

Diurnal Temperature Changes of Air over Water Areas. The temperature of a large water surface is but slightly affected by solar short-wave radiation. Except when the sun stands high above the horizon, most of this radiation is reflected as by a mirror and is projected back to outer space. When the sun is directly overhead, little radiation is lost by reflection, but since water offers little resistance to the solar rays, they penetrate to great depths before being completely absorbed. The heat thus distributed through a great volume of water can have little effect on the surface temperature. The effect is further reduced because of the high specific heat of sea water.

Some of the heat which the sea gains from the sun is used in producing evaporation from the surface. In the process, the surface water increases in salinity, and therefore in density; it sinks, and is replaced by colder water from below. For this reason also, the net temperature rise is very small. (Very shallow water is an exception. In this case, the bottom is heated by unabsorbed radiation and, by contact, warms the water.)

At night, outgoing radiation cools the surface of the ocean. This increases the density of the surface water so that it sinks and is replaced by lighter and warmer water from below. Thus both by day and by night the processes of nature operate to keep the surface of the ocean at a nearly constant temperature; the usual diurnal change amounts to less than 1° F.

Since the temperature of the sea surface changes but little that of the air close above it is also nearly constant. This effect, however, prevails for only a few hundred meters upward. Above this altitude we find a layer in which the tem-

perature variation is controlled by radiation only.   Here the
diurnal variation of temperature may be considerably greater
than that at the surface.   Above this layer the effect of radiation gradually decreases until there is practically no diurnal
variation, the temperature remaining fairly constant through
day and night.

Figure 5–3 illustrates these phenomena.   Curve No. 1 is
a typical temperature-height curve for night, Curve No. 2
for noon, and Curve No. 3 for a time about two hours later
when the air is receiving its greatest heat from radiation.   We

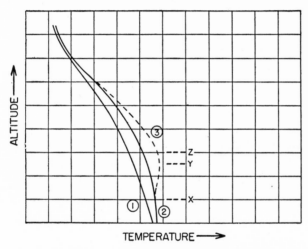

Fɪɢ. 5–3.   Diurnal variation of temperature with altitude, over ᴡᴀᴛᴇʀ areas.

see that between night and noon the surface temperature increases but slightly, whereas that above the surface layer increases considerably because of radiation.   In the upper atmosphere, the radiational effect is very small and there is little
temperature change.   Curve No. 3 shows a not unusual condition, in which the radiational effect is sufficient to produce
an inversion, with resulting stabilization, above the layer controlled by surface contact.

As the day wears on and radiational effect decreases, the
air becomes cooler, and the curve moves back toward the left.

Daytime stability is lost with the change from a negative lapse rate (that of inversion) to a positive. Above altitude Z, however, the reverse is true: here the lapse rate has *increased* during the day, producing unstable conditions; in the evening, as the upper part of this layer radiates the heat acquired during the day and cools, it returns to a state of stability.

To sum up: Over water areas, the lower part of the atmosphere tends toward stability during the day and toward instability at night. Above this lies another layer which tends toward instability during the day and toward stability at night. In the upper atmosphere, there is little diurnal temperature change.

The marked difference between diurnal variation of stability of the lower atmosphere over land areas and that over water areas should be remembered, for this difference has a considerable effect upon the weather.

Temperature Changes in Itinerant Air Masses

An *air mass* may be defined, preliminarily, as an extensive portion of the atmosphere, homogeneous throughout, with properties more or less uniform at each level. (Air masses will be discussed in detail in Chapter VII.)

A *warm air mass* is any air mass whose temperature at ground level is higher than that of the surface over which it lies or travels. An example is an air mass originating in the tropics and traveling toward the polar regions over a surface which becomes progressively colder.

A *cold air mass* is any air mass whose temperature at ground level is lower than that of the surface over which it lies or travels. An example is an air mass originating in the polar regions and traveling toward the tropics, or over a warm ocean current.

As it travels, a warm air mass is cooled by contact with the colder surface. A marked stability is produced in the lowest layer. Convection is retarded, so that the cooling is limited to the lower strata. This effect is modified, however, by the diurnal temperature variation. A land surface with a temperature only slightly lower than that of the overlying air may be warmed by the sun sufficiently to nullify this tendency. The lowest layer of the air then becomes unstable, the effect spreading upward through the mass. Nightfall, however, cools the surface and re-establishes stability in the air mass. Under these conditions, the warm air mass is stable at night, but unstable during the day. But if the warm air mass is traveling over a much colder land surface, or over a sea surface, where the diurnal temperature variation is small, it will remain stable through both day and night.

A cold air mass is heated from below as it travels. The lapse rate of temperature in the lower layers is increased; instability is produced, with convectional currents which carry heat and moisture to higher and higher levels. This is the process described on page 80 (Figure 5–2). This effect also is modified by the diurnal heating and cooling of the surface. When the difference between the air and surface temperature is large, instability will persist through both night and day. When the difference is small, however, the lower layers of air may become stable at night, returning to a state of instability after sunrise.

The equilibrium of itinerant air masses is affected much more by land surfaces than by sea surfaces. The effect of the general surface temperature along the route over which the air mass travels is usually stronger than that of the diurnal variation, except over tropical oceans, which have fairly constant surface temperatures.

Convection

Cloud forms reveal the presence of ascending and descending air currents. We know that clouds of the cumulus type do not float; rather, the minute drops of water which compose them are continually falling, but falling in a rising current of air. The turkey buzzard, soaring to a higher level without flapping a wing, makes use of this principle. He is not using magic to escape the law of gravity; he is falling all the time at a certain rate. But he has learned to do his falling in air currents which are ascending at a *faster* rate.

Rising air currents may be expected beneath a cumulus cloud, and especially just ahead of it; over a sandy beach, a desert, a paved highway; over ploughed dry ground; over smokestacks, and over large buildings, especially those with wide, flat roofs. Descending air currents may be found over lakes and streams, swamps, and wooded areas.

Knowledge of vertical currents is of major importance to pilots of power-driven aircraft; it is of *vital* importance to glider pilots. The few examples given here merely suggest the possibilities in this field. The wise pilot will study the subject in detail, by observation. At low altitudes, especially in taking off and landing, failure to observe and heed indications of descending air currents may mean disaster.

How do convectional currents affect the weather?

We know that, when air near the surface is heated so that the temperature-lapse rate exceeds the dry-adiabatic rate, air becomes unstable. It rises and is replaced by denser air from above. The ascending currents thus created carry heat and moisture to the higher levels. Instability is the cause of various weather phenomena, such as gustiness, turbulence, and cumulus clouds with the showers and thunderstorms which develop from them.

Unstable air rises until it reaches a state of stability. The height of its ascent depends upon the thickness of the unstable layer. Convectional phenomena are determined by the temperature-height curve, the thickness of the unstable layer, and the altitude of the condensation level. Since these factors are of major importance to the aviator let us examine several typical situations:

(*a*) The unstable layer does not extend up to the altitude of the condensation level.

(*b*) A completely stable layer overlies the unstable layer, the condensation level lying within the unstable layer.

(*c*) The condensation level lies at the top of the unstable layer, which is covered by a conditionally unstable layer, above which the air is stable.

(*d*) Same as (*c*) but with freezing temperatures in the conditionally unstable layer.

Situation (a)—Figure 5-4. Since the air is stable above S, convectional currents are prevented from rising above that level. As they cannot reach the condensation level at C no clouds are formed. This situation frequently occurs in the early morning after clear, calm nights. After sunrise, the

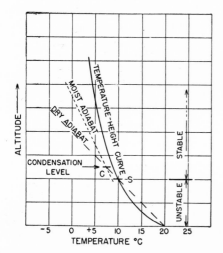

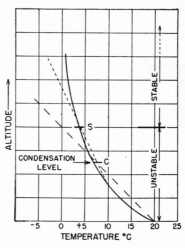

Fig. 5-4. Convection. Situation (A).   Fig. 5-5. Convection. Situation (B).

depth of the unstable layer increases as the temperature near the ground increases. One may visualize the adiabats' sliding to the right. Point S slides up along the temperature-height curve and along the dry-adiabat until it reaches altitude C, the condensation level. Here clouds begin to form. The ground temperature need rise only about 2 degrees to produce this effect. Point S then marks the intersection of the moist-adiabat and the temperature-height curve. Further heating of the ground air will cause it to move more rapidly. The clouds formed will be of the cumulus type. Further developments will depend upon the shape of the temperature-height curve higher up.

Situation (b)—Figure 5–5. Since, in this case, the atmosphere is unstable up to altitude S, the convective currents follow the dry-adiabat up to altitude C; at this altitude clouds will start to form. Above C, the rising air cools at the moist-adiabatic rate, losing more and more of its water vapor through condensation. At S, it achieves a stable state. By its own momentum, some of this air rises slightly above S, but in the process is cooled to a temperature below that of its surroundings and sinks back to S. The clouds formed are of the flattish cumulus humilis variety, or fair-weather cumulus, their bases being at altitude C and their tops at altitude S.

Situation (c)—Figure 5–6. Currents of unstable air rise readily to altitude C. At first, only the thinnest of cumulus humilis forms, for as soon as the current strikes the stable part of the conditionally unstable layer, it is prevented from going higher. However, an increase of only 1° C in the temperature at the surface—so that the foot of the temperature-height curve moves to about 21° C (the adiabats moving to the right accordingly)—will send point S upward. The cumuli produced then will grow to great heights. They will be thick and billowing and may even tower in turreted castellations, showing great internal motion. This form is the cumulus congestus. Although it does not produce precipitation it may do so if it develops into cumulo-nimbus which is described in the next paragraph.

Situation (d)—Figure 5–7. This situation is the same as (c) except that the upward-growing clouds finally reach an altitude, beginning at F, at which the temperature is below

freezing.   An important change in the cloud occurs: the tiny
water droplets formed by condensation congeal into ice crystals.   The ice crystals are active nuclei; water will gather
on them forming raindrops or hailstones which grow in size
until the ascending currents can keep them aloft no longer.
The formation of ice crystals is often visible: stray feathery
wisps appear near the cloud summit.   The entire top of the
cloud may soon lose its billowy shape, becoming ragged and

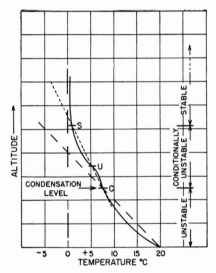

Fig. 5–6. Convection.
Situation (C).

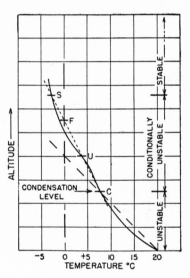

Fig. 5–7. Convection.
Situation (D).

furry and spreading out fanwise into a great "anvil."   The
anvil is composed chiefly of ice crystals which cause precipitation in the cloud.   In this case, a cumulus congestus has
changed to a cumulo-nimbus of the thunderstorm variety.
Heavy precipitation may be expected from it with possible
hail, lightning, and thunder.

By watching the development of cumuli, noting particularly the changes in their upper parts, one often can predict
the weather for several hours in advance.   For example:

Cumulus humilis (Figure 4–17)..........No precipitation will occur.
Cumulus castellatus (Figure 4–10) ....Precipitation may develop.
Cumulus congestus, with ice crystals.....Precipitation will occur soon.
Cumulo-nimbus, with anvil (Figure 4–21)..Heavy precipitation, probably with hail, lightning, and thunder, may be expected.

When cumuli dissolve instead of growing larger, it is a sign that the atmosphere is becoming stable. This is frequently observed in the evening as the air settles down after the heat of the day. The cumuli often flatten out into bulging rolls or break up into layers, then break up into cumuli humilis and evaporate completely.

Precipitation resulting from convection is never steady or lasting, but always of a showery nature, with variable intensity, caused by the ascending and descending currents within the cloud from which it falls.

Over land areas, when convection is the result of diurnal heating, cumuli reach a maximum in the afternoon, dissolving in the evening. Over water areas, where the diurnal temperature variation is small, the maximum of convective clouds occurs at night. However, when the cause of instability is the fact that the air mass is traveling toward warmer areas and consequently is being heated continuously from below, the formation of cumuli with resulting precipitation continues though the day and night.

Thermal Thunderstorms—(Figure 5–8)

The common thunderstorms of summer (*thermal thunderstorms*) are the result of temperature differences and ascending air currents caused by uneven heating within a given body of air. A concrete or macadam road becomes appreciably hotter than a grassy meadow; a plowed field absorbs more heat than the shady woods; the sandy beach becomes hotter than the sea. Air in contact with these warmed surfaces is heated by conduction. As it rises, it cools in conformance with the dry and moist adiabats corresponding to its state of temperature and humidity. (See Figures 5–1 and 5–4 to 5–7.) At the dew point the heat of condensation is added to the temperature of the air and still stronger vertical currents are produced. The clouds formed are cumulo-nimbi. These are described under *Situation* (*d*) and are illustrated in Figure 5–7.

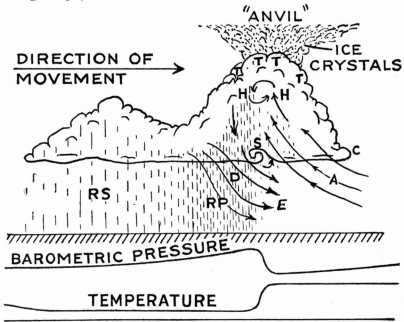

FIG. 5–8. A cross section of a typical cumulo-nimbus (thunderstorm) cloud showing the air currents involved as well as the formation of hail and areas of rain. *A* is the inflowing-ascending air; *D*, the outflowing-descending air; *C*, the storm collar; *S*, roll of "scud," where *A* and *D* meet; *E*, wind gust; *H*, hail; *T*, thunderheads; *RP*, primary rain; *RS*, secondary rain.

As the raindrops grow around their nuclei they increase in weight until they fall. If they grow larger than about 1/6 inch in diameter, their falling velocity exceeds 24 feet per second. Such a velocity, however, will cause these large drops to split into smaller drops, which will fall more slowly. If the ascending currents have a vertical velocity greater than the falling rate of the drops, the drops will be carried upward again, growing, falling, and splitting repeatedly. It must be remembered that the ascending currents are not steady; they come in a succession of gusts and lulls. When the ascensional velocity of the currents is reduced sufficiently, the raindrops will fall out of the cloud.

It is the splitting process, described above, which produces lightning and thunder. When a drop is split, its initially neutral charge of electricity apparently is separated into its component positive and negative charges. The smaller of the resulting droplets have one charge, and the larger have the opposite charge. The smaller droplets are carried upward; the larger droplets tend to gather near the cloud's base or to fall to the ground. Repetition of this process soon builds up tremendous charges of static electricity in different parts of the cloud. When the difference of electric potential between these charges becomes sufficient to break down the insulating effect of the air, a lightning flash occurs, followed by its resulting thunder. Lightning may be produced by the opposite charges in a cloud and in the ground, or in two clouds.

Thunderstorms, particularly of the thermal type, are often accompanied by hail. Hailstones are merely frozen raindrops. Often many successive layers of ice are built up around the drops as they are carried up and down within the cloud.

Some people believe that a hail-bearing cloud can be recognized by its peculiar color and "boiling" characteristics. (See Figure 4–22.) Probably such clouds do carry hail. Any fully developed thunderstorm, however, is more than likely to carry a dangerous load of hail and *should be avoided if possible.*

Many rules have been given for flying in thunderstorms; the safest rule is to avoid them. The hazards of hail may be very great. Vertical currents are often so strong that an aircraft cannot be controlled. Updrafts often extend to such heights that few planes could climb above them. Worse yet, the strong downdrafts often extend all the way down to the surface and may force the aircraft into a crash landing in spite of all efforts to climb.

Even when it is possible to fly above the storm there remains the danger of bad icing conditions. The time used in climbing would allow for many miles of level flight around the storm—a far safer procedure. Usually a thunderstorm of the thermal type just described is local in character and little time is lost by flying around it.

Other types of thunderstorms, which may be termed "mechanical thunderstorms" (in contrast to the thermal type), will be discussed in Chapters VI and Chapter VII since they are more closely associated with the subject matter thereof.

Inversions

Figure 2–1 indicates that the temperature of the atmosphere normally decreases with altitude. The reverse of this condition, called an *inversion,* is illustrated by Curve No. 1, Figure 5–2, and Curve No. 3, Figure 5–3. Inversions develop readily and frequently near the earth's surface during calm, clear nights. They are sure to occur when warm air travels over a cold surface. They may develop above the surface because of radiation as shown by Curve No. 3, Figure 5–3. An inversion may be a few feet or several hundred feet thick, according to the conditions. Since the air of an inversion is stable, convectional currents cannot exist within it. For this reason an inversion is called a "lid," since it prevents the air below it and that above it from mixing.

The altitude of an inversion determines the depth of the layer which can be stirred by convection and turbulence. The diurnal temperature range is affected by this depth. If the inversion lies at low altitude the diurnal change in temperature will be large, for all the heat carried by the convectional currents will be confined to a shallow layer of air. On the other hand, a high inversion tends to restrict the diurnal range of temperature. Inversions at low altitudes are more easily destroyed by diurnal heating and mixing of the air than are high inversions which may persist through both day and night.

Inversions are of great importance to the aviator since all land fogs and morning mists and most, if not all, sea fogs occur only in the presence of inversions and are limited in vertical range by the height of the lid.   Land fogs are dispersed when the lower atmosphere assumes its normal lapse rate and the lid disappears.

Even without an outside air thermometer the aviator may easily observe the height of an inversion.   Dust and smoke frequently are stopped by an inversion and spread out in a distinct layer of haze the top of which coincides with the base of the stable stratum of air.

An equally important feature of these inversions is their influence on wind velocity.   As outward radiation cools the earth's surface, the air near the surface becomes denser.   Consequently, in a moving mass of air, the lower layer lags behind the upper layers.   The more rapid the cooling, the more pronounced this effect becomes.   On clear evenings, the tops of trees often continue to wave in the wind long after all breeze at the surface has ceased.   Rare occasions have been noted when an inversion has caused a calm at the surface, while at an altitude of 1,500 feet a wind of 40 miles an hour was blowing.   Over the open sea, such extreme conditions are unlikely to occur.   But wherever warm air blows over cold water, inversions occur, with effects in proportion to the amount of cooling of the lower layer of the air.   Thus, over land, small inland lakes and rivers, and coasts, aviators may be favorably or adversely affected by temperature inversions through their influence on the velocity of the surface winds and on the formation of fog.

QUESTIONS

1. Explain the meaning of the following terms: (a) Stability.   (b) Instability.   (c) Neutral stability.   (d) Conditional instability.

2. Define convection.
3. What is an "adiabatic" process?
4. What is: (a) Dry-adiabatic lapse rate? (b) Saturation-adiabatic or moist-adiabatic lapse rate? (c) Pseudo-adiabatic lapse rate? (d) Dry adiabat? (e) Moist adiabat?
5. Define condensation level.
6. What is an inversion?
7. What are convectional currents?
8. Discuss diurnal temperature changes of air over land areas.
9. Discuss diurnal temperature changes of air over water areas.
10. Define: (a) Airmass. (b) Warm air mass. (c) Cold air mass.
11. Discuss temperature changes in itinerant air masses.
12. In what locations are the following most frequently found? (a) Rising air currents. (b) Descending air currents.
13. Why is it of major importance that pilots be particularly observant of these conditions?
14. What various weather phenomena are caused by instability and convectional currents?
15. How far does unstable air rise?
16. When instability exists and convectional currents are rising, explain what happens under the following atmospheric conditions: (a) The unstable layer does not extend up to the altitude of the condensation level. (b) A stable layer lies above the unstable layer, and the condensation level is within the unstable layer. (c) The condensation level lies at the top of the unstable layer, which is covered by a conditionally unstable layer, above which the air is stable. (d) Same as (c) but with freezing temperatures in the conditionally unstable layer.
17. What predictions generally may be made by watching the development of cumulus clouds?
18. Make a sketch of a typical thunderstorm cloud (cumulo-nimbus) showing its different parts, air currents, etc., and the change in pressure and temperature as it passes by.
19. Describe the creation of lightning and thunder in a cumulo-nimbus cloud.
20. Why is an inversion called a "lid"?
21. Why are inversions of particular importance to aviators?
22. How may the height of an inversion be observed without a thermometer?

Chapter VI

CIRCULATION OF AIR: CURRENTS AND WINDS

Wind is air in approximately horizontal motion. Winds are produced by differences of atmospheric pressure, which are themselves ultimately and mainly attributable to differences of temperature.

Air, like all gases, is highly sensitive to the action of heat, expanding or increasing in volume as its temperature rises, contracting or diminishing in volume as its temperature falls. Suppose, now, that the atmosphere over any considerable region of the earth's surface is maintained at a temperature higher than that of its surroundings. The warmed air will expand, and its upper layers will flow off to the surrounding (upper) regions, cooling as they go. The atmospheric pressure at sea level throughout the heated areas will thus be diminished (by the flowing off of the upper layers), while that over the circumjacent cooler areas will be correspondingly increased. As the result of this difference of pressure, there will be a movement of the surface air away from the region of high pressure and toward the region of low, somewhat similar to the flow of water which takes place through a connecting bottom sluice of a vessel as soon as we attempt to fill one compartment to a slightly higher level than that existing in the other.

A difference of atmospheric pressure at sea level is thus immediately followed by a movement of the surface air, or by winds; and these differences of pressure originate in differences of temperature. If the atmosphere were everywhere of uniform temperature it would lie at rest on the earth's surface—sluggish, torpid, and oppressive—and there would be no winds. Fortunately, however, this is not the case. The temperature of the atmosphere is continually or periodically higher in one region than in another, and the chief variations in the distribution of temperature are systematically repeated year after year, giving rise to systematic variations in the distribution of pressure.

Normal Distribution of Pressure

The winds, although caused primarily by differences of temperature, stand in more direct relation to differences of pressure, and it is from this point of view that they are ordinarily studied.

In order to furnish a comprehensive view of this distribution of atmospheric pressure over the earth's surface, charts have been prepared to show average barometric readings for any period, whether a month, a season, or a year, and to cover, as far as possible, the entire globe. These are known as iso-baric charts, from the fact that all points at which the barometer has the same reading are joined by a continuous line called an "isobar."

The isobaric chart of the earth showing average conditions during an entire year shows in each hemisphere a well-defined belt of high pressure known as the "subtropical anticyclone" (1,023 millibars) completely encircling the globe; in the northern hemisphere it has its middle line at about Latitude 35° N.; in the southern hemisphere, at about Latitude 30° S. These middle lines constitute the so-called "meteorological tropics." From the summit or ridge of each of these belts the pressure falls off alike toward the equator and toward the pole, although much less rapidly in the former direction than in the latter. The equator itself is encircled by a belt of somewhat diminished pressure called the *equatorial belt* (1,012 millibars), the middle line of which averages about Latitude 2° N. In the northern hemisphere the diminution of pressure on the poleward slope is much less marked and much less regular than in the southern hemisphere. Minima of about 1,006 millibars occur in the North Atlantic near Iceland and in the North Pacific near the Aleutian Islands, beyond which the pressure increases to form a high-pressure area in the region near the pole. In the southern hemisphere no such minima are apparent; the pressures continue to diminish with fair regularity as higher latitudes are approached, then increase again to form the south polar high-pressure region. The Arctic low (or cyclone) and high (anticyclone) are varible and only of a semi-permanent nature, while those of the Antarctic are fairly steady and permanent. Along the sixtieth parallel of south latitude the average pressure is about 992 millibars.

Seasonal Variation in Pressure

As might be expected from its close relation to the temperature, the whole system of pressure distribution exhibits a tendency to follow the sun's annual motion, the barometric equator occupying in July a position slightly to the northward of its position in January. In either hemisphere, moreover, the pressure over the land during the winter season is decidedly above the annual average, and during the summer season decidedly below it; the extreme variations occur in continental Asia, where the mean monthly pressure ranges from 1,033 millibars (mb) in January to 999 millibars in July. Over the northern ocean, on the other hand, conditions are reversed, the summer pressures being somewhat the higher. Thus, in January the Icelandic and the Aleutian lows increase in depth to 999 millibars, while in July these minima fill up and are well-nigh obliterated. This fact has much to do with the strength and frequency of the winter gales in high northern latitudes, and the absence of gales during the summer. Over the southern ocean, in keeping with its slight contrast between summer and winter temperatures, similar variations of pressure do not exist.

Prevailing Winds and General Circulation (Figure 6–1)

As a result of the distribution of pressure just described, there is in either hemisphere a continual motion of the surface air away from the subtropical anticyclones—on one side toward the equatorial belt, on the other side toward the pole.

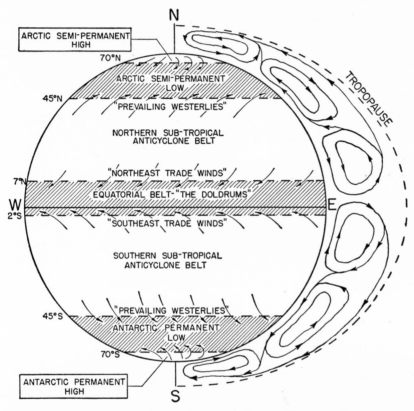

Fig. 6–1. General circulation of the earth's atmosphere.

The first constitutes, in each case, the trade winds, and the second, the prevailing winds of higher latitudes. Upon a stationary earth the direction of this motion would be directly from the region of high toward the region of low barometer, the moving air steadily following the barometric slope or "gradient," increasing in force to a gale where the gradient is steep, decreasing to a light breeze where the gradient is gentle, and sinking to calm where it is absent. The earth, however, is in rapid rotation, and this rotation gives rise to a force (called the "coriolis force") which exercises a material influence over all horizontal motions upon its surface, whatever their direction; it serves constantly to divert them to the *right* in the northern hemisphere, and to the *left* in the southern hemisphere. The air set in motion by the difference of pressure is thus constantly turned aside from its natural course down the barometric gradient or slope, and the direction of the wind at any point is deflected by a certain amount, crossing the latter at an angle which varies between 45° and 90°, the wind in the latter case blowing parallel to the isobars. As a consequence of this deflection, the winds which one would naturally expect to find northerly on the equatorial side of the belt of high pressure in the northern hemisphere become northeasterly to form the northeast trades, while the winds on the poleward side of this belt, instead of being southerly, become southwesterly, forming the "prevailing westerlies" of the northern latitudes. So, too, for the southern hemisphere, the southerly winds of the equatorial slope become southeasterly—the southeast trades—and the northerly winds of the (south) polar slope of the belt become northwesterly, forming the "prevailing westerlies" of the southern latitudes.

The relation here described as existing between the distribution of atmospheric pressure and the direction of the wind is of the greatest importance. It may be briefly stated as follows (Buys-Ballott's Law):

In the northern hemisphere, when you face the wind, the region of low pressure is on your right and somewhat behind you, and the region of high pressure is on your left and somewhat in front of you.

In the southern hemisphere, when you face the wind, the region of low pressure is on your left and somewhat behind you, and the region of high pressure is on your right and somewhat in front of you.

This relation holds absolutely, not only of the general distribution of pressure and circulation of the atmosphere, but also of the special conditions of high and low pressure which usually accompany severe gales.

Trade Winds

The trade winds blow from the subtropical belts of high pressure toward the equatorial belt of lower pressure—in the northern hemisphere from the northeast, in the southern hemisphere from the southeast. Over the eastern half of each of the great oceans they originate much farther away from the equator and their original direction is more nearly from the poles than in midocean, where their direction is almost easterly. They are commonly considered to be the most constant of winds, but although they may blow for days or even weeks with slight variation in direction or strength, their uniformity should not be exaggerated. At times these trade winds weaken or shift. There are regions where their steady course is deformed, notably among the island groups of the South Pacific, where, during January and February, the trades are practically nonexistent. They attain their highest development in the South Atlantic and the South Indian Oceans, and are everywhere fresher during the winter season than during the summer. They are rarely disturbed by cyclonic storms; the occurrence of cyclonic storms within the limits of the trade-wind region is confined, in time, to late summer and autumn months of the respective hemispheres, and, in location, to the western portion of the several oceans. The South Atlantic Ocean alone, however, enjoys complete immunity from tropical cyclonic storms.

The "Doldrums"

The equatorial girdle of low pressure occupies a position between the subtropical anticyclones of the northern and southern hemispheres. Throughout this barometric trough

the pressure, save for the slight diurnal oscillation, is practically uniform, and decided barometric gradients do not
exist. Here, accordingly, the winds sink to stagnation or, at
most, rise only to the strength of fitful breezes, coming first
from one direction, then from another, with cloudy, rainy
sky and frequent thunderstorms. The region throughout
which these conditions prevail consists of a wedge-shaped
area, the base of the wedge resting, for the Atlantic Ocean, on
the west coast of Africa, and, for the Pacific Ocean, on the west
coast of America, the axis of the wedge extending westward.
Throughout February and March it is found immediately
north of the equator and is of inappreciable width; vessels
following the sailing routes frequently pass from trade to trade
without interruption in both the Atlantic and Pacific Oceans.
In July and August it has migrated to the northward; the axis
extends east and west along the parallel of about 7° North
Latitude, and the belt itself covers several degrees of latitude,
even at its narrowest point. At this season of the year, also,
the southeast trades blow with diminished freshness across the
equator and well into the northern hemisphere. They are
diverted, however, by the effect of the earth's rotation into
southerly and southwesterly winds, the so-called southwest
monsoon of the African and Central American coasts.

The "Horse Latitudes"

On the outer margin of the trades, corresponding vaguely
with the summit of the subtropical ridge of high pressure in
either hemisphere, is a second region throughout which the
barometric gradients are faint and undecided, and the prevailing winds correspondingly light and variable. These are the
so-called "horse latitudes" or calms of Cancer and Capricorn.
Unlike the doldrums, however, the weather is here clear and
fresh; the periods of stagnation are intermittent rather than
continuous, and show none of the persistency which is so characteristic of the equatorial region. The explanation of this

difference will become obvious when we realize the nature of the daily barometric changes of pressure in the respective regions, for while the doldrums are marked by the uniformity of the torrid zone with but slight diurnal variation, the "horse latitudes" share to a limited extent in the wide and rapid variations of the temperate zone.

The Prevailing Westerly Winds

On the exterior or polar side of the subtropical anticyclones the pressure again diminishes; the barometric gradients are here directly toward the pole. The currents of air set in motion along these gradients, diverted to the right and left, respectively, of their natural course by the earth's rotation, appear in the northern hemisphere as southwesterly winds and in the southern hemisphere as northwesterly. These are called the "prevailing westerlies" of the temperate zones.

Only in the southern hemisphere do these winds exhibit anything approaching the persistency of the trades. Their course in the northern hemisphere is subject to frequent local interruptions by periods of winds with an easterly component. Tabulated results show that throughout the portion of the North Atlantic included between Latitude 40° and 50° N. and Longitude 10°–50° W., winds from the western semicircle comprise about 74 per cent of the whole number of observations. The relative frequency is somewhat higher in winter, somewhat lower in summer. The average force, on the other hand, decreases from force 6 to force 4, Beaufort scale (see pp. 202 and 337), with the change of season. Over the sea in the southern hemisphere such variations are not apparent; here the westerlies blow through the entire year with a steadiness little less than that of the trades themselves and with a force which, though fitful, is very much greater; their boisterous nature has given the name of the "roaring forties" to the latitude in which they are most frequently observed.

The explanation of this striking difference in the extra-tropical winds of the two halves of the globe is found in the distribution of atmospheric pressure, and in the variations of this in different parts of the world. In the nearly landless southern hemisphere the atmospheric pressure after crossing the parallel of 30° S. diminishes almost uniformly toward the pole, and is rarely disturbed by those large and irregular fluctuations which form so important a factor in the daily weather of the northern hemisphere. Here, accordingly, there is a system of polar gradients quite comparable in stability with the equatorial gradients which give rise to the trades, and the poleward movement of the air in obedience to these gradients, constantly diverted to the *left* by the effect of the earth's rotation (coriolis force), results in the steady westerly winds of the south temperate zone.

Monsoon Winds

Air over land is warmer in summer and colder in winter than that over adjacent oceans. During the summer the continents become the seat of areas of relatively low pressure and, during the winter, of relatively high. Pressure gradients directed outward from the continents during the winter, inward during the summer, are thus established between the land and the sea; these exercise great influence over the winds prevailing in the region adjacent to the coast. Thus, off the Atlantic seaboard of the United States southwesterly winds are most frequent in summer, northwesterly winds in winter; but on the Pacific coast, the wind changes from northwest in summer to southwest with the advance of winter.

The most striking winds of this class are the monsoons of the China Sea and the Indian Ocean. In January abnormally low temperatures and high pressure obtain over the Asiatic plateau, high temperatures and low pressure over Australia and the nearby portion of the Indian Ocean. As a result of the barometric gradients thus established, the southern and eastern coasts of the vast Asiatic continent and the adjacent seas are swept by an outflowing current of air which, diverted to the right of the gradient by the earth's rotation, appears as a northeast wind, covering the China Sea and the northern Indian Ocean. As these winds enter the southern hemisphere, however, the same force which hitherto deflected them to the right of the gradient now serves to deflect them to the left. Here, consequently, the monsoon appears as a northwest wind covering the Indian Ocean as far south as 10°, the Arafura Sea, and the northern coast of Australia.

In July these conditions are exactly reversed. Asia is now the seat of high temperature and correspondingly low pressure, and Australia of low temperature and high pressure, although the departure from the annual average is by no means so pronounced in Australia as in Asia. The baric (barometric) gradients thus lead across the equator and are addressed toward the interior of the greater continent, giving rise to a system of winds whose direction is southeast in the southern hemisphere and southwest in the northern.

The northeast (winter) monsoon blows in the China Sea from October to April, the southwest (summer) monsoon from May to September. The former is marked by all the steadiness of the trades, often attaining the force of a moderate gale; the latter appears as a light breeze, unsteady in direction, and often sinking to a calm. Its prevalence is frequently interrupted by tropical cyclonic storms, locally known as "typhoons," although these may occur well into the winter monsoon season.

One important effect of the seasonal variation of temperature and pressure over the land remains to be described. If there were no land areas to break the even water surface of the globe, the trades and westerlies of the general terrestrial circulation would be developed in the fullest simplicity, with linear divisions along latitude circles between the several members—a condition nearly approached in the land-barren southern hemisphere during the entire year, and in the northern hemisphere during the winter season. In the summer, however, the subtropical belt of high pressure is broken where it crosses the warm land, and the air shouldered off from the continents accumulates over the adjacent oceans, particularly in the northern or land hemisphere. This tends to create over each of the oceans a circular or elliptical area of high pressure, from the center of which the baric gradients radiate in all directions, giving rise to an outflowing system of winds, which by the effect of the earth's rotation is converted into an outflowing spiral eddy or anticyclonic whirl. The sharp lines of demarcation which would otherwise exist between the several members of the general circulation are thus submerged and obliterated. The southwesterly winds of the middle northern latitudes become successively northwesterly, northerly, and northeasterly, as we approach the equator in following the eastern edge of the high-pressure area; and the northeast trade becomes successively southeasterly, southerly, and southwesterly as we continue on around the western edge of the area, receding from the equator. The exact reverse will, of course, be true for the other hemisphere.

Land and Sea Breezes

These phenomena are observed along the coasts of large bodies of water and are more pronounced in summer than in winter. By the effects of solar radiation, the land heats more rapidly during the day than the water, and cools more rapidly during the night. The rising convective currents over the land cause the cooler air over the water to flow in to take its place, producing a wind that blows from the sea, called the "sea breeze." At night the reverse condition develops. The land cools much more rapidly and soon is at considerably lower temperature than the water. The air over the land, cooled by contact, becomes denser and flows out over the water, forcing the warmer and lighter air upward, thus creating a wind that blows from the land, called the "land breeze." These breezes are confined to a rather narrow area along the coast, seldom extending more than about 15 miles inland, although the breezes may be felt considerably farther to seaward, particularly during the daytime. The sea breeze, depending upon the degree of heating of the land surface, may develop into a fresh or strong breeze; the land breeze at night is usually gentle.

In considering, observing, and anlyzing the weather it must be borne in mind that these conditions are superimposed upon the general conditions and one should not, therefore, be misled by them. They will be most pronounced, of course, in the tropics, where land and sea breezes often blow with great persistence; but, in latitudes farther from the equator, stronger winds of a more general character at times may completely prevent the occurrence of these phenomena.

The Deflecting or Coriolis Force (Figure 6–2)

Except for the rotation of the earth, air would tend to flow in a direct path from areas of higher pressure to those of lower pressure—in other words, to follow the direction of the decreasing barometric gradient. The earth's rotation, however, produces a force which prevents this direct flow. There is one (theoretical) exception to this, that is, where the *pressure gradient and flow of air is directly east or west along the earth's equator.* Since this force, called the "Coriolis Force," affects every wind and every weather situation, we must investigate its nature and the manner in which it acts. The principle, though simple, is of great importance to anyone concerned with the weather, and is stated simply in *Ferrel's law,* as follows: "When a mass of air starts to move over the earth's surface, it is deflected to the right in the northern hemisphere and to the left in the southern hemisphere, and tends to move in a circle whose radius depends upon its velocity and its distance from the equator."

Figure 6–2 represents the earth rotating from west to east. The equator, four parallels of latitude, and a meridian of longtitude are shown. The meridian is shown in two successive positions, the solid line indicating the meridian's position at a given instant, and the dotted line the same meridian's position at a later time. Centers of high and low pressure are indicated by H_1, H_2, H_3, and L_1, L_2, respectively.

On account of the difference in their respective distances from the earth's axis, the linear velocity of H_1 at the equator

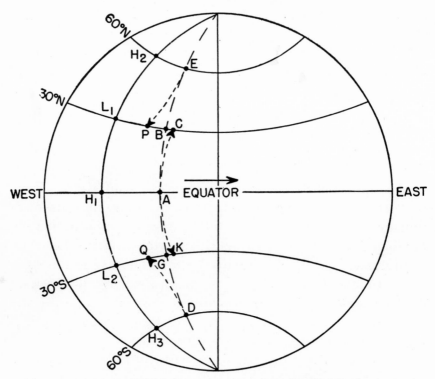

FIG. 6–2.   Effect of the earth's rotation: the Coriolis force.

will be about 1,000 miles per hour, while that of L_1 and L_2 at 30° N. and S. latitude will be about 866 m.p.h., and that of H_2 and H_3 at Latitude 60° will be only about 500 m.p.h.

Suppose that an air particle, under the effect of the pressure gradient, starts from H_1 toward L_1. Considering the particle to be in the free air—i.e., above the effect of surface friction—the particle will continue to move toward the east with the same speed as its point of origin, point H_1, regardless of the velocity imparted to it in a northerly direction by the pressure gradient. While the particle is proceeding from the equator up to the latitude of L_1, the earth will rotate so as to bring the meridian to the position shown by the dotted line. Point H_1 will have moved to A, L_1 to B, and H_2 to E. The air particle, however, in retaining its original eastward component of velocity, will have moved to the eastward a *distance* equal to the travel of point H_1—i.e., H_1-A—and consequently will arrive at a point C, to the eastward of B, such that L_1-C equals H_1-A. Thus we see that the path of the particle *relative to the rotating earth* is indicated by the broken arrow A-C. The particle, instead of following directly along the meridian A-B, has been deflected to the *right*.

Similarly, a particle starting from H_2 will, on account of its *smaller* eastward component, tend to lag behind the motion of the meridian as the particle proceeds southward. Thus, when point L_1 arrives at B, the air particle will arrive at some point, P, to the *westward* of B, so that L_1-P equals H_2-E. Again we see that the particle has been deflected to the right of the direction of the decreasing barometric gradient.

The above discussion will indicate that in the southern hemisphere just the reverse is true, and that air flowing from a higher to a lower pressure area will be deflected to the *left* under the influence of the Coriolis force.

Since the deflecting force tends to keep the particle from moving directly toward the area of low pressure, we may accept without further proof the fact that one component of the deflecting force always acts directly *away* from the low pressure, along the line of the *increasing* barometric gradient. Since the pressure force acts along the direction of the *decreasing* gradients, and this is also always at right angles to the isobars, the pressure force and the outward component of the deflecting force act in exactly opposite directions. The air particle will therefore continue to be deflected until the latter component and the pressure force become equal and opposite. (See Figure 6–3.) Between such balanced forces the air particle can move only at right angles to both of them —i.e., *along the isobar at that point*—and this it does under the force supplied by the remaining component of the deflecting force. So long as these conditions continue to exist, the air will continue to flow parallel to the isobars much as

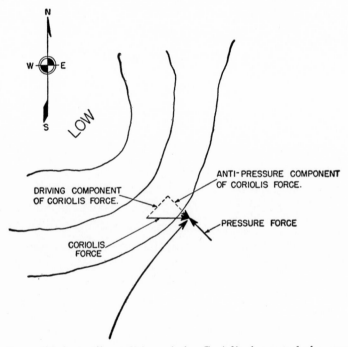

FIG. 6–3. "Balanced" condition of the Coriolis force and the pressure force. In this condition the flow of air is parallel to the isobars.

a river flows between its banks. If the balance of forces becomes upset in any way, the particles then move toward, or away from, the low pressure accordingly. Thus we see that the circulation of the air about an area of low pressure (Figure 6–4) has a counterclockwise rotation in the northern hemisphere, and a clockwise rotation in the southern hemisphere. The rotation about an area of high pressure is just the reverse in each case.

Geostrophic Wind

The velocity attained by the wind when blowing under the conditions of complete balance of forces, as described in the preceding paragraph, is called the geostrophic wind. Its theoretical value depends upon several factors as expressed in the formula:

$$V = \frac{G}{2\rho\omega \sin \phi}$$

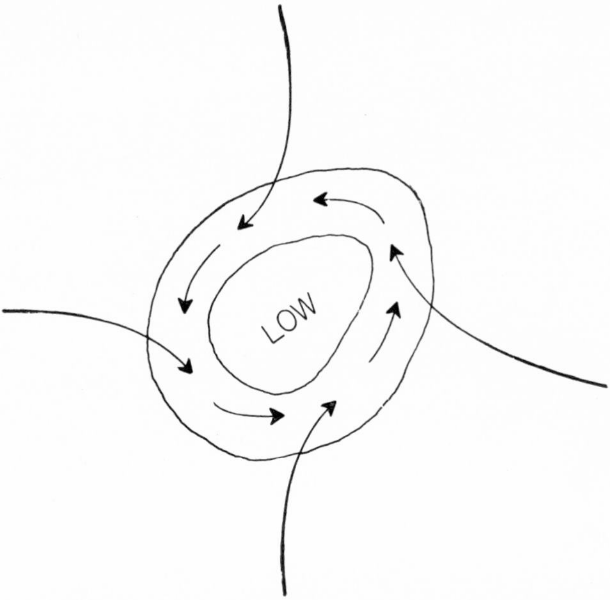

FIG. 6–4. Circulation about an area of low pressure due to the Coriolis force (northern hemisphere).

where V is the velocity, G the pressure gradient force, ρ the density of the atmosphere, ω the angular velocity of the earth's rotation, and ϕ the latitude. Since the atmospheric density is almost constant in a horizontal plane, the velocity of the geostrophic wind is directly proportional to the pressure gradient. Thus the geostrophic wind will be strongest with a steep pressure gradient, which, on a map representing distribution of pressure, may be readily recognized by the fact that the isobars are crowded closely together. Again the flow of the air between the isobars may be compared to the flow of a river between its banks: the narrower the river, the swifter its current.

It should be borne in mind that the geostrophic wind blows, or is approached, only in the "free atmosphere" well above the surface, from 1,500 to 3,000 feet (and more) of altitude. The retarding effect of friction with the ground surface serves to keep the surface wind below the geostrophic velocity.

Turbulence

In passing over the uneven surface of the earth with its hills and valleys, forests and open fields, trees and houses, and numerous other obstacles, air movement is transformed from a smooth and even flow to a series of swirls and eddies caused by friction with these obstacles. This results in a series of gusts and lulls in irregular, turbulent flow. The eddies formed by this surface friction may be forced up several hundred feet by the momentum of the swirling gusts. Turbulence caused by friction with uneven ground surfaces is designated as *mechanical turbulence.*

In Chapter V it was pointed out that convectional currents will also produce turbulent flow in the atmosphere, but these variaions are due entirely to uneven distribution of temperature, which cause ascending and descending currents, producing irregular flow. Turbulence resulting from such a cause is called *thermal turbulence,* and the ascending and descending currents are often referred to as *thermals.*

The total turbulence of the atmosphere is caused by the combining of thermal and mechanical turbulence. Either may be present without the other; a rising thermal may be assisted by mechanically produced rising eddies; rising eddies may diminish or completely overcome descending thermals or, on the other hand, may be completely overcome by them.

If the surface layer of air is stable, the mechanical turbulence will be resisted if not damped out completely; if unstable or conditionally unstable, then the turbulent layer near the earth's surface will be deep. Thus we see that the depth of the turbulent layer depends directly upon the stability of the

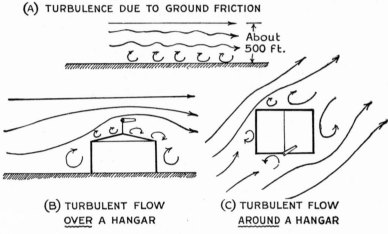

(A) TURBULENCE DUE TO GROUND FRICTION

About
500 Ft.

(B) TURBULENT FLOW
OVER A HANGAR

(C) TURBULENT FLOW
AROUND A HANGAR

Fig. 6–5. Mechanical turbulence and eddies.

surface layer, the strength of the wind, and the roughness of the surface.

Eddies near Obstacles (Figure 6–5). Air flowing along the surface of smooth ground will form small rolling eddies of

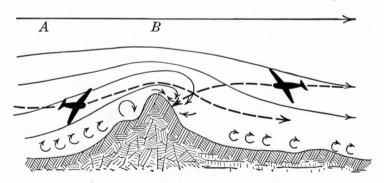

A   *B*

Fig. 6–6 Airflow over mountains.

little consequence, as shown at (A). Air flowing over rough terrain, however, will cause such large eddies as to make a turbulent, "bumpy" layer of a depth which will increase with the wind velocity. Obstacles such as buildings, hangars, etc., create eddies around and over them as shown at (B) and (C). It is, therefore, evident that the downdraft on the lee side makes it dangerous to take off toward a hangar unless one is sure of gaining sufficient altitude to pass well above the hangar roof.

The Effect of Hills and Mountains (Figure 6–6). The flow of air around and, particularly, over hills and mountains should be the subject of serious consideration to any pilot who flies in their vicinity. As shown in the figure, there is less chance of trouble when flying with the wind, for the ascending current on the windward side tends to lift the plane as it approaches the summit, although the pilot should remember the possibility of a stationary eddy that may hang along the side of a steep upslope. On the other hand, the curling downdraft on the lee side of the mountain may be the cause of disaster to a plane attempting to pass over the ridge against the wind, particularly if the wind is strong. Caught in such a downdraft, the plane cannot climb out of it and flies into the side of a mountain just below the summit. Some of the most disastrous crashes can be explained only by just such conditions. The following personal experience of the author will serve perhaps not only to illustrate but to emphasize this point.

We were flying into a strong head wind. As the plane had not a great deal of reserve power, the climb to pass over the mountain (in southeastern New York) was started well in advance. When the plane was about halfway up the slope, with a good thousand feet of altitude above the ground and only a few hundred feet more to climb to the level of the top, the rate of climb began to drop off. The throttle was opened wider and an attempt made to climb more steeply, but this was effective only momentarily. Finally, with motor wide open and at an angle of attack and airspeed to give maximum climb, the plane definitely settled and the mountainside seemed to rise rapidly underneath it. Only by pulling into a vertical bank and "reversed control" turn of 180° was the plane kept from flying into the treetops. After reversing course for about a mile and climbing, then resuming course again still in a climb, the ridge was finally passed over with about 500 feet altitude above the ground. (It is hoped the reader will get as good a lesson from this as did the author, who is quite willing to admit that he was "plenty scared.") The ridge having been successfully gained, however, it was decided to ascertain the effect of the ascending currents on the windward side of the mountain. The plane was turned approximately parallel to the ridge and brought down to about 200 feet above the ground. The throttle was then closed and the plane put into a normal glide. Instead of losing altitude, although gliding downward through the air, the plane actually *gained* 200 feet of altitude in about one minute!

In addition to the effects described above, there are still others of importance to be observed.

Orographic Lifting—Fog, Rain and Thunderstorms. A glance at Figure 6–6 will show in general how the flow of air is affected by mountains and hills. Their upward sloping sides act as "permanent fronts" to lift the onflowing air much more rapidly than even a steep cold front. Streamline flow is altered for a considerable distance above the summit by the momentum of the air ascending the upslope. Given an initial start upward, it may continue so to a considerable altitude above the top before it starts to descend, forming an eddy and then flowing down the lee side of the hill. Since all the air below the point A must pass through the narrow section between the summit and B it can do so only by flowing much more rapidly as it passes the latter point. Thus, even though there may be only a gentle breeze in the valley, the wind may blow with gale force over the top of the hill, creating the dangerous eddy and downdraft described above.

As the air is forced upward on the windward side (mechanical lifting) it will be cooled adiabatically and, if sufficiently humid, fog or clouds of the stratus type may be formed which will extend over and above the top of the hill. Even in stable air, general precipitation may take place on the windward slope, but the downward-flowing current on the lee side is heated adiabatically as it descends so that the clouds are dissolved on the downwind side and the atmosphere becomes clear. When the wind is strong, this condition may often be noticeable as far as 150 miles downwind from a range of mountains. If, on the other hand, the air on the upslope is unstable or conditionally unstable the layer of stratus will change to clouds of the cumulus type, growing upward and possibly producing heavy rain and thunderstorms beyond the summit of the ridge. In some mountainous regions such conditions sometimes persist over considerable periods of time.

Since the top of a hill or ridge may frequently be hidden from view in the clouds from above and because even a slight change in barometric pressure will cause considerable error in the altimeter, it follows that the pilot should avoid entering a cloud in hilly or mountainous regions unless he is sure that he has a large margin of altitude to clear the summit in safety.

U. S. Navy Pilot Charts of the Upper Air

For the use of pilots desiring information on average winds to be expected during any month, the U. S. Navy publishes an "Atlas of Monthly Pilot Charts of the Upper Air—North Atlantic and North Pacific Oceans," H. O. Publication No. 560. By means of "wind roses" in various colors, the charts show the force and direction of the winds blowing during that particular month at the surface and at different altitude levels up to 10,000 feet at principal important observing stations throughout the area of the chart. By studying the charts, the aviator may gain valuable information regarding winds to be expected in general in flying through the areas charted. These charts are obtainable from the U. S. Navy, Hydrographic Office, Washington 25, D. C., at a cost of $1.50 each.

QUESTIONS

1. Define wind. By what are winds produced?
2. Describe briefly the normal average distribution of pressure over the earth's surface. (a) What are its general seasonal variations? (b) What are the "meteorological tropics"?
3. Show by sketch the prevailing winds and general circulation of the air over the earth's surface.
4. Define: (a) Trade winds. (b) Prevailing westerlies. (c) Doldrums.
5. State Buys-Ballott's Law.
6. Explain briefly: (a) Trade winds. (b) Doldrums. (c) Horse latitudes. (d) Prevailing westerlies.
7. What are monsoon winds? Where are they found? What is their cause?
8. Explain briefly the phenomena of land and sea breezes.
9. What is the Coriolis force and what is its effect? What is Ferrel's law?
10. Show by sketch the general circulation of air about an area of low pressure due to the Coriolis force.
11. What is the geostrophic wind and where is it found?
12. Into what two main classes may turbulence be divided? State the cause and effect of each.
13. Show by sketch the typical effect of obstacles and ground friction upon air flow.
14. Show by sketch the air flow over mountains.
15. What precautions must the pilot take when in the vicinity of obstacles or mountain tops?
16. How do the sloping sides of hills and mountains act as "permanent fronts"? What precautions should the pilot take when mountains or hilltops are covered with clouds?
17. What is the Navy Atlas of Monthly Pilot Charts of the Upper Air and what is its purpose?

Chapter VII

AIR MASSES, FRONTS AND DISTURBANCES—
THEIR DEVELOPMENT AND EFFECT

An *air mass* may be defined as a very large parcel of air, ranging from about 500 to 5000 miles in lateral dimensions and from several thousand feet to several miles deep, with properties of temperature, humidity and thermal structure which vary only slightly, or vary linearly, from point to point within the parcel.*

Generation of an Air Mass

Frequently, and in certain particular localities, meteorological conditions are such that the air overlying a considerable area will have little or no tendency to flow toward another area. If such conditions persist for a sufficient period, the overlying air will acquire definite characteristics and properties from the ground up as dictated by the physical and geographical nature of the surface. By the time such a process has been completed, an extensive portion of the atmosphere has become practically homogeneous throughout and its properties have become more or less uniform at each level, fulfilling the definition given above. An air mass has been generated.

An ideal air mass would be identifiable by two important characteristics: its specific humidity and its potential temperature † would be the same everywhere at each successive level. Actually, this never occurs, but the variations in these proper-

---

* P. E. Kraght, in "The Scientific Encyclopedia."

† Specific humidity is defined in Chapter III. Potential temperature is that temperature which the air *would* have if brought (adiabatically) to sea level. The change in temperature would be equal to (about) $5\frac{1}{2}°$ F per thousand feet.

ties are slight and always gradual; there are no abrupt discontinuities within the same air mass.

Conversely, the transition from one air mass to another is generally marked by an abrupt change in various characteristics, and these discontinuities may readily be used to define the boundaries of the air masses.

The region where an air mass is generated, and from which it derives its initial properties, is called its *source*. It may, for example, be the cold, dry polar areas of Asia or Canada, the warm, moist expanse of the Gulf of Mexico, or the dry and burning vastness of the Sahara Desert.

Life History of Air Masses

In order to study, understand, and predict the changes that develop within an air mass, we must consider its origin and movements, which may be considered its life history. These important factors are: first, the source of the air mass; second, its route of travel; and third, its time en route.

(*a*) *Source.* While an air mass lies over its source it absorbs the properties of the surface. The most prolific sources of air masses are the subtropical anticyclone belts and the permanent or semipermanent areas of high pressure in the polar or subpolar regions. Conversely, a *traveling* disturbance is seldom the source of an air mass, since the air within it changes its properties rapidly due to the changing nature of the terrain over which it passes.

(*b*) *Route of Travel.* Once an air mass leaves its source, its physical properties will change in accordance with the nature of the surface over which it travels—whether hot or cold, moist or dry. The changes in physical properties start in the lower layers and travel upward through the mass. The rate at which these changes take place depends upon the degree of difference between the original properties and those of the surface. The general routes of travel of North American air masses is shown in Fig 7–1A.

(c) Time En Route. The *amount* of change in the physical properties of an air mass will depend upon two things: namely, the rate at which it passes over the surface, and the length of time since it left its source.

So long as an air mass passes over a fairly homogeneous surface, the changes within the mass will be fairly consistent throughout the mass; thus its internal irregularities are grad-

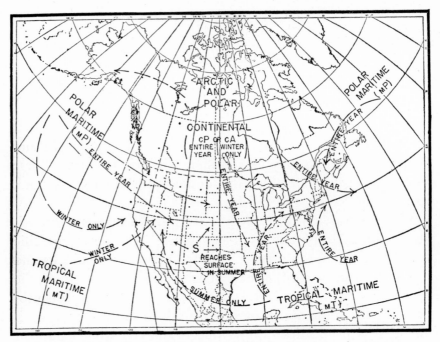

FIG. 7–1A. General movement of North American air masses.

ual. When two air masses meet, however, particularly two from different sources, the transition from one mass to the other along their borders is often abrupt. These differences in physical properties, especially in temperature, along the border or "front" between the air masses, produce great contrasts in energy. Along these boundaries, traveling "depressions" develop from the energy contrasts.

Classification of Air Masses

Air masses are classified according to the various factors which affect their nature, their physical properties, and their internal structure. These factors include a general idea of the latitude and surface nature of their source, the location of their source region, their temperature, relative to the surface over which they travel, and a general indication of their current properties in relation to original properties acquired at their source. The complete classification provides a fairly accurate description of the air mass in its original and its current state.

(*a*) *Latitude of Source.* The four main sources of air masses are the equatorial belt of uniform pressure (the doldrums), the subtropical anticyclone belts, anticyclones in high latitudes, and the great arctic and antarctic regions of ice and snow. We may thus distinguish the air within such masses as:

Equatorial (from the doldrums)
Tropical (from the subtropical anticyclones)
Arctic (from the regions of ice and snow)
Polar (from the anticyclones near the poles)

Since there is relatively little difference between tropical and equatorial air, the one general term "tropical" is used to denote air from these general regions. Petterssen further combines the two terms "arctic" and "polar" under the latter as a broad general term; Bergeron, however, retains the distinction between the two, as in the table on page 123.

(*b*) *Surface Nature of Source.* The nature of the surface over which air travels will definitely affect its properties. The temperature difference between the air and the surface controls the amount of heat absorbed by the air. The air would pick up more moisture over the ocean than it would over a land area. We therefore classify air masses, according to the surface nature of their sources, as *maritime* and *continental*.

(*c*) *Location of Source Region.* An additional classification, by the geographical name of the source region, further describes the properties of an air mass. Thus, air from the Gulf of Mexico (designated "Gulf") would be warm and moist; "Sahara" air would be hot and dry; polar "Pacific" would be cold and wet, etc.

(*d*) *Air-Surface Temperature Difference.* Finally, air masses are classified according to the relative temperature of their surface layer compared to that of the surface over which they travel. An air mass which is warmer than the surface over which it is traveling is called a *warm air mass;* and, conversely, if the air is colder than the surface, it is called a *cold air mass.* The same air mass as it moves may be, successively, a warm air mass and then a cold air mass, or vice versa. Thus, an air mass at 60° F, moving over an ocean whose surface temperature is 50° F, would be called *warm;* but, when that same mass passes inland over a land surface with a temperature of 70° F, it then becomes a *cold* air mass.

Air masses which, by the influences of travel and age, have become or are becoming considerably modified, are additionally designated as "transitional."

For our classification to be complete, we should add that there is one more class of air mass. This is the *high level,* or *superior,* air mass of the middle and upper troposphere, as shown at the bottom of the table.

Identifying the source regions of air masses, and tracing the boundaries or "fronts" between them, are important parts of the meteorologist's work.

As an air mass moves over the varying surface of the earth, it acquires different thermal and moisture characteristics, especially in the lower layers. Such changes in the original properties of the air mass are caused by the radiation of heat from the earth's surface, by mixing, by condensation, or evaporation, and other causes. The mass thus becomes "transitional." The following table defines the source regions most used on weather maps and lists the abbreviations commonly employed to designate them.

Source by—		Local source region	Corresponding air-mass name	Classification, after Bergeron *
Latitude	Nature			
Polar	Continental	Alaska, Canada, and Arctic	Polar Canadian or continental	cA or cAw, winter cP or cPk, summer
		Modified in southern and central United States.	Transitional polar continental	cPw or cPk, winter. cPk, summer.
	Maritime	Colder portions of North Pacific Ocean.	Polar Pacific	mAk or mPk, winter. mP or mPw, summer.
		Modified in central and western United States.	Transitional polar Pacific	cPw, winter cPk, summer.
		Modified over warm portions of Pacific.	Transitional polar Pacific	mP or mPk, winter. mP or mPk, summer.
		Colder portions of North Atlantic Ocean.	Polar Atlantic	mPk, winter. mPw, spring and summer.
		Modified over warm portions of Atlantic.	Transitional polar Atlantic	mPk, winter, spring, and summer.
Tropical	Maritime	Gulf of Mexico, Caribbean Sea, Sargasso Sea, and Middle Atlantic (also southern United States in summer).	Tropical Atlantic	mT or mTk, winter. mTk, summer.
		Modified over northern U. S. or North Atlantic.	Transitional tropical Atlantic	mTw, winter and summer.
		Northern part Pacific trade-wind belt.	Tropical Pacific (usually not found in summer).	mT or mTk, winter.
		Modified in U. S. or over North Pacific.	Transitional tropical Pacific	mTw, winter.
Tropical and sub-polar	High-level	Middle and upper troposphere.	Superior, S.	S, winter and summer.

* Explanation of symbols:

A is Arctic. T is Tropical. S is Superior.
P is Polar. m is maritime. c is continental.
w means the air mass is warmer than the surface over which it is traveling.
k means the air mass is colder than the surface over which it is traveling.

Bergeron's classification gives not only the source region of the air mass but also some idea of its thermal stratification. The source region of the air is designated by "A" for arctic, "P" for polar, "T" for tropical. The nature of source regions is designated by "m" for maritime and "c" for continental. The letters "w" and "k" indicate the air-surface temperature difference—a warm air mass and a cold air mass, respectively. General geographical source areas are designated by "a" for Atlantic, "p" for Pacific, "g" for Gulf (of Mexico).

Cold Masses and Their Properties

Normally, cold masses form in the polar and arctic regions, but in winter they may form over the large land areas in latitudes as low at 25° N. During their generation these masses, having been cooled from below by contact with the cold surface, will have acquired the following properties:

(*a*) Low temperature, with consequent low specific humidity.

(*b*) A gradual lapse rate with marked stability, particularly near the surface.

As the mass moves away from its cold source toward a warmer area, contact with the warmer surface will develop instability in its lower layers. This condition will spread upward, destroying any inversions and producing convective currents and (if sufficient moisture is picked up) clouds of the cumulus and cumulo-nimbus variety.

Cold *continental* and cold *maritime* masses have certain distinct differences by which they may be recognized. All of their typical characteristics as listed in the table below *may* be found, yet several may be missing, depending upon the degree of modification or "transition" which the mass has experienced in its travel. The following examples will illustrate this:

(*a*) From the broad plains of western Canada, in summer a cold continental air mass moves down over Kansas and

Nebraska.   As it travels southward, it is heated considerably by the increasingly warmer surface, yet it acquires little moisture on its journey.   Its humidity and dew point are thus kept low, and its condensation level is kept high.   In spite of the instability created by the steep lapse rate in the lower layers, only scattered cumuli will be formed, with occasional cumulo-nimbus, usually in the afternoon.

(*b*) Winter air from the cold, dry plains of Texas moves southward out over the warm waters of the Gulf of Mexico. It absorbs a considerable amount of moisture from the ocean's surface, bringing the condensation level lower; the warm contact creates a steep lapse rate in the lower layers of this maritime mass and produces strong convective currents, from which develop cumulus and cumulo-nimbus clouds; sharp, squally showers follow, with intermittent breaks of clearing weather.

If the mass of (*a*) above, after being warmed on its journey, had moved out over a cold ocean, a stable state would have

TYPICAL PROPERTIES OF COLD MASSES

Property	*Continental*	*Maritime*
Temperature...	Increasing	Increasing
Humidity......	Fairly constant	Increasing
Lapse rate.....	Steep, unstable	Steep, unstable
Clouds.........	Scattered cumulus, occasional cumulo-nimbus	Plentiful and heavier cumulus and cumulo-nimbus
Precipitation...	Light showers, mostly in afternoon	Heavy, squally showers, mostly in early morning
Cloudiness.....	Pronounced diurnal variation, maximum in afternoon	Slight diurnal variation, mostly in early morning
Sky...........	Considerable bright intervals	Variable between bright and threatening
Cloud base.....	Considerable; seldom below 2,000 feet	Moderate, but seldom below 1,000 feet
Visibility......	Variable, mostly good, except for dust and smoke	Excellent, between showers

been developed in its surface layer, even though its humidity were increased by contact with the water. However, had it moved out over a *warmer* ocean its instability would have been *increased,* with resultant showers of increasing frequency and intensity.

If the mass of (*b*) above had moved back over a cold surface, whether wet or dry, it would have become stable in the surface layer. Also, at the same time, showers from the cumulo-nimbus would have reduced the instability by releasing the latent heat of vaporization above the condensation level.

Warm Masses and Their Properties

The subtropical anticyclone belts are the most prolific sources of warm air masses, although they may also be formed over the continents in summer under the nearly calm conditions or areas of high pressure or anticyclones.

Warm maritime and warm continental air masses also have distinctive characteristics.

A warm maritime mass will be generated with a fairly stable and very humid surface layer. As it travels away from its warm source the increasingly cooler surface serves only to intensify the stability of the lower layer, preventing convectional currents by the strong inversion at the top of the cooled surface layer. Except for the slow cooling incident to outgoing radiation, the air above the inversion will be affected only slightly, although it may become conditionally unstable during the normal diurnal cycle of variation. Meanwhile, if the surface layer becomes sufficiently cooled so as to drop below its dew point, an advection fog will result. If the wind is sufficiently strong to cause a mixing of the air below the inversion, the fog will spread upward to the altitude of the inversion. Mechanical turbulence, however, may heat the air closest to the surface enough to dissipate the lowest part of the fog, resulting in a layer of stratus close to the ground or water. At sea this is almost always the case, so that in a fog a ship's lookout, stationed low in the "eyes" of the ship, can usually see much farther ahead than a lookout stationed aloft.

Warm continental masses form over dry land surfaces under stagnant or quasi-stagnant conditions during the summer, particularly in the subtropical anticyclone belts. With the exception of those generated over desert regions (such as the Sahara and Arizona deserts) such masses will be conditionally unstable. As they travel toward cooler areas the stability of the lower layer is increased by cooling from below and the formation of an inversion. The air above that, however, will change but little *because* of the inversion and will tend to remain conditionally unstable. The mass thus acquires the typi-

TYPICAL PROPERTIES OF WARM MASSES

Property	*Continental*	*Maritime*
Temperature....	Decreasing	Decreasing
Humidity.......	Low; fairly constant	High; increasing
Lapse rate......	Conditionally unstable	Conditionally unstable
Clouds.........	Very few; high	Hazy, stratus-type or fog
Precipitation....	Little, if any	Steady, light
Cloudiness......	Clear, or a few scattered	Variable to overcast
Visibility.......	Good	Poor, hazy

cal properties of a warm mass below the inversion and those of a cold mass above. Warm air masses generated in the desert regions will there acquire marked instability by their contact with the hot sands. The convective currents resulting will produce "dust devils" or "whirling dervishes," small but rather violent whirling dust clouds that travel along the surface, or, in extreme cases, terrific sandstorms covering extensive areas. As these masses move into contact with cooler surfaces the instability decreases and they gradually become stable in the surface layer. On account of the extremely low humidity of the entire mass even to great altitudes, few if any clouds will form.

Superior Air Masses

The pilot may be apprised of the presence, location, and properties of *superior air masses* through weather reports of conditions in the upper air, now obtained twice daily as a matter of routine.   (Reports of *Upper Air Data* are covered in a separate section in the chapter on Weather Reports, page 189.)

Superior air is believed to be developed by strong subsiding motions.   It is most frequently observed at higher or intermediate levels of the atmosphere over the southwestern part of the United States.   However, it may at times be found at the surface, particularly over the South Central States.   Its reactions are similar to other air masses with like properties at lower altitudes.   Superior air is usually cold and dry when aloft, but when brought down by general sinking (called *subsidence*) it is heated adiabatically as it descends and produces warm, dry winds down mountain sides and long downward slopes known as Chinook or Foehn winds.   In this air relative humidities are usually less than forty per cent and are frequently *very low.*

Superior air is observed in both winter and summer.   With such low relative humidities no cloud forms are present and the visibility is usually very good.   Thus flying conditions in such air masses are excellent.

With strong westerly circulation, superior air frequently overruns the mT (maritime tropical) air mass moving north from the Gulf of Mexico.   When the mT air is shallow the overrunning superior air will put a lid on all convective activity, preventing shower or thunderstorm conditions.   When the mT air mass is deep and superior air is present at high levels, the dry superior air which is relatively cold tends to steepen the lapse rate.   Under this condition the convective activity within the mT air mass will be increased and will extend to higher levels.

Fronts and Frontal Zones

A *front* or *frontal zone* is a relatively narrow belt marking the boundary between two dissimilar air masses.

In Chapter VI our study of the general circulation of the atmosphere, as illustrated in Figure 6–1, showed us that this circulation is conducive to the generation of great air masses (see page 99). The general source areas are the respective pressure belts surrounding the earth. Where the air masses come together frontal zones or *fronts* are formed and may be maintained so long as the air of the two masses continues to converge toward a line. In Figure 6–1 two main frontal zones are readily apparent.

Air flowing down from the poles meets air flowing from the poleward side of the subtropical anticyclones to form the *polar fronts,* where the warm tropical air meets the cold polar air. These two general fronts are the most important, since they are responsible for a major part of the weather experienced over a great portion of the earth. They are much more clearly defined over the oceans than over the continents. These fronts move poleward in summer and towards the equator in winter. In the northern hemisphere the polar front extends in a general line from the United States to Norway across the Atlantic Ocean, and from eastern China to the United States across the Pacific.

From the equatorial slopes of the subtropical anticyclones the trade winds bring air which converges in the doldrums to form the *equatorial front.* Since there is little temperature difference between the air flowing in from the north and the south and since, also, the opposing barometric gradients near the middle of the belt are small, this front is not well defined and there is little activity along it.

Other major fronts, but of a much less persistent nature, often develop (and disperse) between the polar maritime masses and the arctic (and antarctic) air nearer the poles. When these exist, they are called the *arctic* and *antarctic fronts.*

Cold Fronts and Warm Fronts. Temporary fronts may form between (or even within) various traveling air masses. They also develop between old and young maritime polar air masses. When two itinerant and dissimilar air masses come together, a front is formed between them along the mutual boundary zone. When, in the frontal zone, the advancing cold air of one mass is displacing the warmer air of the other mass at the ground surface, the front is known as a *cold front;* and, vice versa, when the advancing warm air of one mass is displacing the colder air of the other at the ground surface, the front is known as a *warm front.*

Quasi-stationary Fronts. When there is no displacement of the warm or cold air along the frontal zone, i.e., when the front ceases to move, or wavers, it is then known as a *quasi-stationary front.*

In the study of the weather, the question of the formation, location, development, and dissipation of fronts is of the greatest importance. Each air mass is a storehouse of tremendous amounts of energy; temperature difference is the driving force tending to release this potential energy and convert it to kinetic energy. The greater the temperature difference, the more rapidly is the energy released and the more violent is the resulting reaction. This reaction, of course, occurs where dissimilar air masses meet, resulting in traveling depressions and storms.

Frontogenesis. Thus fronts are generated by the meeting of masses of different temperature, or by the creation of a steep temperature gradient along the horizontal, *within* a mass, so that a temperature discontinuity occurs. This process is called *frontogenesis,* and *the frontal zone lies along the line of discontinuity.*

Frontolysis. Fronts are destroyed by the release of their contained energy in frontal activity, by the merging and mixing of the air of the two masses along the frontal zone, and by the resultant reduction of the steep temperature gradient until it is no longer a narrow discontinuity but, instead, a broad zone

of gradual transition. This process of the weakening or de-
struction of a front is called *frontolysis*.

Isobars

On a weather map lines joining points of equal barometric
pressure are called *isobars*. The system of isobars on a
weather map greatly resembles the system of contours on a
topographical map. A contour is a line at every point of

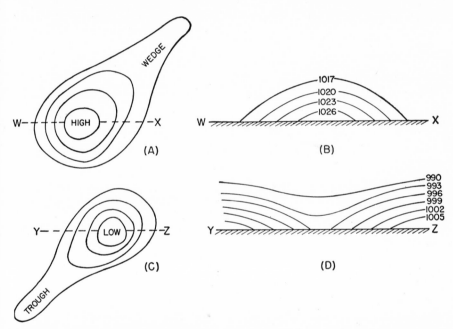

Fig. 7–1B. High-pressure area, or "eminence," and a low-pressure area,
or "depression," are represented by isobars as a "hill of air" and "valley of
air," respectively; shown on a horizontal plane at (A) and (C), and in vertical cross section at (B) and (D).

which the elevation above sea level is the same; at every point
on an isobar the barometric pressure is the same.

A region where the atmospheric pressure is higher than that
of other surrounding regions is called a HIGH or EMINENCE.

A region where the atmopheric pressure is lower than that
of other surrounding regions is called a LOW or DEPRESSION.

An elongated area of high pressure extending from an eminence is called a WEDGE.

An elongated area of low pressure extending from a depression is called a TROUGH.

If we think of isobars as contours depicting the atmospheric topography, the area represented by a HIGH represents a hill of air; the area represented by a LOW represents a depression, or valley. This conception is further suggested by the use of the words HIGH (for the hill of air) and LOW (for the valley). This has also been well brought out in an article on "The Technique of Drawing Isobars on Weather Maps," which appeared on the back of the Pilot Chart of the Upper Air—North Atlantic,* for December, 1938. Figure 7–1B illustrates the conception described above.

On a topographic map, contours close together indicate a steep slope; on a weather map, isobars close together represent a steep hill of air, or steep "gradient." In contrast with the topographic hill, however, an air hill is *fluid,* and therefore tends to flow down into the valley—the closer the isobars, the faster the rate of flow (wind velocity). Surface winds, then, always blow out from a HIGH, and in toward a LOW. If the earth were stationary, this flow might follow the actual direction of the gradient—i.e., perpendicular to the isobars—between the two centers. Because of friction, however, the rotation of the earth (i.e., the Coriolis force), and related factors, wind in the northern hemisphere is always deflected toward the right and approaches the trend of the isobars, blowing more or less along them, as illustrated in Figures 6–2, 6–3, and 6–4. Wind, therefore, blows spirally outward from a HIGH in a generally clockwise direction, and spirally inward toward a LOW, in a counter-clockwise direction (Figure 6–4). (*Note:* Remember that in the southern hemisphere the directions of rotation are just the reverse.) Although individual exceptions may be noted occasionally on actual weather maps

---

* Chart 1400a, U. S. Navy Hydrographic Office, Washington 25, D. C.; 10¢.

(due to local conditions), for the most part the arrows indicating wind direction follow this general rule.

This regular circulation of winds about a pressure center is more pronounced near the surface; on account of the effect of the prevailing winds at higher levels, it becomes less definite as the altitude increases. The HIGHS and LOWS themselves move across the United States from west to east, at a rate usually in excess of 500 miles a day (from about 20 to 30 miles per hour). LOWS usually move in an easterly to north-of-east direction, and HIGHS in an easterly to south-of-east direction. LOWS and HIGHS in summer are marked by less energy and slower movement than those of winter.

Isallobars

Isallobars are lines joining points of equal pressure tendency. Their use on a weather map is optional. They are drawn in curves in the same manner as isobars and are usually composed of short dashes. Their spacing is usually for one whole millibar per 3-hour interval.

Isallobars, taken together, form an *isallobaric field,* indicating regions of greatest (or least) pressure rise or fall, as the the case may be. Subject to various modifying influences, low-pressure centers tend to move toward regions of the most rapidly falling pressure, and, conversely, high-pressure centers tend to move toward regions of maximum rising pressure. Isallobars and isallobaric fields are often found to be as useful in forecasting as the pressure field itself.

Isotherms

Isotherms are lines of equal temperature, usually drawn for 10° intervals. They are optional on printed weather maps. When drawn on manuscript maps they are usually drawn in blue, lightly so as not to be confused with the heavy blue lines used to indicate cold fronts.

Relation of Isobars to Indicated Altitude—Altimeter Setting

As has been stated in an earlier chapter, the common altimeter is simply a form of aneroid barometer. Therefore it is well to remember that in flying "across the isobars" from a high-pressure area into an area of lower pressure the instrument will be affected by the reduction in atmospheric pressure and will indicate an altitude *higher* than the true altitude. The same is true, of course, if the pressure decreases while the plane is in flight even though it returns to its original point of departure. For this reason altimeters are provided with a barometric scale, by which they may be adjusted to the pressure in the vicinity of flight, so that they indicate actual heights, and not dangerously misleading altitudes.

For example, suppose the pressure at New York is 1,021.0 millibars, and at Chicago it is 1,010.2 millibars. These pressures correspond to altimeter settings of 30.15 and 29.83 inches, respectively. Under these conditions, if a pilot left New York with his altimeter adjusted to the pressure there, upon landing at Chicago his altimeter would be overreading and would *indicate* that he had over 300 feet more altitude than he actually had. Under conditions of instrument flights, this error might easily mean the difference between safety and disaster.

Pressure differences of this magnitude are quite common, and differences of twice this amount are not unusual. The difference of altitude in feet corresponding to the difference in barometric pressure should be considered as approximate only, since this also varies somewhat with the temperature. Accurate altimeter correction must therefore include a correction for the temperature as well. As a general rule, however, it may be said that each tenth of an inch (or each 3 millibars) of difference of pressure corresponds to an apparent difference in altitude of 100 feet. The important thing is that the altimeter should always be adjusted for the barometric pressure prevailing at the time *in the region of flight.* The necessary information for making this adjustment is given in the hourly weather broadcasts, as explained in Chapter VIII.

Traveling Disturbances

Previous sections have covered the generation and properties of warm and cold air masses of different varieties, and the various weather phenomena that develop within the masses as they journey across the surface of the earth after leaving their respective sources. All these changes have been internal changes, entirely due to heating and cooling of the air by its contact with the underlying surface.

With an understanding of the above, we may now examine more intelligently the effects produced by the meeting of masses of different temperatures and the weather phenomena which develop in the frontal zones that mark their common boundaries.

The three types of traveling disturbances are: cols, cyclones (or depressions), and anticyclones (or eminences). Each of these is a different type of pressure distribution.

Cols. The area between two depressions and two anticyclones forms a "saddle-backed" region on the weather map, called a *col,* similar to two hills and two valleys on a topographical map. The three typical forms of cols are illustrated in Figure 7–2.

The col is one of the most treacherous types of barometric distribution; sometimes it marks a locality of brilliantly fine weather, and at other times, it is broken up by severe thunderstorms. In the middle of a col there is no gradient, and therefore a calm, while, all around, the winds and weather conform to the usual law of isobars. The weather is dull, gloomy, and stagnant. In summer, violent thunderstorms are found in different portions of a col; in winter, fogs are frequent in such regions.

The type of col shown in Figure 7–2 (B) may be expected to give fair and settled weather. Here we have two small "hills" of air (called wedges) flowing down into two broad "valleys." The effect is very slight, pressure and temperature differences are readily equalized, and fair and settled weather results.

Conversely, Figure 7–2 (C) indicates just the reverse situation. Here two large "hills" come rushing in with a great deal of energy to fill up two narrow "valleys" or *troughs*. The effect is violent, with a rapid development toward worse weather.

Figure 7–2 (A) indicates a col of uncertain conditions, which may develop to those of (B) or (C).

Cols are prolific regions for the formation of fronts; the most active frontogenesis takes place in their vicinity. The

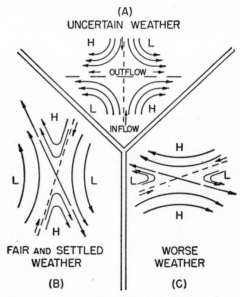

(A)
UNCERTAIN WEATHER

FAIR and SETTLED
WEATHER
(B)

WORSE
WEATHER
(C)

Fig. 7–2.   The three types of cols with their expected resultant weather.

fronts formed tend to lie close to the axis of outflowing air and not very far from it. Other pressure distributions with their wind systems, particularly troughs of low pressure, are also sources of frontogenesis.

Wave Theory. A disturbance of the equilibrium of the surface between a body of air and a body of water causes waves which travel along that surface. The waves in the water are visible; those in the air above the surface, though invisible, are just as real, coinciding and moving with the water waves. A gust of wind, as a source of energy, causes small waves in the water-air surface. If the wind continues to blow, the waves will build up according to the velocity of the wind, i.e., in proportion to the rate at which the energy is applied to the surface. If the wind velocity becomes great enough the tops of the water waves will be seen to curl over forward in the form of "white caps," which merely indicates that the common surface between the air and water has become unstable and the two fluids are tending to whirl together.

Now let us assume that we have two dissimilar air masses contiguous to each other: one, a *cPk* mass (cold, dry and dense), flowing from the northeast along the frontal surface; the other, an *mTw* mass (warm, moist and less dense), flowing from the southwest along the frontal surface.

The equilibrium along the frontal surface can be disturbed in various ways—friction between them, irregularities of underlying terrain, etc. When such a disturbance occurs, a wave is created which will continue until its energy is dissipated. Although the wave between two air masses does not hold to the same shape as the wave in an air-water surface, it obeys the same physical laws. Small waves—analogous to ripples produced on water by a short gust—often die out before becoming unstable, if the source of energy is removed or neutralized. However, the warm, moist air from the *mTw* air mass generally supplies a source of great energy, flowing into the initial incursion of the wave in the front, causing it to build up finally to the point of instability. Then the two masses along that part of the front whirl together and begin to mix, starting another process which is called "occlusion," described later in this chapter. As this mixing continues the temperature differences along that portion of the front are destroyed, the source of energy is cut off (i.e., "occluded"), and the wave dies.

A disturbance such as occurs incident to an atmospheric wave moving along a frontal surface is known as a *wave cyclone* or *cyclone*. It is also called, variously, a *depression* or a *low,* and the meaning of these latter two terms is explained in the two sections following.

Traveling Depressions

A cyclone, now usually spoken of as a depression, is a region of low barometric pressure, frequently designated merely by the term LOW. Depressions usually move in a general easterly direction, carrying their weather and wind systems with them as they travel. A description of the process of the birth, development, and death of a depression will be found beginning on page (148), but let us consider the "mature" disturbance first.

Figure 7–3 represents a typical depression with its pressure and cloud distribution, its circulation and fronts, grouped about a well-developed center of low pressure. The thin solid lines are isobars, the circulation of the winds about the center and across the isobars being indicated by the arrows. The cold front is represented by the heavy solid line, and the warm front by the double line. Imagine the entire disturbance to advance in an east-northeast direction at a rate of about 30 miles an hour, or 720 miles a day, as shown by the long broken arrow (A-B).

The lower part of Figure 7–3 shows that along the warm front the warm air, being lighter, is forced forward and upward along the gradually sloping surface of the colder underlying air. The mechanical lifting and forward flow of the warm air results in the cloud sequence shown. Thus the approach of the warm front is marked by increasing and lowering clouds, followed by rain, which becomes heavier as the front approaches, and subsides after it passes.

As the cold front approaches (lower left of Figure 7–3), the warm air is again lifted as the colder air pushes under it. Alto-cumulus and cumulo-nimbus clouds form, usually accompanied by brief but heavy rainfall of a squally, showery type. The figure shows a narrow band of nimbo-stratus

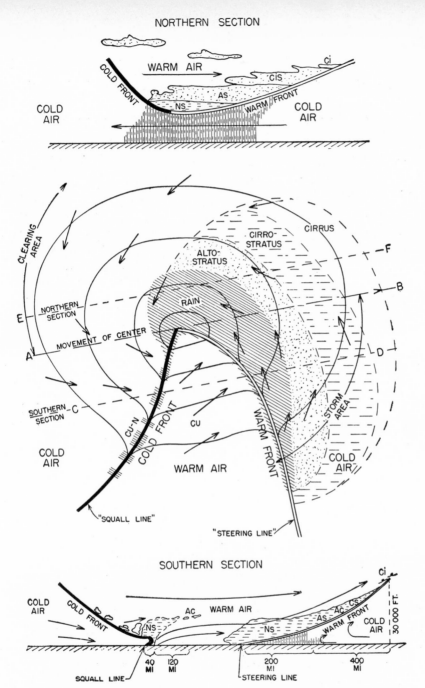

NORTHERN SECTION

COLD FRONT

WARM AIR

Ci

CiS

AS

COLD
AIR

NS

WARM FRONT

COLD
AIR

CLEARING
AREA

CIRRUS

CIRRO-
STRATUS

ALTO-
STRATUS

F

E

NORTHERN
SECTION

RAIN

B

A

MOVEMENT OF CENTER

D

SOUTHERN
SECTION

C

CU-N

COLD FRONT

CU

WARM FRONT

STORM
AREA

COLD
AIR

COLD
AIR

WARM AIR

COLD
AIR

"SQUALL LINE"

"STEERING LINE"

SOUTHERN SECTION

COLD
AIR

COLD FRONT

Ac

WARM AIR

Ci

NS

NS

As Ac Cs

WARM FRONT

COLD
AIR

30,000 FT.

40
MI

120
MI

200
MI

400
MI

SQUALL LINE

STEERING LINE

FIG. 7–3.   Typical depression, with sections through the front at *E-F* and
C-D. Isobars shown as full lines; air circulation shown by arrows. The
diagram above represents the condition found in the Northern Hemisphere.

Note: In the Southern Hemisphere the above diagram would be reversed,
top-for-bottom but *not* right-for-left, and the air circulation would be *clockwise.* For practice, the student should draw a diagram for the Southern
Hemisphere.

clouds along the front, but in many cases this is entirely absent.

As the cold front passes and the colder air behind it comes in contact with the surface of the area so recently occupied by the warm air, the air near the surface is heated, and strong vertical currents are set up. This warm air, meeting the cold air at higher levels, results in the formation of clouds—usually cumulus or cumulo-nimbus. The resulting weather characteristics of such areas are clear periods alternating with occasional showers.

An observer at any station over which the disturbance passed would stand successively under different parts of the storm, and would experience the various kinds of weather that it brings. If his station lay on the track of the storm center, his successive positions within the storm area would fall along the line of the broken arrow, AB; if the storm center passed to the north, his station would be found on—and he would experience the weather found along—such a line as CD; if the storm center passed to the south, his path through the storm would be found along such a line as EF. In the case of his being on the track of the center, he would note at first weak southeasterly winds, increasing in strength and shifting somewhat to the south, with falling pressure, rising temperature, and increasing cloudiness with rain or snow. On the close approach of the center, when the barometer reaches its lowest reading, the winds commonly weaken, and shortly thereafter turn more or less abruptly to the northwest and often increase to gale force as the barometer rises and the temperature falls. The rain soon ceases, the clouds break away, and the wind resumes its more customary direction and velocity.

If the observer's station lies to the south of the track, at first there will be no abrupt change in the course of the wind. High cirrus clouds will be followed by cirro-stratus which thicken and lower steadily to alto-cumulus, alto-stratus (with the beginning of light rain becoming heavier and steady), and finally nimbo-stratus with steady, heavy precipitation. The wind, beginning from the southeast, will veer slowly through the south until the warm front passes over, at which time there is usually a fairly well-defined wind shift of at least 30 to 45 degrees to the southwest, with a rise in temperature and a break in the sky from nimbo-stratus to strato-cumulus and cumulus. This situation continues with fairly even temperature and pressure until shortly before the cold front approaches, heralded by alto-cumulus quickly followed by alto-stratus and then heavy cumulo-nimbus with squalls, heavy showers (thunderstorms in the summer), a drop in temperature, and a strong shift in the wind to the northwest, a rapidly clearing sky, and excellent visibility. Clouds, if any, are light and scattered, of the "fair-weather" variety.

If, on the other hand, the observer's station lies to the north of the storm track, the winds will begin in the east, shifting gradually through the northeast and north to the northwest; this counter-clockwise change in wind direction is called *backing*. The cloud formations passing over are successively cirrus, cirro-stratus, alto-stratus, and nimbo-stratus. The rain clouds do not break away so rapidly as they do with the passage of the warm front in the southern sector; instead, the precipitation diminishes more gradually and there is no sudden change in temperature at the surface. The reason for this (as shown in the "Northern Section" of the figure) is that the frontal surfaces, both warm and cold, are well above the ground.

The abnormal shift implied by the term *backing* is simply explained. European stations, whence these terms have come to us, lie generally to the southeast of the tracks of their stronger winter storms, and hence the ordinary shift of the winds is from the east through the south to the west, or "with the sun," as it is often called; it is only when an exceptional storm center passes farther south than usual, or only at the distant stations in northern Europe, that the winds turn "against

the sun," and therefore this change came to be looked upon as
the reverse of the normal order.

There is still much to be learned about the origin, maintenance, and exact nature of depressions, but new ideas and
theories are aiding considerably in forecasting. One of the
most detailed studies, the work of Prof. V. Bjerknes of Norway, is summarized briefly below.

Professor Bjerknes laid stress on the importance of reporting wind directions by compass degrees rather than by the
nearest intercardinal direction. In this way he was able to
establish firmly the lines of convergent and divergent wind
systems and their attending phenomena during the passage of
the cyclonic storms which traverse the North Sea and pass up
along the coast of Norway. He developed a system for the
determination of the path of the cyclone, not heretofore mentioned and which, if followed, will materially aid a forecaster
in his predictions of weather for any portion of the world.
The usual theory of cyclonic circulation is that the air flows
spirally inward where there is a central core of upward-
flowing air. His investigations revealed that the upward
flow of air takes place mostly in the southeastern quadrant.
Although it is substantially true that the air outside of a radius
of 100 miles flows spirally inward, yet close investigation reveals that, upon nearing the storm center, there are two distinct lines of convergent winds, which Bjerknes conveniently
called the *steering line* and the *squall line*.   (See Figure 7–3.)
The theory of the great air masses had not been developed
then, but it is interesting to note that the steering line and
squall line, as shown in older works, correspond to the position
of the warm and cold fronts, respectively, at the ground level.
Observe that the lines of convergence are those toward which
the wind blows in from both sides, and lines of divergence
are those from which the wind blows out on both sides.

The steering line to the southeast of the storm center is
where the inflowing warm air from the south meets and flows
upward and over the cooler surface air to the eastward of the

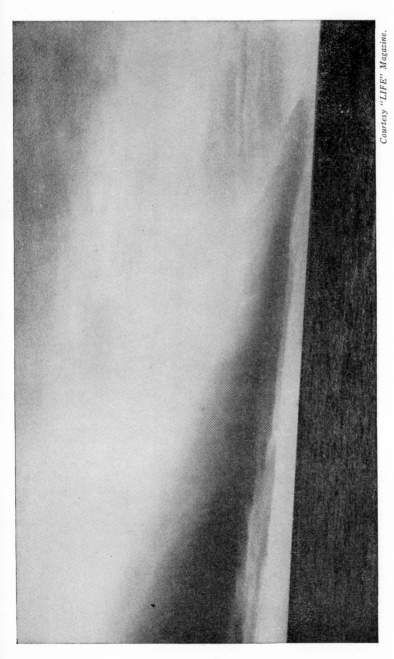

FIG. 7–4. This long nimbus cloud (cumulo-nimbus arcus) is a true "line squall." It marks the edge of a cold front. The cloud is moving to the right. At its far end, rain is falling. An airline pilot confronted with the scene above would quickly translate it into the diagram of Figure 7–5. A mass of cold air is wedging into an area of warm air. When this happens, a weather disturbance inevitably occurs. Here the disturbance takes the form of a sudden, violent rainstorm.

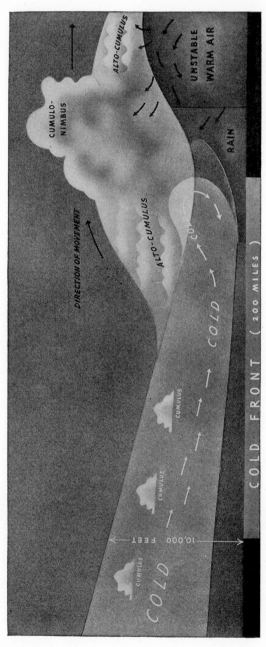

Courtesy "LIFE" Magazine.

FIG. 7–5. To pilots the approach of a cold front is a sign of possible danger. Inside the cumulo-nimbus there is always great disturbance. The air eddies violently upward. The hail pelts so hard that it can dent a plane's wings.

Once past the cold front, however, the pilot finds good flying weather. The air is clear and smooth. The only clouds he sees are the scattered cumulus, remnants of the storm he has just passed through.

storm's progress, causing rains far in advance of the storm's center.

The squall line to the southwest of the storm center is where the cold northwesterly surface winds wedge under the warm southerly winds, lifting them mechanically to produce cumulo-nimbus clouds with southwest shifting to northwest squalls and often thunderstorms.

Professor Bjerknes indicates that the path of the cyclone is a line drawn tangent to the steering line at the storm center. This is usually approximately correct, but recent studies show that lines of barometric tendency, called *isallobars,* are more dependable for this purpose than the older method.

Through the courtesy of *Life* magazine we are enabled to reproduce an actual photograph showing the formation along a pronounced cold front (Figure 7–4) with a diagram illustrating its internal and surrounding weather phenomena (Figure 7–5). Figure 7–6 shows a warm front; in this diagram the student should note carefully that the scale of distance has been greatly foreshortened as compared to that of Figure 7–5. The actual slope of a warm front averages about 1/100, and varies from about 1/50 to 1/200. On the other hand, a cold front is steeper, averaging roughly about 1/60 and varying from about 1/40 to 1/80.

Frontal Thunderstorms

In a frontal zone between two dissimilar air masses the motive power to create an atmospheric disturbance (particularly of local character) is provided principally by the difference in temperature between the two masses coupled with their respective relative humidities. When these two properties are sufficiently accentuated, local thunderstorms will occur along or near the front. The greater the temperature difference and the greater the relative humidity of the two air masses, the more violent will be the resulting local disturbance, distinctive in character according to the type of front.

Warm-front thunderstorms are caused by the lifting of conditionally unstable air flowing up the gradual slope of a warm front. They are generally scattered in the area *ahead*

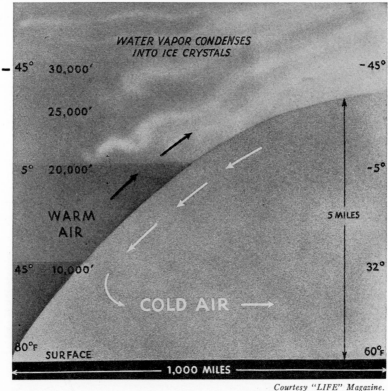

Courtesy "LIFE" Magazine.

Fig. 7–6. A diagrammatic cross section of a warm frontal surface. Cirrus forms when warm air meets cold and overruns it. Forced up over the cold mass, warm air ascends farther and farther as it travels into colder regions (note temperatures at right of picture). Its vapor freezes quickly. Steady winds can blow cirrus a thousand miles from its place of origin. It should be noted that the necessary foreshortening of the diagram makes the slope of the frontal surface appear very steep, whereas it is actually about 1 mile in 200.

of the surface front, and usually originate in the alto-stratus clouds above the cold air. When *heavy* thunderstorms occur ahead of the surface front, their preliminary release of moisture often leaves the warm-front rain area "spotty."

Cold-front thunderstorms are caused by the mechanical lifting of warm moist air by the undercutting cold air of a cold front. The steeper slope of the cold front forces the warm air up more rapidly; thus the cold-front type is usually more violent than either the thermal or the warm-front type. The cold-front thunderstorm usually does not extend to such high altitudes as the warm-front type.

Upper-front thunderstorms. Both warm- and cold-front thunderstorms may be produced by warm and cold fronts aloft in the same manner as described above. These are called *upper-front thunderstorms*. This type is generally recognized easily since little or no turbulence will be encountered in the shielding layer of cold air between the thunderstorm cloud base and the ground.

Line squalls. Another type of thunderstorm, called the *line squall,* presents an even more serious problem. It is always associated with a cold front. The vertical currents often are stronger than those in the thermal type of storm. The line squall (as its name implies) may extend along a front for several hundred miles so that it is impossible to fly around it.

Along a cold front, when cold air runs under the warm air which it replaces, currents of ordinary intensity are produced; but when cold air runs *over* the warmer air, violent vertical currents are set up as the lighter air finally breaks through the colder and heavier air above it. In either case a series of thunderstorms may develop almost simultaneously, occasionally in an almost unbroken line as much as several hundred miles in length. The violently active clouds associated with line squalls usually extend only to an altitude of about 6,000 feet and it is sometimes possible to fly above them; however, their vertical currents which are common to all thunderstorm clouds *may* extend up to 15,000 or 20,000 feet and may exceed velocities of 100 miles per hour. Though many line squalls are of moderate intensity any attempt to fly through or over a storm of this type is extremely hazardous.

Tornadoes. Some thunderstorms, especially those which develop from highly aggravated line squall conditions, develop a violent whirling motion of the air over a small diameter (from a few feet to several hundred yards) extending like a great twisting, funnel-shaped tube from the cloud base down to the earth's surface. This is called a *tornado.* The barometric pressure at its center is extremely low. It is the most concentrated, most violent and most destructive type of storm, and the shortest lived, sometimes lasting but a relatively few minutes. It is easily identified at some distance by its very dark, funnel-shaped cloud, as shown in Fig. 4–23, on page 66.

Mechanical thunderstorms. All of the above types of local disturbances (as well as the orographic type) being initiated by the mechanical lifting of conditionally unstable air, are referred to as *mechanical thunderstorms* in contradistinction to those of a purely thermal character, discussed in Chapter V. However, some thunderstorms may combine the characteristics of both the thermal and mechanical types.

Development of Depressions

The way in which the meeting of dissimilar air masses produces the various meteorological reactions is further illustrated in Figure 7–7. (Note: The sketches depict the successive situations at the *ground level.*) At (A) cold air (*cPk*) is shown flowing from the northeast, with warm air (*mTw*) flowing from the southwest, such as we would find typically along the polar front. The surface between the two air masses and along which they move is referred to as "the surface of discontinuity," since along this line occur rapid changes in temperature, humidity, and wind direction.

Along the front the usual tendency is for the warm mass to make a small initial incursion to the northward. When this happens, the cold air, to the left of the incursion, starts to swing around behind it, making a bulge to the southward, as at (B). This becomes more and more pronounced as the

wave builds up, producing a rotary (or "cyclonic") circulation in a counter-clockwise direction. A wave, such as in
(C) or (D), may be from 200 to 600 (or more) miles across

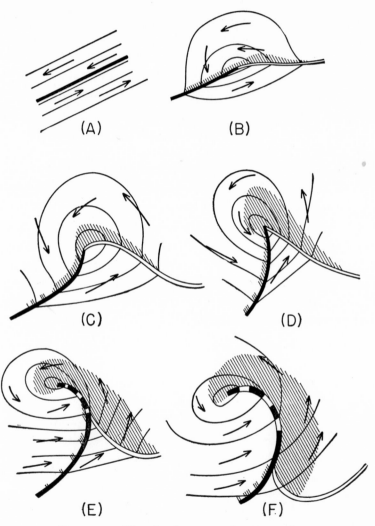

Fig. 7–7. The development of a depression.

the base. Thus there is, at this stage, a large volume and
weight of air moving in a circular path. Centrifugal force
tends to throw the air outward, and thus to reduce the pres-

sure at the center. This is particularly effective upon the warm mTw air as it flows upward over the heavier cPk under the warm front. Both the rotation and the upward flow tend to expand the warm air in that vicinity, and a definite area of reduced atmospheric pressure is created.

Contrary to the explanation above, it should be noted in the sketches that the winds *at ground level* flow inward *toward the center*. This is explained by the fact that the reduction of pressure, caused by the ascension and expansion of the warm air, is sufficiently great to overcome the centrifugal effect and to cause the surface air to flow in to replace the ascending warm air and to fill the expanding bulge of the cold front. So long as the mTw air flows in, from the warm sector between the two fronts, it will, successively: (1) rise over the cold air under the warm front, (2) precipitate its water vapor content, (3) be reheated by the latent heat of condensation, (4) rise still higher and spread out in the upper atmosphere and, at the same time, (5) be thrown outward by the centrifugal force of rotation. The process just described supplies the energy to *maintain* the low pressure which, in turn, sucks in cold air into the cold front bulge and warm air into the center, only to expand the latter and throw it out violently aloft.

So long as the source of energy (the mTw air) is available to go "up the funnel," the disturbance will continue; but, when the cold front finally catches up with the warm front and "occlusion" occurs (E) and (F), the mTw air is cut off and the cyclone dies of "old age."

Occlusion

Ordinarily the cold front advances more rapidly than the warm front, and (as mentioned above) overtakes it. When the cold air from the back of the depression overtakes the cold air in front of the depression, the warm air is lifted entirely from the ground, and is said to be occluded, and the

area in which such a situation exists is called the occlusion
as is also the process itself.   If the overtaking air behind the
cold front is colder than that ahead of the warm front (because of a different path of travel or other reason) the situation will be as shown in Figure 7–8(A) ; the warm front will
be lifted from the ground into the upper atmosphere.   In
this instance, within the occlusion, the passage of the cold
front will be marked by a drop in temperature at the surface.

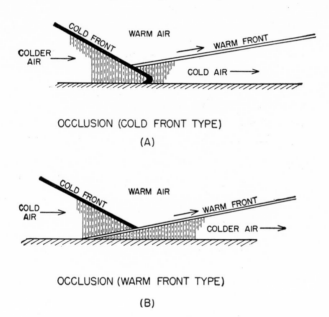

Fig. 7–8.   Cross section through simple occlusions.

This is known as a "cold-front type" occlusion. If, however, the colder air is under the warm front, then the cold
front will be lifted into the air so that it passes overhead, and
the passing of the combined fronts will be accompanied by
a *rise* in temperature at the surface, as shown in Figure
7–8(B).   The cold-front type of occlusion is characterized
by squally rain and falling temperature, the warm-front type
by low cloud and continuous rain or drizzle with rising temperature.

Upper Fronts

A front is termed an *upper front* whenever there is a "very cold" layer next to the ground and the frontal activity takes place above the top of the "very cold" air. Upper fronts occur in winter frequently when the eastern portion of the continent is covered by a cold *cP* air mass and a cool *mP* air mass moves in from the Pacific northwest. Figure 7–9 shows an upper cold front east of the Rocky Mountains.

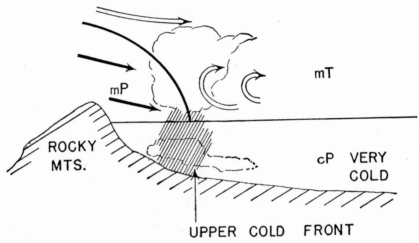

FIG. 7–9. A very cold layer of continental Polar air overlies an area east of the Rockies. A warm mass of maritime Tropical air has migrated north from the Gulf of Mexico, forced aloft by the heavy cP. When a cool maritime Polar mass flows in from the Pacific Ocean over the mountains it forces its way under the mT but, on contacting the cP, it flows across its upper surface just as though it were the surface of the ground. All frontal activity, between the mP and the mT, takes place *aloft* at the top of the cP layer.

Frequently an upper front is the remnant of an old occlusion. When the two cold air masses which have forced the intervening warmer air aloft have attained homogeneity, the front on the ground dissolves and all that is left is the trough of warmer air aloft. The boundary between the surface cold air and the warm air aloft then becomes an upper front.

When an *mP* air mass moves east of the Rocky Mountains with strong westerly winds invading a mass of *mT* air moving north under southerly winds, the stronger westerly winds aloft advance the colder air aloft well ahead of the surface position of the front. This creates an area wherein a blanket of cold heavy air lies over the warm moist air beneath. Although this is a condition indicative of great instability, this situation may, under certain circumstances, persist for periods of 12 to 24 hours. In the meantime, when the warm *mT* air finally breaks through the cold air above, it does so with great violence, causing at least severe thunderstorms if not a series of tornadoes throughout the area.

Fronts between Superior and Tropical Air Masses

In the summer, maritime Tropical air may spread far to the north and yet, at times, it may show little or no frontal activity at the surface. On a surface weather map of the area, there would appear to be merely a large, uniform mass

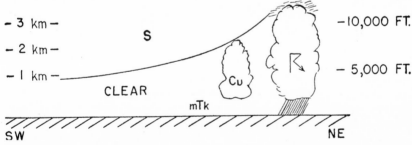

Fig. 7–10. Upper front between S and mTk air masses. This situation is not uncommon in the United States, particularly during the summer season.

of *mT* air; and yet despite its apparent uniformity there would be thunderstorm areas and others which remain clear. Here again is a situation where data on the upper air are a necessary aid to the meteorologist. Figure 7–10 shows a typical cross-section through the area, revealing the cause of what would seem to be an inconsistency. We find that a Superior air mass is overlying the *mTk* which is very broad and shallow. The upper front between the *S* and the *mTk* usually lies between the 1,000 and 10,000-foot levels and is marked by a pronounced temperature inversion and a very sharp moisture discontinuity. The slope of the front is small, rising slowly from the Southwest Plains States eastward toward the Atlantic seaboard. In ascending through the front there is usually a wind shift from south toward west.

In the region of the Central Plains States the diurnal heating is usually enough, at least during the warm season, to effect a rather complete convective dissipation of the shallow *mTk* stratum. The resulting mixture remains too dry, however, for convective showers to occur, as indicated in the "CLEAR" area of the figure. The significance of this stratification pattern lies in the impossibility of convective showers and thunderstorm formation even in summer. About 11,000 to 12,000 feet seems to be the usual minimum depth of the *mTk* air mass required in cases of this type of stratification in order for thunderstorms to develop during the day. It should be borne in mind that the *S* air to the west had been warmed adiabatically during its subsidence to the lower levels, whereas that at the high levels in the east is still relatively cold and dry and tends to steepen the lapse rate. Under this condition the convective activity within the *mTk* air mass will be increased and will be extended to the higher levels required for the generation of thunderstorms.

Southern Hemisphere Diagrams

The student should bear in mind that the diagrams and discussions given here apply only, in the form shown, to the northern hemisphere. For a better understanding, it is recommended that the student reproduce Figures 7-3 and 7-7 as they would be drawn to represent conditions in the southern hemisphere. Bear in mind the following: the top (north) and bottom (south) of the diagram will be interchanged, but the left (west) and right (east) of the diagram will *not* be interchanged; the "northern section" will appear at the south (bottom) of the diagram and will then become the "southern section," and vice versa; the direction of the rotation of the winds will be reversed; the direction of travel of the depression will be generally *south* of east instead of as shown in Figure 7–3.

Unstable Air in Depressions

In the preceding discussions and diagrams, for the sake of simplicity, the cloud systems shown and the phenomena described have been such as would occur if the air were in a stable state. It should be borne in mind, therefore, that a state of instability or conditional instability will superimpose its typical phenomena upon the conditions described for the stable state. For example, since most of the air in warm air masses invading the United States from the Gulf of Mexico is in a state of conditional instability, when it is forced up along the warm front to such an altitude that it becomes unstable, towering cumulus turrets will build up above the top of the ordinary layer-cloud formation, superimposing a showery or even thunderstorm condition upon the steady precipitation from the stratus-type layer. When conditionally unstable air is similarly forced up along a cold front, it serves only to intensify the violence of the squalls and thunderstorms which naturally occur at a cold front; in fact, these are exactly the conditions which produce our most violent and destructive "line squalls." (See Figure 7–4.)

Troughs of Low Pressure

Quite frequently, an elongated area of low pressure, called a *trough,* will extend from a depression, as illustrated in Figure 7–1. The isobars of such a trough may have either a U-shape or a V-shape. U-shaped troughs *usually* contain no fronts, while V-shaped troughs always do. U-shaped troughs contain unsettled to bad weather and in them secondary fronts *may* form. In V-shaped troughs the meteorological elements vary rapidly, the center of the depression is toward the open end of the V, and the front passes through the sharp angles of the V-shaped isobars.

Wind-shifts and Fronts

As shown in Figures 7–3 and 7–7 both the warm and cold fronts are marked by a change in wind direction, particularly in a "young" depression. The cold front is usually more pronounced as a "wind-shift line" than the warm front. As the front passes, the wind shifts more or less abruptly to the right as one faces the wind. The pilot should bear well in mind the shift in wind direction which will occur as he passes through a frontal surface. In the "northern section," to the north of the depression center, if the pilot rises through the frontal surface, he will experience a shift of the wind from an easterly to a westerly direction, and the reverse in descending. In the "southern section," to the south of the center, he will experience a clockwise wind-shift if he rises through a warm front or descends through a cold front. Conversely, if he rises through a cold front or descends through a warm front, he will experience a counterclockwise shift in wind direction. The amount of the shift is frequently so great as to require a radical change in the heading of the aircraft in order to make good the desired track.

Tropical Cyclones

A tropical cyclone—the "cyclone" of the Indian Ocean, the "hurricane" of the West Indies and the South Pacific, and the "typhoon" of the West Pacific and China Sea—consists of a vast whirl of rapidly moving air currents surrounding a calm and relatively small center or vortex.

For a better understanding, let us see how a hurricane is created. Somewhere in the sultry and humid doldrums of the eastern Atlantic Ocean a large patch of air becomes heated over the warm sea. Suddenly it starts to rise, all in one big ball, like a giant balloon encased in its own sluggishness. In its place cooler air rushes in from all directions, not as a gentle breeze but as a great wind racing to fill the void left by the ascending "balloon." There we have the beginning: Warm moist air rising rapidly in the center; more moisture-laden air rushing in from all sides.

The Coriolis force starts the system spinning. The rising air aloft, cooling as it goes, suddenly starts to produce rain, torrents of it, and at the same time releases the terrific energy held in the "cylinder" of this gigantic heat engine. More and more air is sucked in from the surrounding area, warming and humidifying over the warm sea as it comes in. The system whirls faster; the winds increase, to blow the tops from the waves in a sheet of white flying spray. Finally the centrifugal force, tending to throw the rotating air outward, balances the force sucking the air in toward the center. This results in the formation of a "cylinder" of air standing at the center with walls literally hardened so that air cannot get in from the outside while that on the inside remains idly stagnant. It is the "eye" of the hurricane—from two to ten miles in diameter. One comes upon it suddenly, out of a roaring, seething, drenching storm into a soft, balmy calm of light, variable airs and a bright blue sky overhead. The sea swell still runs high, but it is long and smooth. Just as suddenly the other side of the "eye" is reached. One can see the clouds and rain approaching and hear the roar of the wind as it bears down from the *opposite* direction. It strikes your ship like the blow of an enormous sledge hammer; she stops nearly dead in the water and shudders under the impact, finally struggles onto a new course to "ride out" the storm till it passes. The hurricane whirls on across the ocean, "feeding" on the warm, moist air as long as the supply lasts. And so it continues until the hurricane moves in over the land, or over cold water, and the throttle of the great heat-engine is closed, and it gradually comes to stop, and disperses. (The author has just given you a description of his own experience in passing through the "eye" of a West Indian hurricane.)

Although tropical and extratropical cyclones have many similarities, such as low pressure centers, abundant precipitation, same instantaneous wind directions, and the like, and although it may be impossible to say just when a tropical cyclone on its way to higher latitudes becomes extratropical, nevertheless they usually differ from each other in several important respects. Among these differences are:

(*a*) The isobars of the tropical cyclone usually are more symmetrical and more nearly circular than those of the extratropical.

(*b*) The temperature distribution around the vortex of the tropical cyclone is practically the same in every direction, while about the extratropical it is very different.

(*c*) The tropical cyclone contains no frontal surfaces of discontinuity, whereas the extratropical always does.

(*d*) In tropical cyclones rains are torrential and more or less evenly distributed on all sides of the center. In the extratropical, rains vary greatly in nature and intensity in different quadrants.

(*e*) Tropical cyclones usually have calm, rainless centers, 2 to 10 miles or more in diameter, while the extratropical rarely shows this characteristic whirl phenomenon.

(*f*) Tropical cyclones are most frequent during summer and early fall of the hemisphere in which they occur, while the extratropical are strongest and most numerous during the winter months.

(*g*) Tropical cyclones often move to higher latitudes, where they assume more or less completely the characteristics of the extratropical cyclone. The extratropical cyclone, on the other hand, never invades the regions of the tropical nor assumes its distinctive characteristics.

(*h*) The pressure drop of the tropical cyclone generally begins with the winds; in the extratropical, it usually begins much sooner.

(*i*) The tropical cyclone has no anticyclone "companion"; the extratropical cyclone usually has—to the west of it.

Tropical cyclones occur over the tropical portions of all oceans except, possibly, the South Atlantic. They are most numerous in the western Atlantic (including the Gulf of Mexico), the Bay of Bengal, the western Pacific (including the China Sea), where their comparative annual frequencies are, roughly, about 4, 8, and 24, respectively. They seldom originate closer than 5 or 6 degrees to the equator, but most frequently between latitudes 10° to 20°. In fact, they seem to originate almost entirely along the belt of doldrums, and therefore, since this belt follows the sun, to appear at higher latitudes during summer and lower or not at all during late fall or winter.

Tropical cyclones vary greatly in diameter. Initially, such storms may be no more than 50 miles across, but when well developed they may have diameters of 200 to 500 miles. The clouded area incident to typhoons, always much more extensive than the surface area of the storm, may even be as much as 1,000 miles across.

The shape of the cyclone, as given by the isobars, appears usually to be that of an ellipse whose diameters are to each other, roughly, as 2 to 3, with the longer axis in the direction of travel.

The direction of the wind is spirally inward at an angle of 30°, roughly, to the isobars, counterclockwise in the northern hemisphere, clockwise in the southern. At an elevation of only from 2,000 to 2,500 feet the inflow is said to cease, and above this level the winds are spirally outward. These horizontal motions also necessitate a correspondingly strong upward component around the vortex or inner portion of the storm, and a slower downward component over a much greater surrounding area.

The velocity of the wind varies greatly in different tropical cyclones and even more greatly in different portions of the

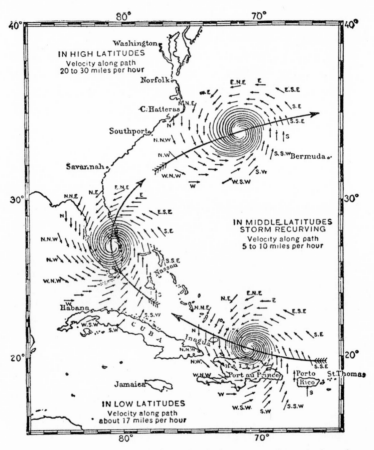

Fig. 7–11. Characteristic track and wind system of tropical cyclone of Northern Hemisphere.

same storm. Near the center, or within the "eye" of the storm, which may have a diameter of from 2 to 10 miles or more, the wind is very light and the sky clear or only partly covered with clouds. Away from this center the winds often reach destructive velocities of from 100 to 125, or even 150 miles an hour, but they decrease in violence rather rapidly with increase of distance from the center, dropping to only moderate winds of 30 to 40 miles an hour at a distance of, say, 200 miles.

The speed of travel of the storm center has a direct effect upon the velocity of the winds in the different quadrants of the storm area. This is because the translational speed of the storm is superimposed upon the velocity due to the pressure gradient within the storm itself. This will tend to increase the wind velocity in that semicircle of the area wherein the winds are blowing in the same general direction as the storm's movement along its track, and will decrease the wind velocity in that semicircle wherein the winds are blowing in a general direction counter to the direction of movement of the storm center. For example: In the lower part of Figure 7-11, the storm is moving along its track in a northwesterly direction at a speed of about 17 m.p.h. Suppose the wind due to the gradient, at a certain given radius, is 80 m.p.h. Then, superimposing the storm's translational velocity thereon, we would find a velocity of $80 + 17 = 97$ m.p.h. at the given radius and 90° to the right of the direction of the storm track; but at a similar point 90° to the *left* of the storm track we would find a velocity of $80 - 17 = 63$ m.p.h., or 34 miles per hour less than in the eastern semicircle. In the middle of Figure 7-11, the maximum difference in velocity between the eastern and western semicircles would be from 10 to 20 m.p.h., and at the top of Figure 7-11 between 40 and 60 m.p.h., in each case approximately twice the speed with which the storm center is moving along its track. A glance at Figure 7-12, showing the situation in the southern hemisphere, will also reveal that the more violent winds will always be found in that semicircle which lies generally to the *eastward* of the track. For this reason, this area of the storm has become known among mariners as the *dangerous semicircle,* and the area lying generally to the west of the storm track, wherein the winds are less violent, has become known as the *navigable semicircle*.

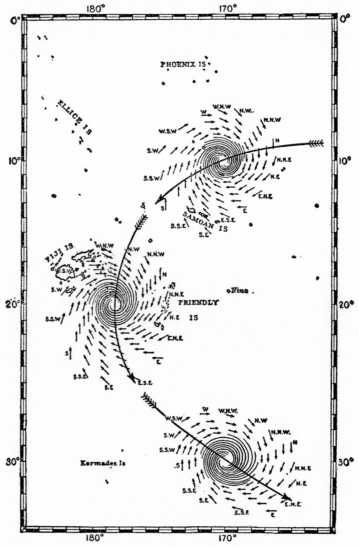

Fig. 7–12. Characteristic track and wind system of tropical cyclone of Southern Hemisphere.

Tropical cyclones of the northern hemisphere first move west, then usually northwest. Many start to recurve in about

Latitude 20°–25° N., turning north and finally moving away to the northeast. In the southern hemisphere the corresponding directions of travel of the tropical cyclone are west, southwest, south, and finally southeast. Typical cyclone paths and latitudes of recurving are shown in Figures 7–11 and 7–12.

The velocity with which tropical cyclones travel varies from almost zero in certain cases, especially at or near the place of recurving (or *inflection,* as it is sometimes called) when this happens to be abrupt, to perhaps 500 miles per day. Over the Bay of Bengal, the Arabian Sea, and the China Sea, the velocity averages about 200 miles per day. Over the Indian Ocean the velocity ranges from 50 to 200 miles per day. Over the western Atlantic the average before and during recurving is about 260 miles per day, but after recurvature—that is, when the cyclones move northeast over middle latitudes—about 400 miles per day.

Anticyclones

An anticyclone is a region in which the barometric pressure is high relative to its surroundings. Since such a region may be visualized as a "hill" of air on the weather map, and as the term "anticyclone" lacks descriptive qualities, the term *eminence* has been suggested and is now coming into some use as a companion-opposite to the term "depression." General acceptance of this term would complete the series of terms now used interchangeably to designate these opposite meteorological situations, thus:

> Cyclone — Anticyclone
> Low — High
> Depression — Eminence

On weather charts an anticyclone is generally shown by a series of closed isobars, the region of highest pressure being the central region. In a well-marked anticyclone, the isobars are roughly circular or oval, the wind blows spirally outward in accordance with Buys-Ballot's law, and the pressure in the central parts is seldom below 1,016 millibars (30 inches Hg). (See Figure 7–13.)

The broad features of the weather in an anticyclone are blue sky, dry, cold air, a hot sun, and a hazy horizon, with very little wind—in fact, the very antithesis of everything which characterizes a depression. As a necessary consequence of this, we find in an eminence strongly marked "radiation weather" * and much diurnal variation.

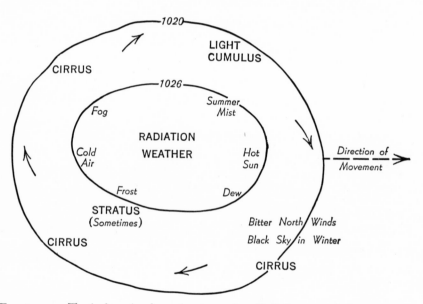

FIG. 7–13. Typical anticyclone (eminence). Full lines are isobars; arrows show air circulation; pressure in millibars. (Northern Hemisphere.)

Ordinarily an anticyclone is thought of as giving light winds, clear skies, and fair weather, but this is not always true, for frequently, over the United States, an anticyclone may bring clouded skies for several days in succession and often rain will develop well toward the center, even in energetic HIGHS.

When reporting stations are close together, as in some of the European countries, it is frequently possible to show kinks

---

* Clear blue sky, brilliant sunlight, low humidity, conducive to rapid reception and emission of solar radiation.

in the isobars which will account for the rains in high-pressure areas. A few such kinks may be observed occasionally in United States maps, but ordinarily the stations are so far apart and the conditions governing the wind direction so uncertain at the observing stations that the isobars have to be drawn smooth over long distances. At such times it is difficult to explain the cause of rain in some sections. (The needs of aviation, however, have already done much to overcome such difficulties through the establishment of more observation stations.) Study of the rainy anticyclones shows that the southern and southwestern parts are those which give the rains and the bad weather. In the southern states, cloudy and dull skies with a drizzle or moderately heavy rains may sometimes exist for two or three days, although the region may be well within the area covered by an eminence.

Anticyclones, like the cyclones, move across the country generally from the west to the east and carry with them their respective weather conditions. Fair weather will prevail from the time the eminence gains control of the weather until it passes by and a low-pressure area moves in to take its place. The rainy type will proceed as described above, but usually the bad weather area will become more pronounced as it reaches the Gulf states.

Although it is commonly considered that eminences give light to moderate winds, it is an interesting fact that an eminence will give about 2½ times as great velocity to the winds as a depression of the same pressure gradient. Another fact that must be noticed is that an eminence of the circular type will give stronger winds than one which has long, straight isobars with the same gradient. The strongest winds of an eminence are found a short way in from the edge and from there they decrease toward the center, where they are light and variable. An energetic depression which develops not far from an eminence will, however, cause steep gradients from the "top" of the eminence to the "bottom" of the depression, with winds of correspondingly greater velocity.

QUESTIONS

1. Define air mass.
2. How is an air mass generated? What is its source?
3. What three factors determine the life history of air masses?
4. How does each of the above factors affect the air mass?
5. How are air masses classified as to: (a) Latitude of source? (b) Surface nature of source? (c) Location of source? (d) Air-Surface temperature difference?
6. What is a transitional air mass?
7. Give in abbreviated forms three examples of air mass designations and explain the meaning of the abbreviations used.
8. What are the typical properties of cold masses from: (a) Continental source? (b) Maritime source?
9. What are the typical properties of warm masses from: (a) Continental source? (b) Maritime source?
10. How may pilots be apprised of the presence, location, and properties of Superior Air Masses? (a) How is superior air developed, and where is it most usually found in the United States? (b) What is subsidence? (c) What are Chinook or Foehn Winds? (d) Describe flying conditions found in superior air masses.
11. What is a front or frontal zone?
12. What is: (a) The polar front? (b) The equatorial front? (c) The arctic (antarctic) front?
13. What are: (a) Cold fronts? (b) Warm fronts? (c) Quasi-stationary fronts?
14. What is: (a) Frontogenesis? (b) Frontolysis?
15. Define: (a) Isobar. (b) Eminence or high. (c) Depression or low. (d) Wedge. (e) Trough.
16. Show by sketch how isobars are used to indicate areas of high and low pressure.
17. What are isallobars? What is an isallobaric field and what does it indicate?
18. What are isotherms?
19. Why is it of importance to the pilot to keep his altimeter adjusted to the barometric pressure in the region of flight?
20. Name the three types of traveling disturbances.
21. What is a col? Show by sketch three types of cols with their expected resultant weather.
22. In what part of a col do fronts most usually form?
23. Describe the formation of a wave in the frontal zone between two air masses.
24. Make a diagram of a typical depression in the Northern Hemisphere showing the fronts, isobars, wind circulation, precipitation areas and general cloud system.

25. Show by sketch a vertical cross section through: (a) The northern section of the depression. (b) The southern section.
26. In a frontal zone, what provides the principal motive power to create an atmospheric disturbance?
27. What causes warm front thunderstorms, and where are they generally located?
28. What causes cold front thunderstorms? How do they differ from the warm front type?
29. What are upper-front thunderstorms and how are they recognized?
30. Describe a line squall. Why is it particularly dangerous to aircraft?
31. Describe a tornado and the typical tornado cloud. Why should it be avoided at all costs by aircraft?
32. What are mechanical thunderstorms? Name five different types.
33. By means of successive diagrams show the development of a depression indicating fronts, isobars, wind circulation and precipitation.
34. What is means by "occlusion"?
35. By sketch show an occlusion of: (a) Cold front type. (b) Warm front type.
36. What is an upper front? What types of storms are caused by persistent upper cold fronts?
37. Show by sketch a typical cross-section through a front between Superior and Tropical air masses.
38. How will diagrams of a depression in the Southern Hemisphere differ from those of the Northern Hemisphere? Draw a diagram of a depression in the Southern Hemisphere.
39. What is the effect of unstable air in depressions.
40. In troughs of low pressure, what shapes of isobars are found? What weather situation usually exists with each of the two shapes? Illustrate by sketch.
41. In passing through frontal surfaces, what changes in wind direction should a pilot expect (in the Northern Hemisphere)?
42. What is a tropical cyclone and by what particular names are they designated in different parts of the world?
43. Describe the creation of a tropical cyclone.
44. What are the typical characteristics of a tropical cyclone compared to an ordinary depression?
45. In what areas do tropical cyclones most frequently occur?
46. How does the diameter of a tropical cyclone vary?
47. What is the shape of a tropical cyclone as given by the isobars?
48. Briefly describe the wind system and air flow in a tropical cyclone.
49. Show by sketch a characteristic track and wind system of a tropical cyclone of: (a) Northern Hemisphere. (b) Southern Hemisphere.
50. How does the speed of travel of the storm center of a tropical cyclone vary?

51. How does the speed of travel of the storm center affect the wind velocity in different sectors of a tropical cyclone?

52. What is meant by: (a) Dangerous semicircle? (b) Navigable semicircle? Why are they so called?

53. Describe by sketch a typical eminence (anticyclone) showing isobars, air circulation, clouds and general weather (Northern Hemisphere).

54. Compare the wind velocity in an eminence to that of a depression of the same gradient.

Chapter *VIII*

WEATHER REPORTS

In recent years, the number of aviators who travel several hundred or even more than a thousand miles in a few hours has greatly increased; there has likewise been a pronounced increase in the length of individual flights. These developments have resulted from improvements in the various safety factors connected with aerial navigation, one of the most important of which is a meteorological service which meets the needs of the modern aviator.

As the pilots cover long distances, it is necessary to obtain a large number of weather reports from all directions. Also, the terminology of these reports must be uniform and standard, and must be based on the same fundamentals. For many years, prior to 1949, close co-operation between the meteorological services of the United States and Canada led to decided similarity in aviation weather reports of the two countries. Now, since 1949, most countries of the world, including the United States and Canada, work together in the International Meteorological Organization, seeking standardization of codes and transmission of data in common units.

Because of the long distances covered in a short period of time, it is also essential that a rapid means of collection and frequent dissemination of weather information be available. Closely associated with this phase is the necessity of having a rather dense and strategically located network of stations in order to show local conditions as fully as possible.

To provide a means for the collection and dissemination of weather information in accordance with the above requirements, the teletype system operated by the Civil Aeronautics Authority, with weather reports under the supervision of the

U. S. Weather Bureau, has been established.   At 30 minutes past each hour, a sequence of airway weather reports are placed on these teletype circuits by the different stations on each circuit, in a designated order.   At the completion of the sequence collection, certain designated stations relay these reports on other teletype circuits with the result that, within the 40-minute period beginning 30 minutes past each hour, every station on a teletype circuit has received a large number of up-to-the-minute airway weather reports within a radius of five hundred miles or more.   In the event of certain specified and decided changes in weather conditions before the time for the next sequence weather collection, the various stations are required to file "special" weather reports showing the changed condition.   In addition to the reports from teletype stations, a few reports are collected by telegraph and telephone and entered on the various circuits.

The U. S. Weather Bureau has qualified meteorologists and observers on duty at all important terminals and at a large number of major airports for the purpose of preparing weather reports and discussing meteorological conditions with pilots. At other airports and weather reporting stations, the reports are prepared by airway observers of the Weather Bureau and by personnel of the Civil Aeronautics Authority, Army, Navy, Air Force, and Coast Guard who are experienced in the necessary procedures.   These reports are the results of years of experience, which have brought about a high degree of accuracy and dependability.   All pilots should train themselves to interpret the various data into safety factors for flight, as numerous occasions will arise when advice of a meteorologist is not available.   Weather conditions to be expected on a flight should be studied before taking off if the pilot wishes to avoid being forced down in some inconvenient location or to avoid an accident which may cause injury or untimely and unnecessary death.

As the experience of pilots varies from about thirty years down to almost nothing, and as the various types of airplanes now in use are equipped for different purposes, it is obvious that flight in some weather situations would be absolutely safe and routine for more experienced pilots flying the better-equipped aircraft, while a flight in the same meteorological conditions by a pilot with little or no experience, in a poorly equipped airplane, would be definitely hazardous to pilot, passengers, and property below. For the protection of all concerned, therefore, the Civil Air Regulations were established by the Civil Aeronautics Board. Among other requirements, these regulations set forth appropriate rules under which flights may be performed according to (1) the equipment of the plane and (2) the meteorological conditions existing in the area of flight. Minima of ceiling and visibility are prescribed to control flights which may be conducted under

(a) *Visual Flight Rules* (VFR), guidance and control of the aircraft being governed by reference to visible objects outside the aircraft; or

(b) *Instrument Flight Rules* (IFR), guidance and control of the aircraft being governed either partly or entirely by reference to instruments within the aircraft.

Flight operations are suspended when weather conditions are below the minima required for operations under Instrument Flight Rules.

Visual Flight Rules (VFR) prescribe the minima as to ceiling, visibility, and distance-from-clouds quoted below:

Ceiling and Distance from Clouds

Aircraft shall comply with the following requirements as to ceiling and distance from clouds:

(*a*) *Within control zones.* Unless authorized by air traffic control, aircraft shall not be flown when the ceiling is less than 1,000 feet, or less than 500 feet vertically and 2,000 feet horizontally from any cloud formation.

(*b*) *Elsewhere.* When at an altitude of more than 700 feet above the surface aircraft shall not be flown less than 500 feet vertically and 2,000 feet horizontally from any cloud formation; when at an altitude of 700 feet or less aircraft shall not be flown unless clear of clouds.

Visibility

(*a*) *Ground visibility within control zones.* When the ground visibility is less than 3 miles, no person shall take off or land an aircraft at an airport within a control zone, or enter the traffic pattern of such an airport, unless an air traffic clearance is obtained from air traffic control;

(*b*) *Flight visibility within control zones.* When the flight visibility is less than 3 miles, no person shall operate an aircraft in flight within a control zone, unless an air traffic clearance is obtained from air traffic control;

(*c*) *Flight visibility within control areas.* When the flight visibility is less than 3 miles, no person shall operate an aircraft within a control area;

NOTE: When the flight visibility is less than 3 miles, operations within control areas are to be conducted in accordance with Instrument Flight Rules. Flight below 700 feet above the surface is not within a control area.

(*d*) *Flight visibility elsewhere.* When outside of control zones and control areas, no person shall operate an aircraft in flight when the flight visibility is less than 1 mile. However, helicopters may be flown at or below 700 feet above the surface when the flight visibility is less than 1 mile if operated at a reduced speed which will give the pilot of such helicopter adequate opportunity to see other air traffic or any obstruction in time to avoid hazard of collision.

NOTE: When traffic conditions permit, air traffic control will issue an air traffic clearance for flights within, entering, or departing control zones when ground visibility or the flight visibility is less than 3 miles. The operator of any airport within a control zone, other than the airport upon which the control zone is centered, may secure continuing permission from air traffic control to conduct operations when the visibility is less than 3 miles provided that such operations, at all times, remain 2,000 feet horizontally and 500 feet vertically from clouds, and traffic patterns are established and observed which avoid conflict with other operations. When outside of control zones and at an altitude of less than 700 feet above the surface, helicopters are permitted to fly when the flight visibility is less than 1 mile because of their special flight characteristics which allow them to proceed at low speed with safety.

Instrument Flight Rules (IFR) apply when the ceiling and/or visibility in the area of flight are less than the minima specified for VFR operations. Under Instrument Flight Rules an aircraft clearance must list (with other required data) another airport, as alternate destination, where current weather reports and forecasts show a trend indicating that the ceiling and visibility at such airport will be at or above the following minima at the time of arrival:

(*a*) *Airport served by radio directional facility.* Ceiling 1,000 feet, visibility 1 mile; or ceiling 900 feet, visibility 1½ miles; or ceiling 800 feet, visibility 2 miles.

(*b*) *Airport not served by radio directional facility.* Ceiling 1,000 feet with broken clouds or better, visibility 2 miles.

(*c*) *Minima at individual airports.* In the interest of safety, at individual airports higher ceiling and visibility minima than required by (*a*) or (*b*) above may be prescribed; and for individual operations at particular airports lower minima may be specified if such reduced minima will not decrease safety.

ELEMENTS IN THE AIRWAY CODE

Airway observations * are disseminated in a code that consists of symbols and numerals arranged in groups with relatively fixed positions. Word and phrase contractions or complete words are used in a specified manner to supplement the coded data.

Grouping of Elements. The elements of the observation are placed in groups as shown in the table on page 174. Spaces separate Groups I to V; and oblique lines (slants), used as mechanical devices, separate numerical data that might otherwise be misinterpreted.

To cover the needs of weather forecasting and aircraft operation, several different types of reports are used, each type being appropriate to the requirements of the situation. Different "Groups" and "Elements" are used to fill the needs of each type of report, as explained later.

Airway observations are recorded and classified as follows:

(a) *Record.* Taken at scheduled hourly intervals..
(b) *Special.* Taken when significant meteorological changes occur at other than scheduled periods.
(c) *Record-Special.* Taken to indicate significant meteorological changes at scheduled periods.

* For complete information on surface weather observations and the transmission of weather reports, it is recommended that the student obtain a copy of Circular N, of the U. S. Weather Bureau, entitled, "WBAN Manual of Surface Observations," November, 1951. It may be obtained from the Superintendent of Documents, Government Printing Office, Washington, D. C., for $1.00.

Group Number	Element Number	Element
I	1	Station identification
II	2	Type of report
III	3	Time of report
IV	4	Ceiling and cloud height
	5	Sky
	6	Visibility
	7	Weather
	8	Obstructions to vision
V	9	Sea-level pressure
	10	Temperature
	11	Dew point
	12	Wind
	a.	Direction
	b.	Speed
	c.	Character
	d.	Shifts
	13	Altimeter setting
VI	14	Remarks

Note: (1) The letter symbol "M" is used to indicate missing data pertaining to an element normally included in a report.

(2) Groups II and III are omitted from record observations since they are transmitted in a regular hourly sequence which indicates the type and time by its heading.

(d) *Local extra.* Taken at designated stations, for local distribution only, for meteorological changes within narrower limits than those requiring a Special Report, but of distinct local importance.

(e) *Check.* Taken at specified stations from which local weather broadcasts are made, within 20 minutes before the broadcast.

Airway Reports of different types are transmitted as follows:

(a) *Hourly.* Transmitting the data of record observations.

(b) *Special.* Transmitting the data of special observations.

(c) *Record-Special.* Transmitting the combined data required when special conditions occur at a usual "record" time.

(d) *Local extra.* Transmitting, for local distribution only, the data contained in local extra observations.

(e) *Check.* Transmitting the data used in the local weather broadcast.

(f) *Correction.* Correcting previously transmitted but erroneous reports.

(g) *Sequence.* This is a special type of report which is composed of the principal record and special reports from all principal stations for each hour, put onto and transmitted over the entire teletype network beginning at 30 minutes after each hour. It is received by all stations with teletype receivers. In this manner the maximum information is made available to all pilots and the air-going public. Since the sequence is arranged in groups of stations along specific airways a pilot can readily check the weather along the route he wishes to fly.

Note: The time is omitted from observations when they are placed in the regularly hourly sequence collection, the time given at the beginning of the sequence applying to all parts of the report.

For each station in the sequence report, the following data are given in the order named:

Station Identification (a 3-letter symbol, assigned by the C.A.A.)
Letter indicating means of determining ceiling.
Ceiling height—in hundreds of feet.
Sky (by code symbol).
Visibility—in miles and fractions of miles.
Weather (by code letters).
Obstruction to vision (by code letters).
Atmospheric sea-level pressure—in millibars and tenths, with the hundreds figure omitted.
Free air temperature—in whole Fahrenheit degrees.
Dew point temperature—in whole Fahrenheit degrees.
Wind direction—to 16 points of the compass.
Wind speed—in knots.
Altimeter setting—in inches of mercury and hundredths, with the tens figure omitted.
Remarks—in contractions, or in complete words if necessary.

Ceiling

In general, the pilot is greatly concerned about how much ceiling he will find along the route of his flight. Ceiling is defined as: The height ascribed to the lowest layer of clouds or obscuring phenomena that is reported as "broken," "overcast," or "obscuration" and not classified "thin" or "partial." In the daytime, ceilings are usually estimated but, if less than 2000 feet, they may be measured by ceiling balloons or a ceilometer. All night-time ceilings are measured by the use of a ceiling clinometer or a ceilometer.

The cloud layer height is reported to the nearest 100 feet up to 5000 feet, then to the nearest 500 feet up to 10,000 feet, and to the nearest 1000 feet above 10,000 feet. When the ceiling is halfway between two reportable values, the lower value is reported.

On the teletype circuits, ceiling height is reported in hundreds of feet preceded by a letter indicating how the ceiling height was determined, as per the following table.

SYMBOL	CEILING CLASSIFICATION
A	Ceiling reported from aircraft in flight
B	Balloon ceiling
E	Estimated ceiling
M	Measured ceiling
P	Precipitation ceiling
W	Indefinite ceiling

When the lower layer of clouds is so scattered as not to form a ceiling (as defined above), the height of the layer is reported, but the ceiling classification symbol is omitted.

Vertical visibility is a ceiling value used to express the distance that an observer within an obscuring medium can see vertically upward into the medium. The ceiling ascribed to an obscuring phenomenon must be classified as "W", "P," or "A."

Sky

Closely associated with ceiling information is the condition of the sky and the presence (or absence) of sky cover or of obscuration.

Sky-cover is a term used to denote one of the following conditions:

(1) Amount of sky covered, but not necessarily hidden, by clouds or obscuring phenomena aloft.

(2) Amount of sky concealed by obscuring phenomena on the ground.

(3) A combination of (1) and (2).

Sky-cover may refer either to the amount of sky covered by a particular layer, or to the total amount covered by all layers. If the sky-cover is opaque (i.e., conceals the sky), the tenths of sky-cover plus the tenths of sky visible will always equal 1.0 (10/10).

The table below sets forth the code symbols for sky-cover, their meaning and explanation. Data regarding sky-cover are reported in ascending order of height using the appropriate sky-cover symbol for each layer, selected in accordance with the summation principles stated in the paragraph immediately following the table.

SKY-COVER SYMBOLS

Symbol and Meaning		Explanation
X	Obscuration.........	Sky completely hidden by precipitation or obstructions to vision (bases at surface).
−X	Partial obscuration....	0.1 to less than 1.0 sky hidden by precipitation or obstructions to vision (bases at surface).
O	Clear..............	Less than 0.1 total sky cover. (This symbol is not used in combination.)
①*	Scattered...........	0.1 to less than 0.6 sky cover.
⑪*	Broken.............	0.6 to 0.9 sky cover.
⊕*	Overcast...........	More than 0.9 sky cover. (This symbol will be used in combination with a lower overcast symbol only if the latter is classified thin.)

* Symbols for thin ("−") and dark ("+") will be prefixed to these symbols in accordance with instructions in the paragraph entitled "Summation" below.

The corresponding height in hundreds of feet is prefixed to each sky-cover symbol. The appropriate ceiling classification symbol is prefixed to the symbol for the ceiling layer only. Heights ascribed to "X" will represent vertical visibility. A numerical value will not be ascribed to "− X" since unlimited vertical visibility is indicated. If the ceiling is variable, the letter "V" is inserted following the ceiling value, e.g., M5V⊕.

Summation. The sky-cover symbol for each layer represents the summation total of all sky-cover at and below that level, including the amount of sky hidden by surface-based obscuring phenomena. In determining summation totals, portions of surface-based obscuring phenomena that do not conceal the sky and portions of upper-cloud layers that are visible only through transparencies in lower layers are disregarded. If any portion of the sky cover is transparent, in addition to the foregoing summation, the summation of opaque sky cover at each level is reported (see examples 7 and 8 below). If, at any level, the ratio of opaque to total sky-cover (summation values) is ½ or less, prefix "—" (thin) is prefixed to the corresponding sky-cover symbol. This prefix is omitted if the ratio exceeds ½. The symbol "+" is prefixed to layers that are unusually dark or threatening.

EXAMPLES

Opaque Sky-Cover

Layers	Summation	Sky-Cover Symbol
(1) 0.4 sky hidden by fog	0.4	−X
0.3 sky-cover at 1000 ft	0.7	M10◑
0.2 sky-cover at 5000 ft	0.9	50◑
(2) Less than 0.1 sky-cover at 500 ft	0.0	—
Less than 0.1 sky-cover at 2000 ft	0.1	20◐
(Total sky-cover 0.1)		
(3) 0.6 sky-cover at 1000 ft	0.6	M10◑
0.3 sky-cover at 5000 ft	0.9	50◑
Less than 0.1 sky-cover at 10,000 ft	0.9+	100⊕ .. (with remark: BINOVC)
(4) 0.1 sky-cover at 1000 ft	0.1	10◐ .. (with remark: KLYR 10◐)
(Smoke aloft)		
0.3 sky-cover at 5000 ft	0.4	50◐
0.1 sky-cover at 10,000 ft	0.5	100◐

Layers	Summation	Sky-Cover Symbol
(5) 0.2 sky-cover at 500 ft	0.2	5 ◑
Sky hidden by snow, vertical visibility 1500 t	1.0	P15X
(6) 0.8 sky hidden by snow	0.8	—X
0.2 sky-cover at 500 ft	1.0	M5⊕

Transparent or Partially Opaque Sky-Cover

Layers	Summation Total	Summation Opaque Portions	Sky-Cover Symbol
(7) 0.8 sky-cover at 500 ft (0.0 opaque)	0.8	0.0	*5 — ◐
(8) 0.1 sky hidden by surface smoke	0.1	0.1	—X
0.7 sky-cover at 1000 ft (0.1 opaque)	0.8	0.2	*10 — ◐
0.2 sky-cover at 5000 ft (all opaque)	1.0	0.4	*50 — ⊕

* Note that the ceiling classification letter is omitted because the layer is classified as "thin."

Remarks. Data pertaining to clouds and obscuring phenomena are appended to the message with other remarks as follows:

Observed	Remarks Appended
(1) Breaks in overcast; one overcast layer only.	"BINOVC," followed by direction of breaks where practicable.
(2) Breaks in higher overcast; two or more overcast layers reported (lower one classified thin).	"BRKHIC"
(3) Higher clouds visible through breaks in overcast not classified thin.	"HIR CLDS VSB"
(4) Direction of breaks in broken layer with ceiling at or below highest instrument minimums. (Omit if breaks are in all quadrants)	"BRKS," followed by direction, e.g., "BRKS N" or "BRKS OVR MID MKR"

Observed	*Remarks Appended*
(5) Obscuring phenomena (smoke, haze, etc.) aloft	"KLYR," "HLYR," etc., followed by height and corresponding sky-cover symbol, e.g., "KLYR 10" ⓓ
(6) Special cloud types (see Weather Bureau Circular S for definitions) a. Towering cumulus	"TWRG CU," followed by direction from station.

Visibility

Next to the ceiling, the most important item in a weather report is visibility, which is the mean greatest distance toward the horizon that prominent objects can be seen and identified by the normal eye unaided by special optical devices, and which distance must prevail over half or more of the horizon. This datum is reported in statute miles or fractions, as described in the table on page 31. Visibility is affected by weather and obstructions.

Weather

Weather elements include all types of precipitation, as well as thunderstorms and tornadoes, and are indicated in weather reports immediately following the visibility, in accordance with the table below.

SYMBOLS FOR WEATHER ELEMENTS

TORNADO or WATERSPOUT (always written out in full) followed by direction from station

T+	Heavy thunderstorm	EW	Sleet showers
T	Thunderstorm	S	Snow
R	Rain	SW	Snow showers
RW	Rain showers	SP	Snow pellets
L	Drizzle	SG	Snow grains
ZR	Freezing rain	IC	Ice crystals
ZL	Freezing drizzle	A	Hail
E	Sleet	AP	Small hail

Elements indicating precipitation are reported to four degrees of intensity, indicated immediately following the element symbol. The unaccompanied symbol means "moderate" intensity; the heavy degree is indicated by a plus (+) sign, the light degree by a minus (—) sign, and the very light degree by a double minus (— —) sign, immediately following the symbol.

Obstructions to Vision

The most important causes of restricted visibility, however, are the result of fog and various foreign substances in the atmosphere. These obstructions to vision are listed in the following table, with the teletype symbol used in airway weather reports.

SYMBOLS FOR OBSTRUCTIONS TO VISION

F	Fog	IF	Ice fog
GF	Ground fog	H	Haze
BS	Blowing snow	K	Smoke
BD	Blowing dust	D	Dust
BN	Blowing sand		

Sea-level Pressure

The atmospheric sea-level pressure, which has been discussed in Chapter III, is essential information for weather map analysis. It is included in the report particularly for the meteorologists' benefit. The pressure is reported in millibars and tenths of millibars with the hundreds figure omitted, as three figures without decimal point. For example: 1008.2 mb would be transmitted as 082.

Temperature

Following the pressure, the free air temperature is reported to the nearest whole Fahrenheit degree. Temperatures below zero are preceded by a minus (—) sign. This information is desirable for determining the likelihood of icing conditions in the atmosphere and proper mixture ratios for efficient engine operation. Also, when considered in connection with the next item of the report—the dew point—it is indispensable in forecasting fog formation.

Dew Point

The dew point is that temperature to which air must be cooled, at constant pressure and constant water vapor content, in order for saturation to occur. In the airway weather report it is reported to the nearest whole Fahrenheit degree. In considering the relationship between the temperature and the dew point, the time of day also must be taken into account. For example, a difference of only two or three degrees in late evening should be considered with concern, as a definite threat of fog, while the same spread a couple of hours after sunrise ordinarily could be dismissed unless some meteorological dissurbance, of a type to reduce the temperature, was in the ofing. The main question to be answered in your mind is this: Are the sun's heat rays available to raise the temperature of the atmosphere?

Wind

Data concerning the direction, velocity and character of air moving horizontally are of importance to the pilot in determining takeoff and landing procedure and as an indication of winds that he may encounter aloft, and to the forecaster. Wind is the horizontal, or nearly horizontal, movement of the air, that is, air naturally in approximately horizontal motion with any degree of velocity. Vertical movements of air are not considered as wind but as air currents. *Wind direction* is indicated as the direction from which the air is moving. If the air is flowing from the southwest toward the northeast, the wind direction would be designated as southwest. Wind direction is reported to 16 points of the compass and is indicated in teletype reports by a single or double arrow, immediately following the dewpoint, pointing in the direction toward which the airflow is taking place. *Wind velocity* is indicated by figures giving the datum in statute miles per hour immediately following the direction arrows. *Gustiness* is characterized by sudden, intermittent increase in speed, with at least 10 miles' variation between peaks and lulls. The peak speed must reach at least 19 miles, and the average time interval between peaks and lulls usually should not exceed 20 seconds. Gusts are indicated by placing a plus (+) sign immediately after the wind speed followed by the peak speed of gusts within 15 minutes preceding the time of observation. A wind direction symbol table appears below.

WIND DIRECTION SYMBOLS

↓ North	↑ South
↓ ↙ North-northeast	↑ ↗ South-southwest
↙ Northeast	↗ Southwest
←↙ East-northeast	→↗ West-southwest
←East	→West
←↖ East-southeast	→↘ West-northwest
↖ Southeast	↘ Northwest
↑ ↖ South-southeast	↓ ↘ North-northwest

Wind shifts are indicated by entry immediately following the last element of the wind data of the report, by use of a direction arrow showing the direction of wind to 16 points of the compass, prior to the shift, followed by the local time and the local time zone letter. *Squalls* are reported by adding the symbol "Q" immediately after the wind speed and preceding the peak speed of gusts within 15 minutes before time of observation.

Altimeter Setting

The last regular datum included is the altimeter setting, which is transmitted in inches and hundredths of inches of mercury from stations having mercurial barometers. Only the last three figures are transmitted, without decimal point. The altimeter setting is a pressure used for setting a pressure-scale type sensitive altimeter in an airplane so that upon the landing of the airplane at an airport the pointers of the instrument will indicate very closely the field elevation above sea-level, provided that the instrument is functioning properly and is free from error, and that the setting was determined by a properly equipped station near the time and place of landing, and was furnished to the pilot just before landing. Because the pressure of the atmosphere varies almost constantly, certain essentials must be adhered to if the datum is to have its proper value. Among these essentials are the following: (*a*) there must be accurate instruments in the airplane and on the ground, recently adjusted, (*b*) the pilot must know the elevation of the airport, and (*c*) the comparison of the instruments must be made when the aircraft is in the approximate vicinity of the ground instrument. The latest altimeter-setting information may be obtained from control towers and C.A.A. broadcast stations by radio while the airplane is in flight.

The altimeter setting is based directly upon the pressure of the atmosphere at the different stations. Variations in this pressure are occurring most of the time; some of the fluctuations are much greater than others. A good portion of the minor variations are diurnal, but the large changes are the results of moving pressure systems.

As the altimeter setting is prepared near the elevation of the airport and is to be used by the pilot principally in the landing of his aircraft, instruments for the measurement of the pressure must be located at the airport and in the airplane. The most accurate device for this is the mercurial barometer. To ensure the correctness of this datum, mercurial barometers have been installed at regularly spaced intervals throughout the country, with a greater concentration in the more populous areas. Because of the size of this instrument, however, its installation and use in the cockpit of an airplane are impracticable and, at times, impossible. Instead, a sensitive altimeter is used as described in Chapter III, p. 18. The accuracy of all these instruments is under constant surveillance, so that they may be comparable at all times when reasonably close to each other.

As stated before, the principal use of the altimeter setting is in the landing of aircraft. We saw in Chapter III that one of the properties of the atmosphere is its decreasing pressure with increasing altitude. Therefore, for the altimeter to be of use the pilot of the airplane must know the elevation of the airport where his landing is to be made. The altimeter-setting datum is the atmospheric pressure in an airplane 10 feet above the elevation of the airport. The information is transmitted by radio to an airplane shortly before its landing at the airport. When it is received, the pilot of the airplane rotates the knob of his altimeter until the figure received comes into position. When the airplane has landed at the airport from which the setting was received, the altitude indicated on the altimeter will be the altitude of the airport. "Altimeter settings include an allowance corresponding to about 10 feet of altitude. The allowance is designed so that a sensitive altimeter calibrated in strict accordance with the U. S. Standard Atmosphere and set in agreement with the existing official altimeter setting will indicate an altitude of about 10 feet lower than the actual altitude of the instrument above sea level. The purpose of this allowance is to cause the altimeter in airplanes to indicate more nearly the altitude of the landing wheels above sea level than the actual altitude of the instrument in an average airplane. If the lowest part of the airplane is more than 10 feet below the altimeter, for example, 18 feet, the pilot must make allowance for the difference, 8 feet in this example, along with all the other possible errors in the instrument." *

Importance of Altimeter Setting. There are, of course, variations in pressure over a period of time at every station. There are also horizontal pressure differences over a given

* U. S. Weather Bureau Circular, *The National Altimeter Setting Program,* May 10, 1939.

area at any instant of time. The changes in the vicinity of an area of low pressure are comparatively much greater than the other changes which are diurnal and small. The pilot must be cognizant of the pressure change if he leaves the area, as well as the change of pressure with the passage of time.

Before take-off the pilot is given an altimeter setting such that when the plane is on the ground the altimeter indicates the known field elevation. If the pressure is changing significantly with time or if the pilot leaves the local area, he must correct his altimeter setting to meet the new amospheric pressure conditions.

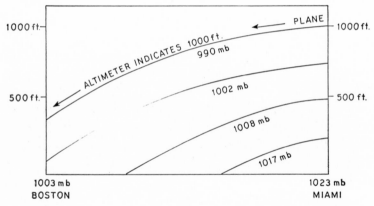

FIG. 8–1.   Effect of change of pressure on altimeter reading.

The importance of adjusting the altimeter setting may be illustrated by a simple diagram, shown in Figure 8–1, which shows a cross-section of isobaric surfaces between Boston and Miami.

The pilot of an airplane leaving Miami, which has a pressure of 1023 mb, for Boston, which has a pressure of 1003 mb, takes off and climbs to an altitude of 1000 feet. At that altitude he will be just about on the 990 mb isobaric surface. If he then maintains an *indicated* 1000 feet, without correcting his altimeter setting enroute, the plane will actually follow the 990 mb isobar as shown. He thus reaches Boston with his altimeter indicating 1000 feet but, the Boston pressure being but 1003 mb, the 990 mb isobar is only *400 feet* above the ground at Boston, and 400 feet altitude is all that he will have. Thus it is seen that a change of 20 mb will result in an error of about 600 feet in altitude.

If the flight were made under Visual Flight Rules conditions, it probably would not cause difficulty since the pilot could see the resultant error. However, suppose the flight were being made under IFR conditions, and during the flight the pressure at Boston had fallen from 1003 mb to 987 mb. The plane, without adjustment of altimeter setting, would fly into the ground a short distance before reaching Boston, if it didn't strike an intervening ridge before that!

Remarks

Certain conditions require the addition of explanatory remarks to the report. These remarks constitute the last part of the observation and of the teletype report. They are composed of the regular symbols and figures combined with appropriate English contractions, or plain English may be used if necessary.

Sample Airway Weather Reports

A working knowledge of the information contained in this chapter can best be obtained through experience. Sample copies of airway weather reports, as well as copies of all other meteorological data transmitted on the teletype circuits, may be obtained from any airport station of the U. S. Weather Bureau. However, to provide a limited study here, three sample reports, with translation, showing the form, are given:

Record-Special report on teletype in airway code:

PIT S2 E15⊕2S−   146/32/28↘18+26↗
1810E/997/Ocnl SW

Translation:

Station, Pittsburgh. Record-Special Observation No. 2 for the day. No time group (since it is included in the hourly sequence). Ceiling estimated fifteen hundred feet, sky condition overcast, visibility two miles, weather light snow. Sea-level barometric pressure 1014.6 millibars, temperature 32, dew point 28, wind northwest 18 knots with peak gusts up to 26 knots in the last 15 minutes; wind shift from the southwest at 6:10 P.M., E.S.T. Altimeter setting 29.97 inches of mercury. Remarks: Occasional snow showers.

Special report on teletype in airway code:

PHL S4   120620E   2①M4⊕¼L–F   ╱13

Translation:

Station, Philadelphia. Special Observation No. 4 for the 12th day of the month; time, 6:20 A.M., E.S.T. Measured ceiling 400 feet. Sky condition, scattered clouds at 200 feet, overcast at 400 feet, visibility one-fourth mile, weather light drizzle; obstruction to vision, fog. Wind northeast 13 knots.

Record report on teletype in airway code:

GVE   30–①E120①20   159/58/47→╱16

Translation:

Station, Gordonsville. No time group (since report is included in the hourly sequence collection). Ceiling estimated twelve thousand feet; sky condition, thin broken clouds at three thousand feet, with broken clouds at twelve thousand feet; visibility twenty miles. Sea-level barometric pressure 1015.9 millibars; temperature 58; dew point 47. Wind, west-southwest 16 knots.

By use of the explanatory teletype weather report (see Appendices, pp. 320–321) any Symbol Weather Report may be deciphered or may be composed from observational data obtained.

Upper Air Data

In recent years the advancement of science has enabled meteorologists to extend their research farther and farther into the upper atmosphere. As a result it has been clearly demonstrated that conditions in the upper air are highly important to accurate—and particularly to long-range—forecasting. Thus there has been a significant trend to employ, more and more, data obtained at levels higher and higher above the surface.

One of the essential factors is the development of new electronic measuring instruments and observational techniques which have rendered the high level data more reliable. These have contributed to theoretical research in the properties of the earth's atmosphere and its circulation.

For useful application of this new knowledge the upper air observations must be routine and regular. Only by such means can reliable information be furnished for the operation of modern aircraft—particularly those with jet propulsion—in regular flights at 25,000 to 40,000 feet, and frequently to higher altitudes.

As explained more fully in the sections on Altimeter Settings, pages 183–187, the pilot who sets his altimeter and, after climbing to his "cruising" altitude, flies at a constant *indicated* height is actually flying along a *constant pressure surface* because the altimeter actually varies its reading by changes in pressure rather than changes in true height. Therefore the selection of constant pressure as the basic factor for upper air charts seems very appropriate.

Routine radiosonde observations, taken twice daily at about seventy stations in the United States, supply data on pressure, temperature, and relative humidity aloft. During the vertical ascent the small automatic radio transmitter carried by the balloon transmits signals indicating the weather data to the recorded at the station below.

The radiosonde observation stations transmit their reports in sequence on the weather teletype. Data are usually reported at each of the following six pressure levels: 850, 700, 500, 300, 200 and 100 millibars. At each level the following data are reported: (1) Altitude of the pressure level, (2) temperature, and (3) relative humidity. Information thus obtained is employed in the construction of upper air weather maps in the form of constant pressure charts at the various levels.

On the constant pressure charts contour lines of the height of the pressure surface are drawn. Depressions (in altitude) in the pressure surface indicate areas of low pressure. Similarly "domes" or eminences in the pressure surface indicate areas of high pressure. Balloons, either manned or unmanned, have proved adequate to observe the lower 100,000 feet of the atmosphere. Above that, other means must be employed.

The development of large, high-altitude rockets was greatly accelerated by the needs of World War II. The continued development of those weapons has provided a valuable means of adding to our knowledge of the atmospheric structure and circulation. Meteorological instruments carried in these great rockets transmit back to the control station, through a telemetering system, valuable data on the atmosphere as they pass through the various levels while in actual flight. With each new flight, with each new altitude reached, a contribution is made to the advancement of our knowledge of the physics of the atmosphere, resulting in turn in better meteorological techniques and more accurate forecasting.

A Word of Caution

The sampling process to determine certain characteristics in mind and material is widely used today. The more samples that are examined, the more true characteristics may be determined. If sampling is at scattered points, many details may pass unnoticed. To get a true picture of conditions, it is necessary to sample all of the items being examined. A weather report is simply the description of a sample of air at a particular point. In periods of bad weather, it is safe to assume that a weather report is representative of no greater area than that included in a radius of five miles. If the average distance between reporting stations is fifty miles, this means that between each two stations there is a distance of forty miles from which no observations are available. In this space, the pilot will frequently find weather conditions which are decidedly different from those at either reporting station. Therefore, the pilot should be cautious on a flight when weather conditions are near the minima for safety.

QUESTIONS

1. Describe briefly the method employed in the United States for the collection and dissemination of weather information over the airways.
2. Under the Civil Air Regulations, what conditions determine the appropriate rules under which flights may be made in aircraft?
3. (a) What do Visual Flight Rules prescribe? (b) What do Instrument Flight Rules prescribe?
4. When are flight operations suspended?
5. What minima are prescribed as to ceiling, visibility, and distance-from-clouds under the following conditions: (a) Visual Flight Rules (VFR)? (b) Instrument Flight Rules (IFR)?
6. Briefly describe the Airway Code used for the dissemination of weather observations.
7. Of how many groups does an airway code message consist, and what elements are reported in each group?
8. How are airway observations classified?
9. What is a "sequence report" and how is it transmitted?
10. List in the prescribed order the data contained for each station in a sequence report.
11. In an airway weather report, how is ceiling indicated?
12. Same as Question 11, but for sky condition.
13. Some as Question 11, but for visibility.
14. Same as Question 11, but for weather.
15. Same as Question 11, but for obstructions to vision.
16. State how the following "Group V" data of a weather report are indicated: (a) Sea-level barometric pressure. (b) Temperature. (c) Dew-point. (d) Wind direction and velocity; wind shifts and squalls. (e) Altimeter setting.

17. Why should a pilot maintain a constant check of the altimeter setting when flying with an aneroid type of altimeter only?

18. Where do "Remarks" appear in an airway weather report, and of what are they composed?

19. Give several examples of weather reports of different types, and their translation.

20. What has recent research in the upper atmosphere clearly demonstrated?

21. What is essential for the practical application of recent research information from the upper atmosphere?

22. What data are collected regularly now, and at what levels, for the construction of upper air constant pressure charts?

23. Describe a constant pressure chart.

24. What contribution have high-altitude rockets made recently in weather research?

25. When weather conditions are at or near the minima for safety, what caution should the pilot exercise relative to conditions indicated on the weather map between reporting stations?

Chapter IX

WEATHER MAPS

The hourly sequence reports described in Chapter VIII show weather conditions as they exist at the time of the observation. It is equally important, however, to know how long good or bad weather conditions will prevail along a certain route. By charting weather conditions on maps at regular intervals, thus providing a composite picture of conditions over the entire area mapped, it is quite easy to study the development and movement of pressure systems, air masses, fronts, wind shifts, fog areas, and precipitation areas.

Nearly all weather forecasting is based on weather maps which show the weather and its development, and its movement from place to place. Several different types of maps are used. Some portray conditions at the earth's surface and others show conditions in the upper air. Some cover the entire Northern Hemisphere, while others cover only local areas as required for special purposes. Practically all weather maps are based on the same principle, so that differences, if they exist, are in minor detail only. This has been accomplished by recent international agreements within the framework of the International Meteorological Organization in its connection with the International Civil Aviation Organization of the United Nations. At U. S. Weather Bureau offices, maps showing conditions at the earth's surface are drawn four times daily or oftener. Maps of upper level temperature, pressure, and humidity are drawn twice a day.

In order to accomplish this a special set of reports, best suited for mapping weather situations, is collected over the teletype networks at 1:30 and 7:30 A.M. and P.M., EST. These are supplemented by others telegraphed or telephoned to designated centers. These reports are then transmitted to all Weather Bureau, Army, Navy, and Air Force stations which prepare weather maps.

To prepare the surface weather maps and present the information quickly and pictorially, two actions are necessary: (1) Weather observers must go to their stations at regular times each day to observe the weather and send the information by wire or radio to the offices where maps are drawn; and (2) the information must be quickly transcribed to the maps. In order to effect economy of space and transmission time, an International Weather Code has been adopted for sending the information and plotting it on the maps.

A great deal of information is contained in each brief coded weather message. If each item were named and described in plain language, a very lengthy message would be required and it would be confusing to read and difficult to transfer to a map. Use of a code permits the message to be condensed to a few five-figure numeral groups, each figure of which has a meaning depending upon its position in the message. Persons trained in the use of the code can read the message as easily as plain language.

The location of each reporting station is printed on the map as a small circle (the *station circle*). A definite arrangement of the data around the station circle, called the *station model,* is used. When the report is plotted in these fixed positions around the station circle on the weather map, many of the code figures are transcribed exactly as sent. Entries in the station model which are not made in code figures or actual values found in the message are usually in the form of symbols which graphically represent the element concerned. In some cases, certain of the data may or may not be reported by the observer, depending upon local weather conditions. Precipitation and clouds are examples. In such cases the absence of an entry on the map is interpreted as non-occurrence or non-observance of the phenomena.

Both the code and the station model are also based on international agreements. Through such standardized use of numerals and symbols, a meteorologist of one country can use the weather reports and weather maps of another country even though he does not understand the language. Weather codes are, in effect, an international language, making possible complete interchange and use of world-wide weather reports so essential in present-day activities.

The international code form for surface reports used by the Weather Bureau beginning January 1, 1949, is shown in abridged form on page 196, together with a corresponding sample message. The symbolic station model used on the maps, a sample station model as entered from the sample message, and an explanation of the symbols with remarks on map entry are also shown.

Many of the elements in the plotting model are entered in values which can be interpreted directly. Some, however, require reference to code tables, which follow the station model and explanation and appear on pages 198–202. For example, temperature (T_dT_d) is given without need for reference to the coded tables: $30 = 30°$ F. However, sky coverage (N) is given as the number 8 in the coded message. By referring to the coded table for N (Table 5), we find that the number 8 signifies "completely overcast" and is shown on the Plotted Report as a completely filled-in circle.

FRONTS

When two air masses from different source regions become juxtaposed, a zone of transition, or front, is formed. As the future locations of fronts are of prime importance to the forecaster and the pilot, it is necessary that they be shown on the weather map. On Weather Bureau maps, this is done in general accordance with the table on p. 203, but there is a decided lack of uniformity in the method of entry on printed maps. Some printed maps have a solid black line for a cold

SYMBOLIC FORM OF MESSAGE

iiiT_dT_d Nddff VVwwW PPPTT $N_hhC_cC_H$ 6$D_c$app 7RRR$_s$

Note: This Abridged Code Shows Only Data Normally Plotted on Printed Maps.

SAMPLE CODED MESSAGE

40530 83220 12716 24731 67220 67228 74542

SYMBOLIC STATION MODEL

SAMPLE PLOTTED REPORT

EXPLANATION OF SYMBOLS AND MAP ENTRIES

Symbols in order as they appear in the message	Explanation of symbols and decode of example above	Remarks on coding and plotting
iii	Station number 405 = Washington	Usually printed on manuscript maps below station circle. Omitted on Daily Weather Map in favor of printed station names.
T_dT_d	Temperature of dewpoint 30 = 30° F	Coded and plotted in actual value whole degrees F.
N	Total amount of cloud 8 = completely covered	Observed in tenths of cloud cover and coded in Oktas (eighths) according to code table in block ❺. Plotted in symbols shown in same table.
dd	True direction from which wind is blowing. 32 = 320° = NW	Coded in tens of degrees and plotted as the shaft of an arrow extending from the station circle toward the direction from which the wind is blowing.
ff	Wind speed in knots 20 = 20 knots = Beaufort force 5	Coded in knots (nautical miles per hour) and plotted in equivalent Beaufort force as feathers and half-feathers on the shaft of the wind direction arrow. See block ❼
VV	Visibility in miles and fractions. (nautical)	Coded in tenths of miles up to 8 miles (Code figure 80) and plotted in miles and fractions.

ww	Present weather 71 = continuous slight snow	Coded in figures taken from the "ww" table (block **6**) and plotted in corresponding symbols same block. Entries for code figures 00, 01, 02, and 03 are omitted from this map.
W	Past weather 6 = rain	Coded in figures taken from the W table (block **9**) and plotted in the corresponding symbols same block. No entry made for code figures 0, 1, or 2.
PPP	Barometric pressure (in millibars) reduced to sea-level. 247 = 1024.7 mb.	Coded and plotted in tens, units, and tenths of millibars. The initial 9 or 10 and the decimal point are omitted.
TT	Current air temperature 31 = 31° F	Coded and plotted in actual value whole degrees F.
N_h	Amount of cloud whose height is reported by "h" 6 = 7 or 8 tenths	Observed and coded same as N. Plotted as code figure given in message. See block **5**
C_L	Cloud type 7 = Fractostratus and/or Fractocumulus of bad weather (scud)	Predominating clouds of types in C_L table (block **1**) are coded from that table and plotted in corresponding symbols.
h	Height of base of cloud 2 = 300 to 599 feet	Observed in feet and coded and plotted as code figures according to code table in block **4**.
C_M	Cloud type 2 = Thick Altostratus or Nimbostratus	See C_L above and table in block **1**.
C_H	Cloud type 0 = No clouds C_H	See C_L above and table in block **1**.
6	Indicator figure	Not plotted.
D_C	Direction of cloud movement 7 = from NW	Observed in accordance with types of clouds present. Coded according to table in block **2** and plotted adjacent to the cloud symbol to which it applies as an arrow showing direction of movement.
a	Characteristic of barograph trace. 2 = rising unsteadily	Coded according to table in block **8** and plotted in corresponding symbols.
pp	Pressure change in 3 hours preceding observation. 28 = 2.8 millibars	Coded and plotted in units and tenths of millibars.
7	Indicator figure	Not plotted.
RR	Amount of precipitation 45 = 0.45 inches	Coded and plotted in inches and hundredths.
R_t	Time precipitation began or ended. 4 = 3 to 4 hours ago	Coded and plotted in figures from table in block **3**
s	Depth of snow on ground	Not plotted.

Code Number	C_L	Description (Abridged From I.M.O. Code)
1		Cu with little vertical development and seemingly flattened.
2		Cu of considerable development, generally towering, with or without other Cu or Sc bases all at same level.
3		Cb with tops lacking clear-cut outlines, but distinctly not cirriform or anvil-shaped; with or without Cu, Sc, or St.
4		Sc formed by spreading out of Cu; Cu often present also.
5		Sc not formed by spreading out of Cu.
6		St or Fs or both, but not Fs of bad weather.
7		Fs and/or Fc of bad weather (scud) usually under As and Ns.
8		Cu and Sc (not formed by spreading out of Cu) with bases at different levels.
9		Cb having a clearly fibrous (cirriform) top, often anvil-shaped, with or without Cu, Sc, St, or scud.

Code Number	C_M	Description (Abridged From I.M.O. Code)
1		Thin As (entire cloud layer semitransparent).
2		Thick As, or Ns.
3		Thin Ac; cloud elements not changing much and at a single level.
4		Thin Ac in patches; cloud elements continually changing and/or occurring at more than one level.
5		Thin Ac in bands or in a layer gradually spreading over sky and usually thickening as a whole.
6		Ac formed by the spreading out of Cu.
7		Double-layered Ac or a thick layer of Ac, not increasing; or As and Ac both present at same or different levels.
8		Ac in the form of Cu-shaped tufts or Ac with turrets.
9		Ac of a chaotic sky, usually at different levels; patches of dense Ci are usually present also.

C_H	Code Number	Description (Abridged From I.M.O. Code)
	1	Filaments of Ci, scattered and not increasing.
	2	Dense Ci in patches or twisted sheaves, usually not increasing.
	3	Ci, often anvil-shaped, derived from or associated with Cb.
	4	Ci, often hook-shaped, gradually spreading over the sky and usually thickening as a whole.
	5	Ci and Cs, often in converging bands, or Cs alone; the continuous layer not reaching 45° altitude.
	6	Ci and Cs, often in converging bands, or Cs alone; the continuous layer exceeding 45° altitude.
	7	Cs covering the entire sky.
	8	Cs not increasing and not covering entire sky; Ci and Cc may be present.
	9	Cc alone or Cc with some Ci or Cs, but the Cc being the main cirriform cloud present.

Cloud Abbreviation	Code Number	Dc	Cloud Direction	Rt	Time of Precipitation	h	Height in Feet (Rounded Off)	Height in Meters (Approximate)	N	Nh	Sky Coverage
St or Fs-Stratus or Fractostratus	0	NONE	No Clouds, or Calm	0	No Precipitation	0	0 - 149	0 - 49	○	0	No clouds.
Ci-Cirrus	1	↙	Northeast	1	Less than 1 hour ago	1	150 - 299	50 - 99	⊖	1	Less than one-tenth or one-tenth.
Cs-Cirrostratus	2	↓	East	2	1 to 2 hours ago	2	300 - 599	100 - 199	◔	2	Two- or three-tenths.
Cc-Cirrocumulus	3	↘	Southeast	3	2 to 3 hours ago	3	600 - 999	200 - 299	◑	3	Four-tenths.
Ac-Altocumulus	4	←	South	4	3 to 4 hours ago	4	1,000-1,999	300 - 599	◕	4	Five-tenths.
As-Altostratus	5	↖	Southwest	5	4 to 5 hours ago	5	2,000-3,499	600 - 999	⬤	5	Six-tenths.
Sc-Stratocumulus	6	↑	West	6	5 to 6 hours ago	6	3,500-4,999	1,000-1,499	◕	6	Seven- or eight-tenths.
Ns-Nimbostratus	7	↗	Northwest	7	6 to 12 hours ago	7	5,000-6,499	1,500-1,999	⊖	7	Nine-tenths or overcast with openings.
Cu or Fc-Cumulus or Fractocumulus	8	→	North	8	More than 12 hours ago	8	6,500-7,999	2,000-2,499	⬤	8	Completely overcast.
Cb-Cumulonimbus	9	NONE	Unknown, or Variable	9	Unknown	9	Above 8,000 or no clouds	Above 2,500 or no clouds	⊗	9	Sky obscured.

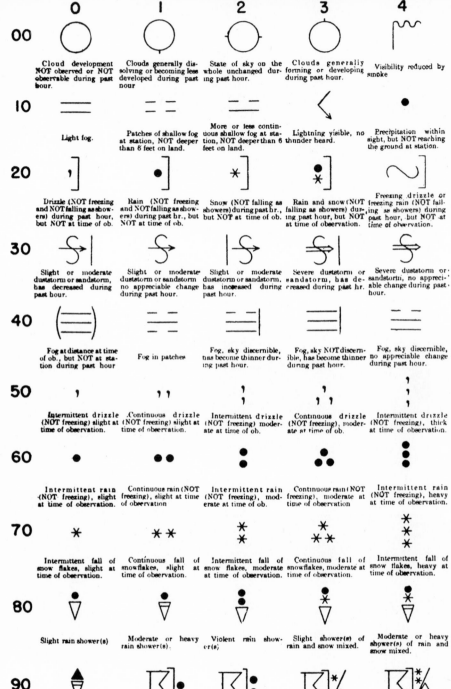

	0	**1**	**2**	**3**	**4**
00	Cloud development NOT observed or NOT observable during past hour.	Clouds generally dissolving or becoming less developed during past hour	State of sky on the whole unchanged during past hour.	Clouds generally forming or developing during past hour.	Visibility reduced by smoke
10	Light fog.	Patches of shallow fog at station, NOT deeper than 6 feet on land.	More or less continuous shallow fog at station, NOT deeper than 6 feet on land.	Lightning visible, no thunder heard.	Precipitation within sight, but NOT reaching the ground at station.
20	Drizzle (NOT freezing and NOT falling as showers) during past hour, but NOT at time of ob.	Rain (NOT freezing and NOT falling as showers) during past hr., but NOT at time of ob.	Snow (NOT falling as showers) during past hr., but NOT at time of ob.	Rain and snow (NOT falling as showers) during past hour, but NOT at time of observation.	Freezing drizzle or freezing rain (NOT falling as showers) during past hour, but NOT at time of observation.
30	Slight or moderate duststorm or sandstorm, has decreased during past hour.	Slight or moderate duststorm or sandstorm no appreciable change during past hour.	Slight or moderate duststorm or sandstorm has increased during past hour.	Severe duststorm or sandstorm, has decreased during past hr.	Severe duststorm or sandstorm, no appreciable change during past hour.
40	Fog at distance at time of ob., but NOT at station during past hour	Fog in patches	Fog, sky discernible, has become thinner during past hour.	Fog, sky NOT discernible, has become thinner during past hour.	Fog, sky discernible, no appreciable change during past hour.
50	Intermittent drizzle (NOT freezing) slight at time of observation.	Continuous drizzle (NOT freezing) slight at time of observation.	Intermittent drizzle (NOT freezing) moderate at time of ob.	Continuous drizzle (NOT freezing), moderate at time of ob.	Intermittent drizzle (NOT freezing), thick at time of observation.
60	Intermittent rain (NOT freezing), slight at time of observation.	Continuous rain (NOT freezing), slight at time of observation	Intermittent rain (NOT freezing), moderate at time of ob.	Continuous rain (NOT freezing), moderate at time of observation	Intermittent rain (NOT freezing), heavy at time of observation.
70	Intermittent fall of snow flakes, slight at time of observation.	Continuous fall of snowflakes, slight at time of observation.	Intermittent fall of snow flakes, moderate at time of observation.	Continuous fall of snowflakes, moderate at time of observation.	Intermittent fall of snow flakes, heavy at time of observation.
80	Slight rain shower(s)	Moderate or heavy rain shower(s).	Violent rain shower(s)	Slight shower(s) of rain and snow mixed.	Moderate or heavy shower(s) of rain and snow mixed.
90	Moderate or heavy shower(s) of hail with or without rain or rain and snow mixed, not associated with thunder.	Slight rain at time of ob.; thunderstorm during past hour, but NOT at time of observation.	Moderate, or heavy rain at time of ob.; thunderstorm during past hour, but NOT at time of observation.	Slight snow or rain and snow mixed at time of observa.; thunderstorm during past hour, but not at time of observation.	Mod. or heavy snow, or rain and snow mixed or hail at time of ob.; thunderstorm during past hour, but NOT at time of observation.

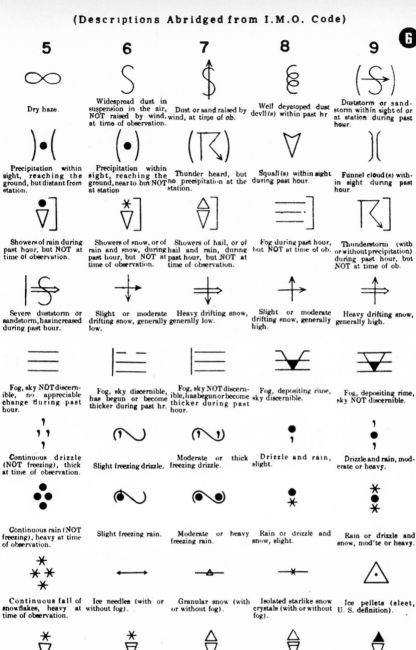

5	6	7	8	9
Dry haze.	Widespread dust in suspension in the air, NOT raised by wind, at time of observation.	Dust or sand raised by wind, at time of ob.	Well developed dust devil(s) within past hr.	Duststorm or sandstorm within sight of or at station during past hour.
Precipitation within sight, reaching the ground, but distant from station.	Precipitation within sight, reaching the ground, near to but NOT at station	Thunder heard, but no precipitation at the station.	Squall(s) within sight during past hour.	Funnel cloud(s) within sight during past hour.
Showers of rain during past hour, but NOT at time of observation.	Showers of snow, or of rain and snow, during past hour, but NOT at time of observation.	Showers of hail, or of hail and rain, during past hour, but NOT at time of observation.	Fog during past hour, but NOT at time of ob.	Thunderstorm (with or without precipitation) during past hour, but NOT at time of ob.
Severe duststorm or sandstorm, has increased during past hour.	Slight or moderate drifting snow, generally low.	Heavy drifting snow, generally low.	Slight or moderate drifting snow, generally high.	Heavy drifting snow, generally high.
Fog, sky NOT discernible, no appreciable change during past hour.	Fog, sky discernible, has begun or become thicker during past hr.	Fog, sky NOT discernible, has begun or become thicker during past hour.	Fog, depositing rime, sky discernible.	Fog, depositing rime, sky NOT discernible.
Continuous drizzle (NOT freezing), thick at time of observation.	Slight freezing drizzle.	Moderate or thick freezing drizzle.	Drizzle and rain, slight.	Drizzle and rain, moderate or heavy.
Continuous rain (NOT freezing), heavy at time of observation.	Slight freezing rain.	Moderate or heavy freezing rain.	Rain or drizzle and snow, slight.	Rain or drizzle and snow, mod'te or heavy.
Continuous fall of snowflakes, heavy at time of observation.	Ice needles (with or without fog).	Granular snow (with or without fog).	Isolated starlike snow crystals (with or without fog).	Ice pellets (sleet, U. S. definition).
Slight snow shower(s).	Moderate or heavy snow shower(s).	Slight shower(s) of soft or small hail with or without rain or rain and snow mixed.	Moderate or heavy shower(s) of soft or small hail with or without rain or rain and snow mixed.	Slight shower(s) of hail, with or without rain or rain and snow mixed, not associated with thunder.
Slight or mod. thunderstorm without hail but with rain and/or snow at time of ob.	Slight or mod. thunderstorm, with hail at time of observation.	Heavy thunderstorm, without hail, but with rain and/or snow at time of observation,	Thunderstorm combined with duststorm or sandstorm at time of ob,	Heavy thunderstorm with hail at time of ob.

Beaufort Number	ff	Miles (Statute) Per Hour	Knots	Beaufort Number	ff	Miles (Statute) Per Hour	Knots
0	◎	Calm	Calm	9	(symbol)	47-54	41-47
1	(symbol)	1-3	1-3	10	(symbol)	55-63	48-55
2	(symbol)	4-7	4-6	11	(symbol)	64-72	56-63
3	(symbol)	8-12	7-10	12	(symbol)	73-82	64-71
4	(symbol)	13-18	11-16	13	(symbol)	83-92	72-80
5	(symbol)	19-24	17-21	14	(symbol)	93-103	81-89
6	(symbol)	25-31	22-27	15	(symbol)	104-114	90-99
7	(symbol)	32-38	28-33	16	(symbol)	115-125	100-108
8	(symbol)	39-46	34-40	17	(symbol)	126-136	109-118

❽

Code Number	a	Barometric Tendency	
0	(symbol)	Rising, then falling.	
1	(symbol)	Rising, then steady; or rising, then rising more slowly.	Barometer now higher than, or same as, 3 hours ago.
2	(symbol)	Rising unsteadily, or unsteady.	
3		Rising steadily, or steady. (not plotted)	
4	(symbol)	Falling or steady, then rising; or rising, then rising more quickly.	
5	(symbol)	Falling, then rising.	
6	(symbol)	Falling, then steady; or falling, then falling more slowly.	
7	(symbol)	Falling unsteadily, or unsteady.	Barometer now lower than 3 hours ago.
8		Falling Steadily. (not plotted)	
9	(symbol)	Steady or rising, then falling; or falling, then falling more quickly.	

❾

Code Number	W	Past Weather	
0		Clear or few clouds	
1		Partly cloudy (scattered) or variable sky.	Not Plotted
2		Cloudy (broken) or overcast.	
3	(symbol)	Sandstorm, or duststorm, or drifting or blowing snow.	
4	≡	Fog, or smoke, or thick dust haze.	
5	,	Drizzle.	
6	•	Rain.	
7	*	Snow, or rain and snow mixed, or ice pellets (sleet).	
8	▽	Shower(s).	
9	(symbol)	Thunderstorm, with or without precipitation.	

front, a double line for a warm front, and dot-dash line for an occluded front, instead of as given in the table.

The large majority of fronts which the average pilot will encounter are classified as cold or warm surface fronts. As they are boundaries at the surface between air masses of different characteristics, it is to be expected that the passage of a front at an observation station, involving as it does a change from one air mass to another, will produce certain changes

CHARACTER OF FRONT	ON WORKING CHARTS	ON PRINTED CHARTS
Cold front at the ground	Continuous blue line	
Cold front aloft	Broken blue line	
Warm front at the ground	Continuous red line	
Warm front aloft	Broken red line	
Stationary front at the ground	Alternate red and blue lines joined together to form a continuous line	
Stationary front aloft	Alternate red and blue broken line	
Occluded front	Continuous purple line	
Occluded front aloft	Broken purple line	
Frontogenesis	Line of red or blue dots; alternating red and blue dots if front is stationary	The word FRONTOGENESIS is added
Frontolysis	Line of short slants across the front of same color as the front itself.	The word FRONTOLYSIS is added

in the meteorological elements. These changes are of decided importance in determining the position of fronts on the weather map and are listed in the table on page 204.

After the fronts, isobars, and centers of pressure have been located, the various air masses which the fronts delineate should be labeled to show their basic characteristics. The study of air masses is centered about the characteristics attained in their source regions and the modifications they undergo as they travel. These basic characteristics are indicated by their designating letters as explained in the table on p. 123.

The thermodynamic classification is often omitted due to similar temperature characteristics. Designators for polar air masses are entered in blue, and those of tropical origin are entered in red.

When a polar air mass moves southward through central Canada to the midwestern United States, it has had a conti-

CHANGES IN METEOROLOGICAL ELEMENTS INDICATING A
FRONTAL PASSAGE

	Cold Front	*Warm Front*
Temperature	Falls	Rises
Dew point	Falls	Rises
Wind direction	Shift from southerly to westerly direction	Shift from easterly to southerly direction; less prominent than cold front
Pressure Tendency	Falling, then rising. See 4 under a, Table 8	Falling, then steady. See 6 under a, Table 8
Precipitation	Showery of variable intensity	End of steady precipitation
Cloud System	Cumulo-nimbus. See 9 under C_L, Table 1	Fractocumulus or fractostratus. 6 under C_L or 2 under C_M, Table 1
Thunderstorms (if they occur)	At surface position of front	Several hundred miles in advance of surface position of front
Ceiling and Visibility	Lowest values in vicinity of front	Lowest values in vicinity of front

nental trajectory and it is colder than the surface over which it flows. The designation of this air mass is *cPk*. If a tropical air mass moves into the southern part of the United States from the Gulf of Mexico, it has had a maritime trajectory and, in the winter, it is warmer than the surface over which it flows. The designator for this air mass is *mTw*.

Frequently, two air masses from the same basic type of source region have different trajectories but later become mixed over another region. When this happens, a plus (+)

sign is placed between the designators of the two air masses. This commonly occurs in the case of $cPk + mPk$.

When an air mass has been exposed to modifying influences for a long period of time, it gradually assumes the characteristics imparted by these influences and becomes "transitional." For example, if a cPk mass moves to a position over the Atlantic Ocean about latitude 30° N—a source region of considerable mT air which later flows into the eastern United States—it gradually loses its cPk characteristics and assumes those of mTk. This transitional process is indicated on the weather map by inserting an arrow between the designator of the original characteristics and those newly attained; in this case, $cPk \rightarrow mTk$.

Quite often, the air mass at the surface differs essentially from the air masses in the intermediate levels of the atmosphere. The surface air mass, in these cases, is indicated in the usual manner, but the designator for the upper air mass is placed above the surface mass designator, and then a horizontal line is drawn between the two. For example, if mTw air is flowing over mPk air, the designation is

$$\frac{mTw}{mPk}$$

Areas in which precipitation is falling at the time of the observation should be indicated in green in accordance with the following:

(*a*) Shower areas, principally snow flurries and sprinkles, are represented by a series of small, inverted triangles: ▽▽ ▽ ▽▽

(*b*) Drizzle areas are represented by a series of comma-like symbols: ,,,

(*c*) Intermittent precipitation areas are shown by open diagonals (hatching): / / / /

(*d*) Continuous precipitation areas are indicated by smooth light shading: ▱

DRAWING THE WEATHER MAP

There are several factors which influence the order in which a map analyst draws the various elements of his analysis on the basic weather map. These factors include delayed receipt of reports, type of map and impending weather, historical sequences available, relative difficulty of analysis in specific areas, time required for completion, etc. Moreover, very often the various elements of the analysis are drawn concurrently, or certain elements are skeched in lightly, or mentally, before other elements are drawn in their final form.

In general, however, the various elements of the analysis are usually entered in the following order (*optional*) :

1. Fronts.
2. Isobars.
3. HIGH and LOW pressure centers.
4. Air mass symbols.
5. Areas of various types of precipitation.
6. Isallobars.   (*Optional.*)
7. Tracks of HIGH and LOW pressure centers.   (*Optional.*)

In the interest of simplicity and readability for the beginner, only the first three elements have been drawn on the sample maps included in this book, to be studied with the next chapter, "Weather Forecasting."

The very general instructions given here on the entry of the various map analysis elements do not cover all of the questions and possible alternatives that arise in the drawing of manuscript weather maps. They relate only to the *mechanics* of the entry of map analysis elements, in order to arrive at standardization of map entry methods and uniformity in map appearance. The ultimate objective, of course, is a neat and legible map, smoothly and accurately drawn, that is truly representative of prevailing atmospheric conditions.

Finding and Delineating Fronts

Note the first three items shown in the table on page 204. Change in temperature, dew point, and wind direction constitute a triple indicator of a frontal passage. Therefore, to find the location of a frontal zone, examine the data plotted around the various stations shown on the weather map, comparing each to its neighbor, successively. Unless the approximate position of a front is known, it is often most convenient to begin at the right and proceed to the left horizontally across the map. Compare each station successively with the one to its left and note whether the change in the "indicators" is gradual and regular or rapid and irregular. You may proceed for some distance before you note any *marked* change. The temperature and dew point may change quite regularly only a few degrees and the wind from 10 to 20 degrees in direction. Then suddenly you find that the temperature and dew point drop (or rise) as much as 5° to 15° F and the wind shifts 30° to 60° or more to the right. Here make a short, light pencil line between the two stations concerned, the direction of the line tending to separate the stations, not to join them. Now compare the nearest two stations both above and below the short pencil line. If you find a similar indication of such a discontinuity, mark it as before. Now keep proceeding above and below by pairs of stations, and soon you will find that your short pencil lines have grown into a definite suggestion of a continuous line, straight or curving as it may occur. Sometimes not all three of the indicators will change significantly, but only one, especially the wind or temperature. Sketch in the line lightly as you go; its general direction will help you to find the next pair of stations between which the discontinuity, or front, lies. Proceed over the rest of the map in similar manner, sketching in the fronts; you may soon find some of them joining up with others in curves or even in sharp points. Sketch in all you can find.

Tracing Isobars

Now start sketching in the isobars in a similar manner, at any convenient place. Pick any pair of adjacent stations having an atmospheric sea-level pressure respectively above and below any one specific isobar you have decided to plot.

Isobars are drawn with a black lead pencil, lightly at first. For uniformity of line, a mechanical pencil is recommended. Isobars are spaced, usually, 3 mb apart. The series to be plotted is then chosen so that the value of each isobar is evenly divisible by the interval chosen, in this case, 3. Thus the series will run 1005–1008–1011, etc., above and below. Intermediate isobars 1.5 mb apart are sometimes drawn in areas in which it is desired to make a more detailed study.

General Rules. All pressures higher than the value of a specific isobar should be on the same side of that isobar, while all pressures lower than the value of that specific isobar should lie on the other side. However, some latitude is allowable here in order to provide a smooth, continuous line. (This is quite permissible since various isolated "spots" of slightly higher or lower pressure actually do occur, due to local conditions or other causes.)

An isobar must never meet, join, or cross another isobar. Since isobars are lines drawn through points having equal pressure, it is obvious, then, that an isobar can only meet itself and never another isobar.

An isobar can never come to an end *within* the area of observations, but must come back to the starting point and form a closed curve. When an isobar reaches the border of the map or to a place where there are no more observations, it stops only for lack of further observations; at this point we place the appropriate value of the isobar. But within areas of observations there are never any unterminated isobars.

Two separate and distinct isobars through points having the same pressure may approach closely in an area of light winds, and there may not be enough observations there to show exactly how they should be drawn, but, in any event, they must not cross or merge. Figure 9–1 shows isobars which may be drawn in either of two ways. Pressure in the middle, at A, may be higher or lower than the reading (12) shown at the ends of the isobars; if there is no observation at A we may not know, for sure, so we can only use our best judgment and draw the lines accordingly. In the case at the left (Fig. 9–1) we assume that the pressure at A is lower than 12.0 and in the case at the right we assume that it is higher than 12.0.

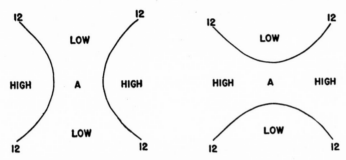

Fig. 9–1. In the absence of barometer readings in the vicinity of A, the isobars may be drawn two ways.

If pressure is appreciably higher on both sides of an isobar than it is along the isobar, a mistake has been made. It is probable that the isobar has been drawn through an area of low pressure when it should have encircled it. This is illustrated in Figure 9–2. Likewise, when pressure is considerably lower on both sides than it is along the isobar, the region through which the isobar has been drawn is probably an area of high pressure which should be inclosed by the isobar. The wind arrows should indicate the correct way to draw the isobar.

Isobars are crowded in areas where the wind is strong and farther apart where the wind is light. This rule helps when observations are scanty.

The wind generally does not blow across the isobars from low to high pressure. Wind will not blow from low to high pressure any more than water will run up hill, but many weather maps are carelessly drawn to show wind blowing up the barometric slope. However, because of local obstructions to a free flow of air, there are some exceptions to this rule over land, but never in the open sea.

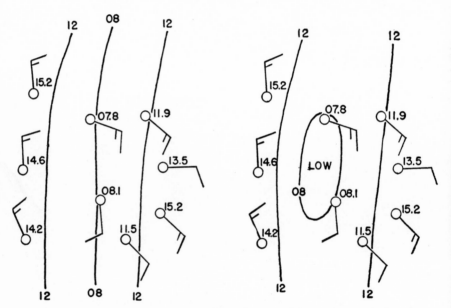

FIG. 9–2. At left, isobar drawn through area of low pressure is in error. It is correctly drawn at right.

Example. For an example of tracing isobars, turn to Figure 9–3. Select at random a point about the middle of the Atlantic Coast as a starting point—say, Cape Hatteras, Lat. 35° N., Long. 76° W. The Cape Hatteras station pressure reads "108" (i.e., 1010.8 mb) and Norfolk (just north of it) reads "064" (i.e., 1006.4 mb). So let us start with the 1008 mb isobar. Since 1008 is about halfway between the two values, 1006.4 and 1010.8, we start this isobar crossing the coast about half way between the two stations. Now, con-

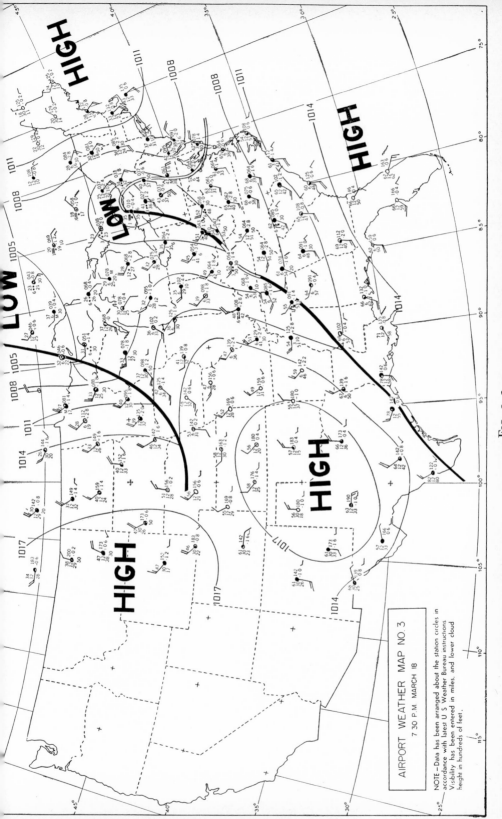

AIRPORT WEATHER MAP NO 3
7 30 P.M. MARCH 18

NOTE – Data has been arranged about the station circles in
accordance with latest U S Weather Bureau instructions
Visibility has been entered in miles, and lower cloud
height in hundreds of feet.

FIG. 9-3.

tinuing the trace, we see that the 1008 mb isobar must pass
between those stations whose pressure readings on the map
are, successively:—108 and 064; 112 and 064; 102 and 075;
085 and 064; 091 and 078.   Then the cold front is encountered, so we anticipate a change (to the right) in the direction
of the isobar.   The change is usually sharp—from 60 to as
much as 150 degrees—but sometimes, particularly in crossing
a warm front, the change may be small.   The inflection of
the line always points away from the center of low pressure.
After crossing the cold front the 1008 mb isobar is found to
continue on between pairs of stations whose pressures read
successively as follows: 085 and 068; 108 and 054; 098 and
064; 102 and 075; 095 and 078; 098 and 078, when the second
cold front is encountered.   There the isobar again turns
sharply to the right and shortly runs out of the area of data
recorded.

Now, trace the next higher isobar, 1011 mb, noting that
its position relative to each pair of stations it passes is roughly
proportional to the difference between them and the amount
that 1011 is above or below the respective station pressures.

To trace the next *lower* isobar, i.e., 1005 mb, we find that,
since there is no pressure that low along the coast line, we must
look inland until we find a pressure low enough to start the
trace.   Coming in from the coast, we find "047" near central
West Virginia, close to the front.   From this point the 1005
mb isobar may now be traced, finally forming a closed loop
and indicating that the center of low pressure is within it.

(Practice following the trace of isobars on maps already
completed and you will soon learn how to draw them for
yourself, quickly and smoothly.)

Now, following the principles demonstrated in the above
examples, proceed to the remaining areas of the map, drawing in the isobars lightly until all desired areas have been
covered.

Centers of High and Low Pressure

Next, find in each enclosed (or partly enclosed) area the station having the highest, or lowest, pressure. That station is considered to be the center of the high (or low) pressure area, and it is marked HIGH or LOW as appropriate.

Fronts in a Depression

In drawing the map the beginner may easily become confused as to how to draw the shape of the fronts running into—or meeting in—a depression. A little study of the shapes shown in the five weather maps at the back of the book as well as the various diagrams of Figure 7–7, page 149, showing the successive positions and shapes of fronts in the development of a typical disturbance will help the student to follow the fronts into the center.

Occluded Front

It is less easy to trace out an occluded front, its definition often not being clearly indicated; but as an additional help the student may observe (on Maps No. 4 and No. 5, pp. 335–6) the typical way that the isobars come into the front in a "V" (making a trough) while they approach or turn away from it on either side.

Air Masses and Precipitation Areas

After the above points have been covered (i.e., fronts, isobars, and centers of pressure), the student should proceed to identify, and mark appropriately, the various air masses and areas of precipitation indicated by the data plotted around the respective stations on the map.

Isallobars

The drawing of isallobars, if desired, is similar to the drawing of isobars except that the element pp (pressure change in last 3 hours) is used as the guide instead of sea-level pressure. Isallobars are usually spaced 1 mb apart and are marked plus (+) where the pressure is increasing, minus (—) where it is decreasing. A zero (0) isallobar is drawn between the + 1 and — 1 indicating where there has been no pressure change, or "steady." One particular characteristic of isallobars is that they have no characteristic change in direction when crossing a front; in fact when close to a front they frequently run close together and nearly parallel to it for long distances.

Movements of Pressure Centers

Tracks of high- and low-pressure centers may also be marked on maps if desired. The symbol to indicate successive positions of pressure centers 6 hours apart is a small black square with white diagonals. The track followed is made by a line of short arrows joining the successive positions and pointing in the direction of movement.

The purpose of the above explanation of the construction of a weather map has been solely to give the student a general idea of some of the mechanical processes which the map analyst employs in map drawing. For those interested in delving more deeply into this interesting field, reference should be made to special texts and pamphlets, or to experienced analysts, for such information.

Winds Aloft Map

Another important map prepared in meteorological offices is the winds aloft map, which consists of a series of small charts, arranged four to a sheet. On these charts, reports at prescribed intervals from pilot-balloon and radiosonde stations in this and adjacent countries are entered, showing wind direction and velocity at even thousand-foot elevations above sea level to 16,000 feet, then at 20, 25, 30, and 35 thousand feet (and higher). By plotting these reports on a map, a composite picture of the wind direction and velocity at various elevations can be quickly obtained. The pilot can determine readily the elevation at which the strongest tail wind or the least head wind prevails. To the forecaster, this map is a handy tool which can be used in his analysis of the movement of pressure and frontal systems.

By means of "facsimile" machines connected into a network (described later in this chapter), winds aloft maps (and others) are now transmitted, completely drawn, to most stations every six hours. As a consequence, the drawing of winds aloft maps at the individual stations has been greatly curtailed, the facsimile maps being used instead. On these charts the wind velocity is indicated by "feathers" or a flag on the shaft of the wind arrow. It does *not* correspond to the values of the Beaufort Scale. Instead, the following values are used:

> A full feather equals 10 knots.
> A half feather equals 5 knots.
> Small triangular flag equals 50 knots.

Typical examples of these Winds Aloft Maps for March 8, 1950, will be found in the Appendix (pp. 322–327).

AUXILIARY CHARTS

On the same sheet as its daily weather map, the U. S. Weather Bureau includes four auxiliary charts, each devoted to depicting the situation as to certain specific items which contribute to making up the whole composite picture. These are described in the following paragraphs. The following maps are illustrated in the Appendix.

Temperature Chart (see p. 328)

Temperature data from about 175 stations in the United States are entered. The figures above the station dots denote maximum temperatures reported from these stations during the 24 hours ending 1:30 A.M., E.S.T.; the figures entered below the station dots denote minimum temperatures during the 24 hours ending 1:30 P.M., E.S.T., of the previous day.

Light gray shading, labeled "Higher" or "Lower," indicates the areas where current temperatures recorded at 1:30 A.M., E.S.T., are at least 10° higher or lower than 24 hours earlier.

Precipitation Map (see p. 329)

Precipitation data from about 175 stations in the United States are entered. When precipitation has occurred at any of these stations in the 24-hour period ending at 1:30 A.M., E.S.T., the total amount, in inches and hundredths, is entered near the station dot. When the figures for total precipitation have been compiled from incomplete data the amount on the map is underlined.

The geographical areas where precipitation has fallen during the 24 hours ending at 1:30 A.M., E.S.T., are shaded.

700-Millibar Map (see p. 330)

Contour lines, isotherms, and wind arrows are shown on the insert chart for the 700-millibar constant pressure surface. Solid lines are drawn to show height above sea level and are labeled in feet. Dashed lines are drawn at 10° intervals of temperature and at 32° and are labeled in degrees Fahrenheit. Wind direction is shown by arrows and wind speed by feathers (or a flag) as on the Winds Aloft Maps. This chart corresponds in time approximately to the Continental Map described below.

Continental Map (see p. 331)

The insert map of nearly the entire North American continent shows the surface pressure pattern and frontal analysis twelve hours earlier than the principal chart (the daily weather map). Areas of current precipitation are shaded.

TELETYPE, RADIO AND FACSIMILE MAP DISTRIBUTION

Teletype and Radio

At the WBAN * Analysis Center, located at the U. S. Weather Bureau in Washington, D. C., meteorological data from the entire Northern Hemisphere is being constantly received, compiled, and analyzed. After being analyzed, analyses and prognostic data are disseminated over teletype and radio networks covering the United States and its outlying possessions.

A wide field of information is covered by this teletype and radio system.

Facsimile Weather Maps

From master weather charts prepared at the Analysis Center completely drawn maps are transmitted over the facsimile network, using telephone lines for transmission. This service covers all Army, Navy, and Air Force weather stations and most of the major airports of the continental United States. By means of the new radio-facsimile machines selected naval vessels, equipped with radio-facsimile receivers, are supplied with facsimile weather charts at sea.

A great wealth of weather information is furnished in over 50 transmissions daily to stations and to ships by means of this revolutionary and highly useful invention.

QUESTIONS

1. Through what medium have international agreements been reached to attain uniformity on an international weather code and the arrangement of weather data on weather maps?

---

* "WBAN" derives its name from the letters representing the *activities who* furnish its personnel, viz., Weather Bureau, Army, Air Force, and Navy, all working in a common cause.

2. How and when are weather reports collected and disseminated for the preparation of the regular weather maps?
3. Describe in general the information most generally contained in a weather code message.
4. Show how the various weather data are grouped about a station circle in accordance with the standard "station model."
5. Explain the meaning of each symbol appearing on the station model.
6. On Weather Bureau maps, how are fronts of different types generally shown?
7. What changes in the meteorological elements indicate a frontal passage?
8. How is an air mass whose meteorological characteristics are changing, indicated on a weather map?
9. When an air mass in the upper atmosphere overlies another air mass at the surface and is of different characteristics, how is this condition indicated on a weather map?
10. How are the following precipitation areas shown on the weather map, and in what color? (a) Showers. (b) Drizzle. (c) Intermittent precipitation. (d) Continuous precipitation.
11. In what order are the various elements generally entered on the map?
12. What is the "triple indicator" of a frontal passage, and how is it used in finding and dilineating fronts on a weather map?
13. Describe how isobars are drawn and placed on a map.
14. State briefly the general rules pertaining to isobars.
15. How are centers of high and low pressure marked on a map?
16. Explain how to draw fronts in a depression.
17. Discuss the tracing of an occluded front.
18. How are isallobars drawn and spaced, and what are their characteristics?
19. How are the movements of pressure centers indicated and marked?
20. What are winds aloft maps and how are they arranged? (a) What elevations are covered in a series? (b) What purpose do they serve? (c) Explain the wind velocity indicators placed at the tail of the wind arrows on these maps.
21. Describe the four auxiliary charts printed with the Weather Bureau's Daily Weather Map, as follows: (a) Temperature Chart. (b) Precipitation Map. (c) 700-Millibar Map. (d) Continental Map.
22. Describe the field of information disseminated by the WBAN Analysis Center.
23. Discuss facsimile weather maps, how they are transmitted, and to whom they are furnished.

Chapter X

WEATHER FORECASTS

The completion of the weather map marks the end of the first big step in the preparation of a forecast. A good forecaster must be particularly adept at these three things: He must be able (1) to analyze the meteorological situation quickly and accurately, (2) to advance the current situation through the period of the forecast, and (3) to express the expected conditions in a few concise sentences.

Of great value in forecasting is a thorough knowledge of the topography of the area. Ordinarily the major phases of weather situations are controlled by air mass and pressure systems, but local conditions of topography frequently alter the normally expected weather, and at times cause weather conditions different from those usually associated with certain pressure systems and air mass distributions. For example, compare the weather for the Cleveland-Pittsburgh-Buffalo area with that for the New York-Philadelphia-Washington area when the winds are about 20 miles per hour or more from the west or northwest during late fall and early winter. In the former area, because of the influence of the Great Lakes and the eastward upslope of the terrain, snow flurries and squalls, with extremely variable ceilings and visibilities, and icing conditions in clouds, are experienced for several days in succession, while in the latter area sloping toward the sea, the prevailing conditions are: varying cloudiness, generally scattered or broken, with good ceilings and visibilities, and icing conditions at altitudes sufficiently high to be usually of small concern to the pilot.

The effect of local topography on certain weather conditions varies so much that it is impossible to include in this book the many and varied axioms and rules used by local fore-casters in different parts of the country.   Rather, the problem of forecasting will be presented along general lines.   Through experience, most pilots quickly become familiar with local peculiarities in weather situations.

The U. S. Weather Bureau has established Airway Fore-cast Centers at the following places:

Albuquerque, N. M.	Los Angeles, Calif.
Atlanta, Ga.	Miami, Fla.
Billings, Mont.	Minneapolis, Minn.
Boston, Mass.	New Orleans, La.
Chicago, Ill.	New York, N. Y.
Dayton, Ohio	Salt Lake City, Utah
Denver, Colo.	San Francisco, Calif.
Fort Worth, Tex.	Seattle, Wash.
Kansas City, Mo.	Washington, D. C.

These forecast centers are maintained for the purpose of in-forming pilots, transport operators, and other aviation interests of weather conditions which may be expected in flights and at terminals throughout the country.   Regional or route and terminal forecasts are prepared every six hours and released just after 5 and 11 A.M. and P.M., E.S.T., over the teletype circuits of the C.A.A.   These forecasts are for an eight-hour period beginning at 5:30 and 11:30 A.M. and P.M., E.S.T. Should unanticipated weather conditions develop, special fore-casts may be issued at any time.   The terminology used is generally similar to and has the same limits and meanings as described in Chapter VIII on airway weather reports.   In order to shorten the time required for transmission on the tele-type circuits, certain abbreviations for long or frequently used words are employed.   Airway forecasts include expected ceil-ings, conditions of the sky, visibilities, weather conditions, ob-structions to visibility, winds aloft, wind shifts, icing condi-tions, and movements of pressure and frontal systems.

To analyze the current map properly, a detailed study should be made of the maps covering at least the two preceding six-hour periods. The life history of preceding developments must be known before future trends may be analyzed.

Pressure Gradients

In the analysis of the map, the degree of development of several factors must be determined, and an appropriate weight given to each. The pressure gradient is the first of these factors to be studied. By comparing the current map with preceding maps, it is easy to determine whether the gradient has increased or decreased—indicated by the isobars being closer together or farther apart, respectively. An increasing pressure gradient results in an increased wind velocity, increasing turbulence, and, if in the vicinity of an area of low barometric pressure, causes air from widely separated regions to flow more rapidly into the center of the disturbance, bringing about worse weather conditions in the form of precipitation, low ceilings, and low visibilities.

If the pressure gradient of the map is rather flat—that is, if the isobars are far apart—the winds are light; the air is not so turbulent and is homogeneous as to temperature and humidity over a fairly large area, and good flying weather is rather general. This situation, however, because of the lack of convective air currents at night, quite often leads to the formation of ground fog and accumulation of smoke particles in the atmosphere near the surface of the earth. These obstructions to visibility will continue into the morning daylight hours until the air is heated sufficiently to evaporate the fog particles or to set up convective currents which will disperse the smoke into the upper air. If fog or smoke overlies a cold surface—for example, ground which has been exposed to cold air currents for several days—a longer period of time will be required for its dispersion.

Pressure Tendencies

As barometric pressure is the identifying characteristic of *highs* and *lows,* its importance in the meteorological situation cannot be overestimated.   However, as this pressure varies at most points from day to day with varying weather conditions, it is just as essential to study this changing pressure in relation to the different weather situations that follow.   A systematic classification of wind-barometer data and subsequent weather conditions soon results in a list of indications upon which dependable forecasts may be made.   Seasonal and diurnal variations will occur and should be noticed on every occasion.   The greater the number of cases listed, the more reliable the system becomes and the greater is the opportunity of noting exceptions.

The following wind-barometer indications for the United States were prepared by the late Professor E. B. Garriott when he was chief forecaster for the Weather Bureau.

Wind Direction	*Sea-level Barometric Pressure (mb)*	*Character of Weather Indicated*
SW to NW	1019.3 to 1022.7 steady	Fair, with slight temperature changes, for 1 to 2 days
SW to NW	1019.3 to 1022.7 rising rapidly	Fair, followed within 2 days by rain
SW to NW	1022.7 and above, stationary	Continued fair, with no decided temperature change
SW to NW	1022.7 and above, falling slowly	Slowly rising temperature and fair for 2 days
S to SE	1019.3 to 1022.7, falling slowly	Rain within 24 hours
S to SE	1019.3 to 1022.7, falling rapidly	Wind increasing in force, with rain within 12 to 24 hours
SE to NE	1019.3 to 1022.7, falling slowly	Rain in 12 to 18 hours
SE to NE	1019.3 to 1022.7, falling rapidly	Increasing wind, and rain within 12 hours
E to NE	1019.3 and above, falling slowly	In summer, with light winds, rain may not fall for several days. In winter, rain within 24 hours

Wind Direction	*Sea-level Barometric Pressure (mb)*	*Character of Weather Indicated*
E to NE	1019.3 and above, falling rapidly	In summer, rain probable within 12 to 24 hours. In winter, rain or snow, with increasing winds, will often set in when the barometer begins to fall and the wind sets in from the NE
SE to NE	1019.3 or below, falling slowly	Rain will continue 1 to 2 days
SE to NE	1015.9 or below, falling rapidly	Rain, with high wind, followed within 36 hours by clearing, and in winter by colder
S to SW	1015.9 or below, rising slowly	Clearing within a few hours, and fair for several days
S to E	1009.1 or below, falling rapidly	Severe storm imminent, followed within 24 hours by clearing, and in winter by colder
E to N	1009.1 or below, falling rapidly	Severe northeast gale and heavy precipitation; in winter, heavy snow, followed by a cold wave
Going to W	1009.1 or below, rising rapidly	Clearing and colder

General weather trends as given above are helpful, or use of them may be more nearly necessary, when one has observations only in his own locality. But if one has a continental weather map, he may study the general weather conditions over a large area first. Then a local forecast may be made more intelligently and more accurately after considering the weather over the whole country and its effect in the vicinity of his own location.

Pressure Systems

To determine the future trend in intensity of areas of high and low barometric pressure, the likelihood of a continued supply of air from the proper source region must be considered. If the warm, moist winds from a southerly direction can pass to the center of the low-pressure area, or if the cold, relatively dry winds from a northwesterly direction continue as a feeder current for the high-pressure area, there will be an increase in the intensity of the pressure system involved. Whenever these supply winds are cut off, there will be a subsequent diminution in intensity.

Blocking Effects

The forecaster must always take into consideration the possibility of blocking effects—that is, the retardation of pressure movements. Blocked conditions occur most frequently and for longer periods in the spring of the year, due in most cases to the impeding effects of cold air masses that move southeastward from Hudson Bay or regions to the east of it and settle over the Canadian Maritime Provinces, where cold coastal waters prevail and tend to accentuate the coldness of the air and retard the movement of the HIGH. Cases are also found in other seasons of the year. Such blocking is not confined to the Canadian Maritime Provinces. Slowing up of storm movement in the region of Iceland is followed 5 or 6 days later by slowing up of storm movement over Newfoundland. The retardation in the Newfoundland region may be felt as far west as the Mississippi Valley. It is believed that retardation in any part of the main storm track is reflected after a proper interval in a blocking to the westward along the main storm track. Blocking of high-pressure areas over the Canadian Maritime Provinces causes very bad flying weather over a considerable portion of the Atlantic Coast east of the Allegheny Mountains. Cold outflowing air flows over the warm Gulf Stream to the south of the cold water of the Canadian Maritime Provinces and its moisture content increases sharply, forming a low stratus "deck" which flows inland along the New England and Middle Atlantic coast with the east wind prevalent in this barometric pressure condition. The low stratus cloud deck will continue for several days, or until the

HIGH moves far enough eastward to set up a southerly wind over the coast.

Associated very closely with blocking effects in the movement of pressure areas is the resultant blocking of the movement of frontal surfaces. Flying weather conditions usually improve rapidly following the passage of a *fast-moving* cold front as the inrushing cold, dry air is moving with sufficient vigor to displace the warm air aloft as well as at the surface. Following the passage of a *slow-moving* cold front, however, a low cloud deck, at times accompanied by precipitation, may persist for several hours. Any further retardation in the forward motion of the front results in the development of worse weather conditions, which may prevail for several days.

Most quasi-stationary fronts actually have warm front characteristics. The cold air mass to the rear of the front is shallow. This lack of vigor gives the front more of the passive characteristics of a warm front than the active ones of a cold front. The slope of the front gradually decreases and becomes much closer to the 1 in 200 ratio, that is, a rise of 1 mile in a distance of 200 miles rather than 1 in 30 to 100 miles.

To illustrate the points brought out in the foregoing paragraph, let us follow the movements of two cold fronts that might occur in the month of November. The first of these cold fronts extends, let us say, from a low-pressure area over southern Indiana to the Gulf Coast east of New Orleans. In 24 hours (7:30 A.M.–7:30 A.M.) the front has moved to a line extending from central New York down along the Atlantic seaboard and over the ocean, well to the east of Florida. The cold front has moved in this eastward direction at a rate of 25 mph, and then continued at this rate eastward across the ocean for the next 12 hours. Yet, almost without exception, the precipitation attending and preceding the front ended, and the cloudiness decreased generally to scattered clouds within an hour or two after its passage. In fact, breaks in the overcast could be noted within 10 minutes after the passage of the front.

The second front, somewhat later in the month, extends, let us say, from a low-pressure area over central Iowa down through Columbia, Mo., to Little Rock, Ark., and Houston, Tex.   In 24 hours (7:30 A.M.–7:30 A.M.), this front has moved eastward to a line extending from Vermont through eastern Pennsylvania, Virginia, on down to the Gulf Coast passing halfway between Alabama and Florida.   Its movement eastward was at the rate of 30 mph in the northern portion and 24 mph in the southern portion.

The slowing up of the movement of this front, however, is evidenced at this time by the warm wave developments over northern Virginia and western South Carolina.   During the next 12 hours this front moves to a line extending southeast of Nantucket, Mass., downward along the Carolina coast, and across Georgia and Florida.   It then becomes quasi-stationary and remains near this position until four days later when a major wave develops and moves northeastward along the coast.

During the quasi-stationary period, several minor warm waves developed, but none was sufficiently strong to alter the general situation.   A strong area of high pressure existed over the Atlantic Ocean to the east of the front, blocking its eastward movement.   Yet, during this period, the weather condition along the Atlantic Coast, east of the Blue Ridge Mountains, was one of almost continuous light rain.   The circulation from the Atlantic Ocean high-pressure area produced a warm, moist southerly current to the east of the front.   Upon reaching the front, this current was forced to ascend over the cold air to the northwest.   The resultant adiabatic cooling by ascent caused copious and, in a few places, heavy, rain along the Atlantic seaboard.

Seasonal and Topographical Influences

When forecasting the movement of areas of high and low pressure, every case must be considered individually.   As a guide, keep in mind that the rate of movement is greater in winter than in summer. The average 24-hour movement of HIGHS in winter is 594 miles as compared with 485 miles during the summer months. For LOWS, comparable rates are 718 miles for the winter months and 477 miles during the summer months. Individual cases will vary considerably according to several factors, most prominent of which are the meteorological condition of the atmosphere over a large surrounding area and the topography of the country.

Some of the meteorological conditions which affect movements are as follows:

(*a*) LOWS and HIGHS tend to repel each other, while adjacent lows tend to unite.

(*b*) LOWS move faster if the following HIGH is pushing eastward vigorously.

(*c*) Blocking effects (discussed above).

Topographic conditions which affect movements of HIGHS and LOWS are as follows:

(*a*) After recurving, as in tropical cyclones, LOWS move faster, particularly if they are over or approaching a large body of water. This is very noticeable in the eastern part of the United States.

(*b*) Mountain ranges which are not parallel to the direction of movement of an area of high pressure have a blocking effect which depends upon the angle and the height of the mountains. Areas of low pressure tend to move parallel to large mountain chains.

In addition to the variations in degree of seasonal coldness with which we are all familiar, there are other seasonal differences:

(*a*) The pressure at the crest of the HIGH is greater, and at the center of the LOW is less, in winter than in summer. This increases pressure gradients in winter, and so produces greater wind velocities.

(*b*) Heavy instability showers frequently occur near the crest of the HIGH in summer; in winter this occurrence is rare, unless aided materially by topography.

Air Masses and Fronts

As air masses move away from their source regions, they are modified by the terrain over which they travel. The lower levels of polar air masses are warmed as they move southward; tropical air masses are warmed in summer and cooled in winter as they move northward. The amount of change depends on the time required for the air mass to move from the source region to the place for which the forecast is to be made. Thus, a slow-moving air mass will be modified more than a faster-moving one. This amount of change must be determined in order to forecast the occurrence of instability showers incident to the warming of the lower levels of a cold air mass, and the occurrence of fog and stratus clouds caused by the cooling of the lower levels of a warm moist air mass. Travel of air masses over large water surfaces is to be specially noted. If the temperature difference between air and water is large, the evaporation of water into the atmosphere may cool and moisten it sufficiently to cause cloudiness and, at times, precipitation.

The movement and the development of the frontal structure must be analyzed to compare its rate of movement with rates shown at preceding periods, and to ascertain whether any intensification is taking place. A slow-moving front frequently develops a secondary low-pressure center which later becomes the main center of the disturbance. The secondary center usually contains worse flying weather conditions and higher wind velocities than the primary center. Many of the northeast storms of the Atlantic Coast result from the development of the secondary center. Intensification of the frontal zone results in a sharper wind-shift line, increased turbulence, and worse weather conditions in the form of heavier precipitation, lower ceilings, and reduced visibilities.

Clouds

As the result of increased emphasis on accurate cloud reporting and the adoption of *The International Atlas of Clouds and of the States of the Sky* in recent years, the value of cloud types as an aid in forecasting has been advanced considerably. Many cloud types are so definitely associated with different portions of low-pressure disturbances that the experienced observer frequently can determine by cloud observations alone whether a period of bad weather has passed or is still in the offing. In certain ways, clouds in the intermediate and lower levels may be divided into two classes: (*a*) layer-type clouds, indicative of air without appreciable convective currents or turbulence, any precipitation from which will be gentle and more or less continuous, and (*b*) cumulo-form clouds, indicative of air with convective currents and turbulence, any precipitation from which will be in the form of showers or precipitation of widely varying intensity.

The first sign of an approaching depression is the appearance of cirrus, generally in the form of hooks ending in a point or small tuft, increasing rapidly to the halo-forming cirro-stratus and then to thickening alto-stratus. From this type of cloud, gentle precipitation soon begins to fall. The veil of alto-stratus gradually lowers and turns into nimbo-stratus, with precipitation becoming continuous and increasing in intensity. The falling precipitation soon saturates the air below the nimbo-stratus and so produces an increasing layer of fracto-cumulus or fracto-stratus. When this condition occurs, the center of the disturbance is close at hand. At the passage of the cold front at the center of the depression, this lower deck of clouds becomes very low, with the ceiling only a few hundred feet, and heavy showery precipitation occurs, indicative of the passage of a cumulo-form cloud, the upper part of which is usually hidden by the lower clouds and heavy precipitation. If the front is moving rapidly and steadily, clearing weather follows its passage very shortly. If for any reason the front is retarded, masses of warm, moist air aloft from the warm sector of the LOW will not be displaced as happens with the rapidly moving front.   Under this condition, strato-cumulus or stratus clouds may form, at times accompanied by occasional instability showers.   Farther to the rear of the depression, small cumulus clouds prevail, indicative of a period of fine weather. This evolution of cloud-forms occurs when the warm sector of the low-pressure area passes to the south of the observer, assuming a general west-to-east movement.

If the warm sector passes over the observer, however, the passage of the warm front usually brings a period of relatively better weather conditions.   The nimbo-stratus and fracto-cumulus or fracto-stratus of the cold sector often give way to an area of alto-cumulus and cumulus or strato-cumulus in the warm sector.   The approach and passage of the cold front results in the same sequence of cloud forms as described in the paragraph above, but the cumulo-form clouds at the front usually may be observed as it passes.

The predominating source of cloud formation is adiabatic cooling of the atmosphere to the dew point, caused by ascent. Main causes of vertically ascending air are turbulence, convection and instability, topography, and frontal surfaces.   In many instances, however, the cloud system is the result of more than *one* of these influences, and the forecaster's analysis must take into consideration the prevalence of each effect.   Any forecast of the development of any cloud system must be based on a humidity high enough to cause a condensation level between the altitude limits of the vertical movement.

The principal cloud type formed as the result of ordinary turbulence is the relatively low stratus deck.   The turbulence must be active enough to reach a very low condensation level, but the air above must be stable to prevent a further ascent of the air and formation of cumulus-type clouds.   This cloud sheet is prevalent when conditions are conducive to the formation of radiation or advection fog, but if the wind is stronger than about 6 or 8 miles per hour, surface turbulence is usually sufficient to prevent the fog from forming at the ground level.

Clouds resulting from convective and unstable action follow the heating of the lower layers of the atmosphere. They may range in size from small cumuli to the massive cumulonimbus. If the temperature lapse rate above the condensation level is less than the moist adiabatic, the tendency for further development of the cloud will be damped by the stability, but will be assisted if the lapse rate is greater than the moist adiabatic.

Unsaturated air which is forced to ascend cools dry adiabatically about 5.5° F per 1000 feet of lift. Air circulations which are forced to ascend over hills and mountains frequently have their temperatures reduced to the dew point in this manner, either below or above the top of the high ground. If the condensation level is below the crest, the ascent above that level produces a cooling at the moist adiabatic rate, about 2.5° F per 1000 feet of lift. These clouds are usually flat-based and not very thick vertically. As the United States is in the belt of the *prevailing westerlies,* the occurrence of these clouds along the western slopes of the Pacific Coast mountains and the Allegheny Mountains is rather common. This effect must also be considered in the case of an easterly circulation along the Atlantic Coast where, although the mountains are considerably lower than the western ranges, the moisture content of an easterly circulation is considerably higher. Easterly circulations in the Rocky Mountain area produce cloudiness only during rather infrequent periods of high relative humidity for that area and during periods of fresh outbreaks of *cPk* air over the Western Plains states. This orographic lifting—i.e., due to mountain ranges—is not confined to the surface layers of the atmosphere, as this lifting would have a lifting effect on the layers immediately above, and upward for a height of several thousand feet. This action frequently results in the formation of clouds above windward slopes and the tops of hills or mountains. Over the windward side the clouds form continuously, while to the leeward of the crest, because of heating at the adiabatic rate of descending air, the clouds dissipate as fast as they form on the windward side.

We have learned previously that the general circulation of the atmosphere in the vicinity of an area of low pressure is inward toward the center, with the wind directions forming an angle of about 30 degrees with the direction of the isobars. This continued inflow, usually restricted to the lower 2000 feet, must be balanced by an outflow in the only manner possible—that is, by ascending and diverging in the upper atmosphere. Close association of converging air flow and cloud systems establishes this as one factor in cloud formation.

One of the primary causes of cloud formation, as mentioned previously, is the ascent of air as a result of frontal surfaces. In the case of the warm front, the ascent is passive and relatively uniform, generally forming a smooth cloud sheet, the elevation of which gradually increases with increasing distance from the surface position of the front. In contrast to this, in the vicinity of a cold front, more rapid, active, and forced ascent takes place due to the underrunning of the cold air and the steeper frontal surface, causing the development of cumulonimbus clouds.

Clouds may be formed, however, independently of adiabatic cooling of ascending air. As a result of uprunning of warm, moist air and its *mixing* with colder air along a warm front surface, condensation and precipitation occur. As the precipitation falls through the cold air between the frontal surface and the ground, the air gradually becomes saturated by evaporation from the falling precipitation. Saturation of this layer of air creates a low layer of fracto-stratus or fracto-cumulus clouds, extending about 200 miles or more in advance of the surface position of the warm front.

Precipitation Areas

The forecasting of precipitation is probably the most difficult duty of the meteorologist. The difficult part is not forecasting that precipitation *will* occur but in stating the time of beginning, the amount expected, and the exact nature since at times a few degrees of temperature change means the difference between rain and some form of frozen precipitation. The occurrence of precipitation—extremely serious when it causes icing conditions in the colder months of the year—is of decided importance at all times because of the resultant lowered ceiling and visibility which follow immediately. Pilots who use airports with unpaved runways should heed the occurrence of heavy precipitation or a succession of rainy days in order to avoid making a dangerous landing on a soggy or water-covered field.

In preparing the forecast of precipitation, the past history of the precipitation area must be studied on previous maps to determine whether that area is changing in size or intensity. The movement of the area through the forecast period must next be decided. A study of pilot-balloon and humidity reports will show the presence or absence of a major flow of moist air into the precipitation area. If the area is to increase in size or the precipitation in intensity, the flow of moist air from some large body of water must be maintained.

Another difficult problem is the forecasting of the place where a precipitation area will originate, as in the case of dry LOWS moving eastward across the Western Plains states into a region where the moisture content of the atmosphere is slowly increasing. No two of these situations are identical, and accurate forecasting is attained only through experience.

A knowledge of topography is a valuable asset in forecasting precipitation. Air which is forced upslope will be cooled, at times to the point of condensation and precipitation. As the main mountain ranges of this country extend in a north-south direction and as the general circulation of the atmosphere is from west to east, at right angles to these mountains, the significance of this fact is readily apparent. An example of this was cited in an earlier paragraph of this chapter concerning the Cleveland-Pittsburgh-Buffalo sector.

The process of condensation is an intermediate step between the water vapor and precipitation stages. Precipitation occurs if the convective and unstable, orographic, or frontal lifting actions are sufficiently strong to continue the process beyond the condensation stage. In the case of convection and instability, the precipitation will be in the form of showers of variable intensity, while orographic and frontal-lifting precipitation types depend on other circumstances. If the front is a warm one or if there is a gradual rise in the terrain, the precipitation will be steady and light, but when the front is cold or the terrain is steep and high, the precipitation is showery and of variable intensity. The exception to this is the occurrence of a warm-front or orographic thunderstorm when the lifting is sufficient to release the conditional instability of the atmosphere. The warm-front thunderstorms occur at relatively high levels and several hundred miles in advance of the surface front and, on account of the height of occurrence, the flying weather conditions below the thunderstorms are not necessarily unfavorable. The turbulent layer of air is usually sufficiently high to permit routine flight in most cases.

Ice Accumulation on Aircraft

In connection with condensation and precipitation, the forecaster must give proper advice on one of the serious hazards of aviation, that is, the formation of ice on aircraft while in flight.

The reason for the existence of water in the liquid state at temperatures well below freezing is not definitely known. It is sufficient to the purpose of this volume to state that it does occur, as verified by many pilots in actual experience.

The aircraft which normally flies in a horizontal plane through a sub-freezing layer of air containing supercooled drops of water attains a temperature nearer that of the air than do the falling water drops. At the instance of impact, the water drop bursts into a thin film over some surface of the aircraft and freezes instantly. This accumulation may become a serious hazard and force an aircraft down within a few minutes, so rapid is its action.

"Contact weather" pilots should make sure that sufficient ceiling exists for a safe journey over the route of their flight. "Instrument weather" pilots should not depend on air with a temperature just above freezing over the warm front surface where ice accretions will not take place unless its elevation and vertical extent are definitely known, as this is generally an extensive area of unfavorable flying weather. If the temperature in this layer is just above freezing, the non-icing layer probably is very thin and another severe icing area is just a few hundred feet higher. If the aircraft is low-powered, the best course is to descend immediately or return to the non-icing area which it has just left.

The foregoing remarks on icing are included at this point to emphasize to the pilot that this subject is one of critical importance, one to which the meteorologist must *always* give careful attention in preparing a forecast.

The matter of icing is so vital to the pilot that a chapter has been devoted to its discussion, Chapter XI.

A thorough comprehension of ice formation on aircraft is a **must** for every pilot.

Diurnal Variations

The presence of water in the atmosphere in the form of clouds or falling precipitation depends almost entirely on the amount of heat energy, or insolation, received by the lower layers from the sun. With the decided diurnal variations in the supply of this energy, it is obvious that there should be similar differences in the occurrence of these phenomena between night and day. This is proved by two meteorological conditions of importance to the pilot which occur rather frequently. The first of these is radiation or ground fog which forms and develops at night and is quickly dissipated by the heat of the sun shortly after sunrise. A more detailed discussion of radiation fog will be found on page 68. The second of these conditions is stratus fog. When the stratus deck is comparatively thin the clouds will be dissipated shortly after sunrise to recur after the next sundown, unless other changes in the composite meteorological situation occur to prevent its formation. If the stratus deck is rather thick, however, or is accompanied by a drizzle, the clearing weather will be delayed or may not occur at all during the day. But as the period of daylight progresses there is usually a slow but steady improvement in weather conditions. The drizzle will stop or become occasional, and the ceiling and visibility will slowly increase until the best conditions prevail about 2 to 4 hours before sundown. As sundown comes and passes, the drizzle increases and the ceiling and visibility lower to near zero conditions which will prevail through the night.

The occurrence of a thunderstorm or showers about sundown of a warm day is of decided importance in the formation of a stratus cloud deck or radiation fog (depending on the velocity of the wind) in the early hours of the night. The precipitation has moistened the warm ground and is now evaporated by the warm ground back into the atmosphere, which already has been cooled to near the dew point or condensation point at a time when the temperature of the air cannot again be increased by the energy of the sun. A quick consequence of this situation is a layer of stratus clouds or radiation fog.

AN ACTUAL WEATHER MAP SERIES

Thus far, in this chapter, a general though brief outline of the principal features of weather forecasting has been given. An actual series of maps at six-hour intervals from 7:30 A.M., E.S.T., March 18, to 7:30 A.M., March 19, is presented at the back of the book to show the practical application of many of these factors in forecasting. (See pages 332–336, incl.)

Data from a very large number of stations were used in preparing the original maps, but for simplicity and legibility only sufficient stations are shown, with partial data, to enable the student to understand the construction and the delineation of isobars, fronts and LOWS and HIGHS.

The problem of ice accretion on aircraft flying through weather conditions similar to the types on this series of maps is generally restricted to the area north and northwest of the center of low pressure. Ceilings elsewhere are at a sufficiently high elevation to permit operations beneath the clouds. At the time of the 7:30 A.M. map of March 18, an extensive area in which icing conditions might be anticipated exists over the Upper Lakes region. With the development of the meteorological situation during the ensuing 24 hours, this area moved eastward and maintained its position relative to the low center.

The occurrence of thunderstorms would be restricted to the vicinity of the cold front, if any occurred. Surface reports do not indicate any great degree of conditional instability of the warm air which is flowing over the warm-front surface and this would preclude the development of warm-front thunderstorms. Cold-front thunderstorms should be expected along the southern portions of the front, or at least where the humidity is higher than along the northern portions.

All pilots should heed a caution concerning flying in the vicinity of thunderstorms as issued by R. M. Stanley of the Bell Aircraft Corporation: "In closing, I would summarize approximately as follows: The interior of a thunderstorm represents a condition of extreme hazard which should never be entered by any pilot without a parachute and recent experience in blind acrobatic flight, and should never be done in an airplane other than a plane of special design incorporating high factors of safety. In fact, it would be on the side of caution to avoid flying below or in the immediate vicinity of clouds of this description due to the extremely high velocity of up-drafts existing beneath such formations and the consequent danger of being sucked up inside the cloud before the plane's air speed can have carried it away from that vicinity."

On the map of 7:30 A.M., E.S.T., March 18, crests of high pressure are located over the central Rocky Mountain section, the St. Lawrence River valley, and the Florida peninsula, while the center of a low pressure area overlies Illinois and Indiana. A cold front extends inland from the Atlantic Ocean through southern Virginia, then curves northwestward and becomes a warm front in the vicinity of Gordonsville. The warm front continues to just east of Pittsburgh, north of Cleveland and Toledo, and becomes a cold front again in the vicinity of Fort Wayne, whence it continues southwestward just east of St. Louis, west of Fort Smith, Ark., east of Fort Worth, and south of Big Spring, ending north of Alpine, Texas.

There is very little bad flying weather in the vicinity of this depression. It should be noted that the warm sector, in the Ohio valley area, is rather broad on this map. This indicates a continued supply of warm, moist air with a consequent increase in the intensity of the storm. The highest pressure in the crests and the lowest pressure in the disturbance should be remembered in order that a comparison may be made when the succeeding map is studied.

On the map of 1:30 P.M., E.S.T., March 18, the center of the disturbance is located just west of Detroit, where a pressure reading of 1002.4 millibars indicates that the center has deepened somewhat from the central pressure of about 1006.8 millibars at 7:30 A.M. The crest of the high pressure over the St. Lawrence River has fallen from about 1021 millibars to about 1016 millibars as a result of the northeastward movement of the disturbance. Slight falls are recorded in the crests of the other high-pressure areas but these falls are mostly diurnal. There has been little change in the pressure gradient except in the eastern Middle Atlantic States, where it has become steeper (indicated by the isobars moving closer together). This will cause an increase in wind velocity.

The front, both cold and warm, has become stationary through the Virginias and in western Pennsylvania but has continued its northward movement as a warm front over Lake Erie. It becomes a cold front just west of Detroit and continues thus southwestward just east of Indianapolis, and Advance, Mo., and west of Shreveport, La., and Corpus Christi, Tex. The warm sector now is not nearly so broad as it was six hours previously; this indicates that the cold front is slowly overtaking the warm front. Their meeting will shut off the supply of warm, moist air to the storm area and cause the occlusion and eventual end of the storm center.

A new development on this map is the formation of a secondary cold front from northwestern Minnesota south-southwestward just east of Fargo and ending just west of Valentine, Neb. The presence of this front is indicated by the pressure rises to the west of the front compared to the pressure falls to the east, and by the southwest to northwest wind shift which is present. Secondary cold fronts which develop in these pressure systems are attended by much better flying weather than the primary front, as the primary front has displaced the warm, moist air far to the south and east and any period of low ceilings, low visibilities, or precipitation will be rather brief, and not so intense when compared with the conditions prevalent with the passage of a primary cold front.

On this map, the size of the unfavorable flying weather area has increased and now includes lower Michigan, eastern Indiana, and northwestern Ohio, with indications of another slight increase in size resulting from the continued inflow of warm, moist air.

On the map of 7:30 P.M., the center of the depression has continued its rather rapid movement east-northeastward and is located over western Lake Ontario. The stationary front in Virginia has become a warm front and moved northward a little, while the warm front through Pennsylvania has moved eastward to the central portion of the State. The front becomes a cold one in the vicinity of Buffalo and continues as such southwestward just west of Pittsburgh and just east of Parkersburg, W. Va., thence just east of Winchester, Ky., where a warm wave has developed. The front again becomes cold in the vicinity of Nashville and continues southwestward, becoming stationary from Houston to the Mexican border. The eastward movement of the cold front had been more rapid than that of the warm front and the width of the warm sector is now just about half the width of six hours before. The continuation of this decreasing width (and there is no evidence on the map to indicate any other tendency) will cause the cold front to overtake the warm front in about six more hours, or by the next map period.

The size of the bad flying weather area has continued to increase and now includes northern Kentucky, eastern Ohio, western Pennsylvania, western New York, and southeastern Ontario. On account of the occlusion of the warm front which should occur in about six hours, the size of this area should not increase much by the time of the next map. But, a detailed study of this map brings out another detail of importance. Pressure changes are often indicative of developing conditions. The pressure at Gordonsville, Va., is steadily falling, with a net change for the three preceding hours of 5 millibars lower, a rather large amount when compared to the amount of change at neighboring stations. This indicates the formation of a secondary storm center, the forecast of which would be further borne out by the direction of the wind at adjacent stations. This formation would result in bad flying weather in the north and east quadrants of the new storm center and accordingly must be forecast.

The best evidence so far found as to the formation of such a secondary disturbance is an incipient cyclonic circulation of the wind or a localized 12-hour pressure fall in the southern end of the trough. The formation of a wave is the earliest symptom and the pressure fall is next. The primary which is in the process of occlusion begins to lose intensity in most cases shortly after the secondary develops, filling up gradually after the secondary reaches a full stage of activity. In a few cases both primary and secondary increase in intensity, but later the primary decreases and the secondary increases further. The best development takes place when the primary moves rather slowly. With primaries of northern origin when the movement is slightly southeast instead of east, the development of the secondary is marked.

The secondary cold front which made its appearance on the preceding map has continued its southeastward movement and lengthened slightly, and now extends from western Lake Superior southwestward to Grand Island, Neb. At the present time, there is no bad flying weather in the vicinity of this front, except near Lake Superior, and there is no evidence of the formation of any appreciable amount thereof, as the front is moving into an area of rather dry air, and the surface temperature discontinuity is hardly noticeable.

The areas of high pressure over the eastern portion of the country have continued to weaken under the influence of the eastward-moving low-pressure area. The cold air supply to the high pressure area over the Western plains states has been cut off or weakened and the crest is spreading and weakening. The pressure gradient west of the cold front has decreased slightly and this tendency will continue.

The map of 1:30 A.M., March 19, reveals the development of some meteorological conditions expected from the 7:30 P.M. map preceding. The main storm center continued its rapid movement and is central in southern Quebec, the exact location being indefinite because of the lack of observational data. The secondary center has developed and has moved to the Delaware Bay area at map time in the vicinity of which rather sharp pressure falls have occurred. Lack of observational data precludes the further study of the primary center, which will continue its journey to the northeastward. As the usual direction of travel of secondary centers is northeastward, the forecast should be based on this fact, with the amount of travel a little more than was shown in the preceding six hours from the vicinity of Gordonsville. This slight increase in rate of movement will be due to the storm center's approaching and passing over a large body of water. Some increase in the intensity of the storm center should also result from the rather broad warm sector which has developed.

As expected, the cold front has overtaken the warm front and the occluded front now extends between the primary and secondary centers through eastern New York and central New Jersey. The warm front previously through southeastern Virginia has moved northward and now extends eastward from just south of Atlantic City. The cold front runs from the secondary center southwestward just west of Roanoke, through Atlanta, and west of New Orleans and Brownsville. The main development in the frontal situation has been the broadening of the warm sector of the secondary low pressure area. This warm sector will supply warm, moist air to the secondary center for from 36 to 72 hours and thus assist its development.

On account of the lack of observations over the Atlantic Ocean, the size of the area of bad flying weather cannot be determined accurately, but, owing to the secondary center development, it now includes eastern New York, and Pennsylvania, New Jersey, Delaware and Maryland, and the northern portion of the Virginias. With the increased rate of movement and intensity of the secondary center, the area of bad flying weather will probably be extended through most of New England, while there should be improvement in weather conditions in the western portion of the above area.

The secondary cold front has continued its eastward movement to eastern Lake Superior southwestward to Moline and then westward to its end, southwest of Omaha. There is still no bad flying weather in connection with its passage except in the vicinity of Lake Superior, and with little discontinuity in temperature and humidity existing, the status quo should be maintained.

The high-pressure area over eastern New England has continued to lose its strength while those over the Florida peninsula and the Western plains states have changed little. The southwestern HIGH is continuing a slow eastward drift.

The final map of the series, at 7:30 A.M., March 19, shows the continuation of the eastward drift of all the conditions of the map at 1:30 A.M. The secondary center has moved northeastward to Rhode Island; its frontal structure remains the same relative to the storm center. The secondary cold front extends southwesterly from Haileybury, Ont., passing southeast of Grand Rapids, Mich., and Chicago, Ill., then south of Kirksville, Mo., and thence slightly northwest to its end, north of Concordia, Kans. Good flying weather continues except in the vicinity of Lake Huron and northward. Another secondary cold front which was just in the field of observation at 1:30 A.M., has continued to move eastward and now lies northeast and southwest over the Dakotas. This front will follow the same course and be attended by much the same weather conditions as its predecessor. A small crest of high pressure over Iowa now separates the two cold fronts.

It has been shown in an earlier chapter that the density of the air depends to a large extent on the temperature of the atmosphere. A study of barometric tendencies of a station in a warm air mass and then in a cold air mass well illustrates this point. Such a station in this series of maps is Indianapolis, which at 7:30 A.M., March 18, was in the warm sector; the tendency was rising, then falling. On the map 6 hours later, the station was just in the edge of the cold air mass. The tendency was falling, then rising. The falling tendency occurred while the station was in the warm air mass and the rising tendency took place with the advent of the colder, denser air after the passage of the cold front. On the map at 7:30 P.M., the pressure was continuing to rise as the colder air continued its eastward flow. A further slight rise took place as the colder air mass continued its eastward course.

After studying this series of maps, some may get the idea that the problem of forecasting is not difficult or involved. It is hoped, however, that the novice will realize that this series is one in which expected conditions followed the normal and usual courses and was selected for that reason. Complicated situations often defy correct analysis by even the best meteorologists.

QUESTIONS

1. At what three things must a good forecaster be particularly adept?
2. Of what value to the forecaster is a knowledge of the topography of the forecasting area?
3. In making a forecast why is it desirable also to study the weather maps of at least the two preceding forecast periods?
4. How is a change in the pressure gradient shown from one map to the next?
5. What is indicated by an increase in the pressure gradient from one map to the next?
6. What is indicated by a flat gradient?
7. How is the future trend determined in the intensity of areas of high and low pressure?
8. What is meant by "blocking effects"?
9. What is the usual result of "blocking effects"?
10. What is the average daily movement of highs and lows in winter and summer?
11. What meteorological conditions affect the movements of highs and lows?
12. How does the nature of the terrain (topographic conditions) affect movements of highs and lows?
13. Is the intensity of highs and lows greater in winter or in summer? What effect does this have on pressure gradient and wind velocities?
14. What condition frequently occurs near the crest of a high in summer? Does this occur in winter?

Chapter XI

ICE FORMATION ON AIRCRAFT

In spite of the progress that has been made toward overcoming the formation of ice on aircraft, condensation at near-freezing temperatures still remains one of the greatest hazards of flight. Prior to the development of instrumental methods for air navigation, no serious difficulty due to icing was experienced because severe icing occurs only in bad weather. The icing hazard has steadily become more serious as developments in instruments and aircraft have permitted operation under more severe weather conditions.

This hazard may result from any combination of the following factors:

(*a*) Increased weight due to the ice accumulation.
(*b*) Loss of lift and added drag due to deformation of the wing contour by the encrusted ice, and the building up of ice on projections in the air stream.
(*c*) Loss of thrust due to deformation of the propeller contour by the encrusted ice.
(*d*) Loss of engine power due to formation of ice in the carburetor or jet engine intake.
(*e*) Loss of control due to jamming of controls by ice accumulation between main and control surfaces.
(*f*) Destructive vibration due to uneven formation or breaking off of ice on the propeller.
(*g*) Icing of instrument system pitot head tubes.
(*h*) Icing of radio and radar masts, antennae, etc.
(*i*) Icing of windshields.

The formation of ice on an airplane is due to the presence of liquid water in the atmosphere which freezes after being deposited on the airplane. The heaviest deposits usually occur on the leading edges of all surfaces, but under certain conditions horizontal surfaces may also become coated with ice. Although the additional weight of the ice is of importance in reducing the airplane's performance, the most serious effect is the deformation of the airfoil, which increases the drag and reduces the lift. In some cases, ice has jammed the control surfaces, but this has now been largely overcome by proper design. Ice formations on the propeller may cause severe vibrations due to the unequal removal of the ice by centrifugal force. Such vibrations may be so severe as to require a reduction in power to prevent structural failure. Under icing conditions an airplane tends to become unstable and will ultimately become uncontrollable. In extremely heavy icing this may occur in a matter of two to three minutes, so that it is essential that the pilot take the correct steps immediately.

In addition to the above effects on the flight characteristics, icing conditions also affect the operation of the external parts of flight instruments, such as air speed heads and radio antennas. Windshields also become coated and, although this is not serious in flight, a clear windshield is still considered essential for a safe landing.

Ice deposits also frequently form in the carburetor and other portions of the intake piping. This is a somewhat different problem because ice may form in these parts at air temperatures well above freezing and in fine weather. Carburetor ice is principally sublimed water vapor which forms because of the expansional cooling and the cooling due to the evaporation of the gasoline. Liquid water in the atmosphere may considerably aggravate carburetor icing difficulties, but is not the primary cause of it.

The effects described in general above will be discussed in detail in the latter part of this chapter.

Although methods have been developed for reducing the hazards of icing, none of these is effective indefinitely under severe icing conditions, and it is of the utmost importance that meteorologists understand the synoptic situations conducive to icing so that they may forecast its occurrence and aid in the selection of the optimum flight path. In order to understand the purely meteorological aspects of the problem it is first essential to consider the physics of the deposition of the ice.

PHYSICS OF ICING

As stated above, ice accretion usually results from the freezing of liquid water drops contained in the atmosphere after they are deposited on the surface of an airplane. Occasionally ice may be formed by the direct sublimation of water vapor, as when an airplane descends from a cold layer to a relatively warm and moist layer. This type of ice is called "frost feathers," is very light and fragile and never forms in large amounts in flight, since the airplane rapidly attains the temperature of its new environment. Heavy deposits occasionally occur on aircraft stored in the open, but this type of ice is not of sufficient importance to warrant an extended discussion.

Because of expansional cooling of air passing over the airfoil, it is possible to have ice form while flying in air with ambient temperature from 32° to 36° F. Ice formation is most common, however, at temperatures from 34° to 5° F (1° to — 15° C), heavy icing being experienced between 15° and 34° F, and the most frequent and most severe between 26° and 34° F.

Since atmospheric ice particles do not cause ice accretion on airplanes, it follows that most icing is due to the deposition of supercooled drops of water on the surfaces. There is considerable evidence of the existence of supercooled water drops in the atmosphere. Most clouds with temperatures above 15° F are composed of water drops, and water clouds have been observed at temperatures as low as — 60° F. Rain drops are often supercooled several degrees, as is evidenced by the occurrence of sleet storms at the surface, and this must be more common in the free atmosphere. It might be noted that it is a relatively simple matter to supercool ordinary tap water in a beaker to — 5° C or — 10° C. Supercooled water is in an unstable or metastable equilibrium, but little is known about the mechanism which will finally produce freezing. It appears that the impact of a supercooled drop on an airplane inevitably initiates the freezing process. It should be noted that the freezing will not be instantaneous, both because the process of crystalization takes time and because the latent heat of fusion must be absorbed. Since the latent heat of fusion of water is about 80 calories per gram, it is clear that the fraction $(1 - t/80)$ of the latent heat must be given up to the environment before freezing is complete, where t is the numerical value of the air temperature in °C.

Three types of ice are recognized: *rime, glaze* (or clear ice) and *frost*. *Rime* is a white, opaque ice of relatively low mass per unit volume. It is friable, often rough, and is apparently composed of a large number of relatively small crystals very loosely held together and with numerous air spaces both between the separate crystals and within the crystals themselves. *Glaze* or clear ice has a solid or continuous structure and may be perfectly clear or it may be opaque due to the inclusion of minute air bubbles. All intermediate forms occur and alternate layers of rime and glaze are often observed. *Frost* is a light, whitish, feathery, crystalline structure of snowlike character. It is similar to frost observed on objects on the ground in the early morning, most commonly in the cooler season of the year following rather humid nights when the surface temperature falls below 32° F. It is formed when the aircraft passes quickly from air at temperature well below 32° F into air which is considerably warmer and of relatively high humidity. The frost deposits when the warm water vapor is chilled suddenly below its fusion temperature (i.e., its dew point for ice) by contact with the very cold surface of the aircraft and sublimates thereon (i.e., passes directly from the vapor to the solid state). Frost deposits are thin. They thaw readily and evaporate quickly as flight is continued in warm air. Frost also may form suddenly on wind shields, but it usually takes longer to thaw and evaporate because the glass windshield warms up more slowly than the metal wing surfaces. Frost may form on the top wing surfaces of aircraft that have been parked in the open overnight without covers when sub-freezing temperatures occur.

Cases of rime outnumber cases of glaze three or four to one. Since rime is more readily removed with the present type of de-icing equipment, glaze is the more serious type. It is observed that freezing rain always produces glaze, whereas clouds may produce either glaze or rime. Very thin clouds usually produce rime. Ice deposits are always heaviest at the leading edge, but rime forms *only* on the leading edge or on small irregularities, such as rivet heads, while glaze may extend back over the horizontal surfaces. The form of the deposit on the leading edge may be blunt or pointed, and there is often evidence of a minimum deposit near the stagnation point with a maximum above and below. Some writers have stated that one shape is characteristic of rime and another of glaze, but it is believed that a deposit of either rime or glaze may build up in any of these shapes, depending on the conditions.

The rate of ice accretion depends upon the combination of a large number of factors but principally depends upon the airspeed, size of the water droplets, density of visible water, and the shape and size of the external area of the airplane. The rate of icing is generally expressed in terms of the rate of increase of the thickness of the deposit in the direction of flight and at the thickest point. The rate is expressed in inches per minute. It has been known to increase as much as 1 inch per minute. The most frequent rate is about $\frac{1}{32}$ inch per minute. Observed icing rates seem to be consistent with our knowledge of the amount of water available in the atmosphere and the aerodynamics of drop deposition.

Although the aerodynamics of the deposition of drops on an airfoil is exceedingly complex, a qualitative discussion is sufficient to bring out the significant factors. For this purpose it is convenient to consider the wing as stationary with respect to the air and the suspended water drops having a velocity equal to the speed of the airplane. The streamlines about an airfoil are illustrated schematically in Figure 11–1. As a suspended water drop approaches the airfoil, it is acted upon by two forces. One is the inertia force which tends to project it along a straight line. As soon as the drop deviates from the streamline on which it was initially located, it acquires a velocity relative to the air and is therefore subjected to a resisting force which tends to move the drop back toward the streamline. Now the inertia force is proportional to the radius of the drop and to the relative velocity of the drop and the air. This means that for large drops the inertia force predominates and the drops travel in nearly straight lines, while the

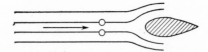

Fig. 11–1. Suspended droplets in streamlines about an airfoil.

small drops are controlled primarily by the resisting force of the air and tend to follow the streamlines.

The size of the airfoil is as important as the size of the drops. Thus, if the airfoil shown in Figure 11–1 were doubled, the streamlines would change in proportion, so that the effect would be simply a change in the scale of the drawing. However, the actual size of the drop would remain the same, and it would therefore appear relatively smaller when drawn to the new reduced scale. Thus a drop of given size will be deflected more by a large airfoil than by a small one. The physical reason for this is that the deflecting force of the air acts over a longer distance in the case of the larger airfoil.

Because of the deflecting action of the airflow, not all of the drops in the volume swept out by the airfoil will be deposited thereon. It follows from the discussion in previous paragraphs that the fraction of the drops in the swept volume actually intercepted by the airfoil will be smaller for small drops and for large airfoils. The effect of the size of the airfoil on the rate of deposition is readily observable, particularly when the icing is due to cloud drops. In such cases, the ice will usually build up most rapidly on small surfaces, such as struts and wires, and relatively much more slowly on the wing. Antenna wires may often collect sufficient ice to cause failure before the pilot begins to observe ice on the wings.

It is next in order to consider the freezing process which occurs after the drops are deposited on the airplane surface. As pointed out above, only a fraction of the latent heat of fusion can be absorbed in raising the temperature of the drop to the freezing point. It is generally assumed that, on impact, a supercooled drop starts to freeze immediately, the latent heat raising the temperature until the freezing point is reached. Since the supercooling in degrees is normally small compared to the latent heat of fusion, only a small fraction of the drop can be frozen in this manner. To freeze the remainder of the drop the latent heat of fusion must be removed in other ways. There are three possible ways in which this heat can be removed from the drop. These are conductive cooling to the air stream, conduction to the airplane surface and cooling due to the evaporation of the drop. All of these processes depend on the temperature difference between the drop and the air, although evaporation cooling could occur in the absence of the initial heating if the relative humidity is less than 100%. Computations for typical conditions indicate that the conduction of heat away from the drop to the airplane surface is large compared to the other two heat losses. Evaporative cooling is undoubtedly relatively more important in cases of icing in freezing rain because the air is seldom saturated. Evaporative cooling is also the sole explanation for the formation of ice at temperatures above freezing, as occasionally reported.

The time required for a drop to freeze evidently depends on the temperature difference between the drop and its environment and on the size of the drop. Now if the freezing time is less than the time between successive arrivals of drops at the same spot, the drops will tend to freeze separately, and it is possible that rime is formed this way. If the freezing time is greater than the time between successive drops, the drops will merge and form a continuous sheet of water which will tend to freeze from the under surface due to conductive cooling. This process would presumably lend to glaze or clear ice. Simple computations made on this basis show that under normal conditions, rime can be formed only in clouds, which is in agreement with observations. Rime formation is favored by small drops, a small amount of liquid water per unit volume of air and low temperatures.

There is one other effect which should be included in any complete study of the freezing process. There is a pressure rise in the air immediately in front of any object moving through the air. This has a maximum at the so-called stagnation point where it has the value of $\frac{1}{2}pv^2$, where p is the air density and v is the velocity of the object relative to the air at a distance from the object. Assuming an adiabatic temperature rise, it is readily found that the pressure rise at 100 m/sec (224 mph) will produce a temperature rise of about 4.8° C (8.7° F). This is the maximum temperature rise which could occur at the stagnation point. The mean rise would be considerably less, but still large enough to be of some importance. There are regions of negative pressure above the horizontal wing surfaces, but measurements have indicated that there is an actual temperature rise over these portions of the wing, presumably due to skin friction. Adiabatic heating of the air appears to be an important factor in the case of propellers, the temperature rise being sufficient to prevent the formation of ice on the outer portions of the blades.

SYNOPTIC CONSIDERATIONS

As noted before, icing occurs in supercooled clouds and in freezing rain. Although there is no lower temperature limit, icing is uncommon at temperatures below about 5° F (— 15° C).   Since ice cannot form at ambient air temperatures higher than about + 36° F (2° C), it is apparent that the temperature is an extremely important item to consider in forecasting icing. It is observed that the highest icing rates occur at the higher temperatures within the range.   Assuming a normal lapse rate of about 3.3° F/1000 ft (6° C/km), the layer within which icing is probable is about 8000 ft (2.5 km) deep.

Icing is most common and most severe in regions of frontal activity and in regions where conditionally unstable air is subjected to orographic lifting.   Statistical investigations by Lacy, Hallanger and McNeal have definitely indicated that icing is most common in actively unstable air.   Thus Lacy reports that in 30 cases of icing the lapse rate averaged 0.5° F/ 1000 ft (0.9° C/km) greater than the moist adiabatic, while in 20 cases of non-icing clouds the lapse rate averaged 0.3° F/ 1000 ft (0.5° C/km) less than the moist adiabatic.

It is generally assumed that rain can only be formed at temperatures above the freezing point.   It follows that icing due to freezing rain can occur only in the presence of a temperature inversion with freezing temperatures below and temperatures higher than freezing above.   This situation may often occur below a warm front.

The discussion of the physics of icing showed that the most important factor determining the rate of icing was the amount of liquid water in the air.   The meteorological processes which release the maximum amount of water are those which involve rapid lifting.   Any process which causes the air to become actively unstable meets this condition.   This conclusion is in agreement with the observations outlined above. Active instability generally results from the lifting of convectionally unstable air masses at frontal surfaces or orographically.   Local convection of the type which produces cumulus clouds probably leads to icing conditions within the appropriate temperature range.   However, aircraft do not fly through active cumulus because of the extreme turbulence, and icing reports in cumulus clouds of this type are rare.

In view of the above discussion, the factors which should be considered in forecasting the occurrence of icing and in selecting the optimum flight path are as follows:

1. Icing may occur in any cloud or rain area in which the temperature is less than about 36° F (2° C), but it is less likely at temperatures below 5° F (— 15° C).

2. The stability of the air mass is of great importance in connection with a consideration of the probability of frontal or orographic lifting.

3. The wind velocity is important, since it determines the rate of forced lifting.

4. Particular attention should be given to frontal regions. Icing is apt to occur in all types of frontal cloud systems, but particularly in the convective clouds in advance of a cold front and the convective clouds above a warm front when the warm air is convectively unstable. Icing due to freezing rain may be expected beneath the warm front when the ground temperature is near the freezing point and rain is falling.

5. Forced lifting at mountain ranges is conducive to icing, particularly if the air is convectively unstable. A combination of frontal activity and orographic lifting represents an extreme hazard.

6. Conditions for icing are similar to those for precipitation, and in the absence of upper air data the precipitation areas may be used as a guide.

7. Other things being equal, the icing will be more severe in air with a high specific humidity than in drier air.

8. Although icing may occur at any season, it is most frequent in the winter in temperate climates. This is due not only to the lower temperatures but to the increased frontal activity. In higher latitudes, icing may be less severe in winter than in the spring and fall, because of the small amount of

water vapor available. Also, at temperatures below about 5° F (— 15° C) most of the clouds are composed of ice crystals.

9. Icing is most frequent and severe around the mean latitude of the polar front and in mountainous regions.

10. If a flight through a frontal zone in which icing is expected is necessary, the flight should be conducted at as high an altitude as possible. If the front is near the take-off point it may be necessary to fly away from the front until altitude is gained. Similarly, if the front is near the terminal, it may be advisable to go by at a high altitude and to let down beyond the terminal.

11. In all cases, flight paths should avoid the juncture of a front and a mountain range unless the flight can take place above the major cloud systems.

12. Since the zone of *severe* icing is seldom deeper than 6500 ft (2 km) at most, because of the temperature limits, it is usually possible to get out of unexpected icing by reducing or increasing altitude. If sufficient ground clearance is available, it is preferable to decrease altitude, since this is more readily accomplished, particularly if ice is forming rapidly.

13. If ice is forming rapidly and it is not possible to reduce altitude, it is better to turn back before attempting to get above the ice.

LOCATION OF ICING ZONES

Ice may form on aircraft parked on the ground, during take-off, during contact flight or during instrument flight through clouds.

The following types of ice formation can occur while aircraft are **on the ground** or **taking off**:

1. Frost may form on the top surfaces at night when the aircraft is left in the open and the temperature falls to 32° F or below with high humidity present.

2. Ice may form on the wings or tail surfaces due to water splash when the aircraft breaks through ice-crusted pools during take-off or taxi. Splash may also ice up brakes or landing gear retracting mechanism.

3. Ice may form on the propeller during warm up if the temperature and dew point are close together and near freezing or if a fog is present and the temperature is 32° F or below.

4. Freezing rain may form on the surfaces of the aircraft if it is allowed to stand in the open during an ice storm.

5. Controls may freeze due to moisture which has collected in and about the hinges.

6. Refrozen precipitation can occur when an aircraft is brought out of a warm hangar into a snow storm. The snow first melts while the surfaces of the aircraft are warm and later freezes as they cool off.

7. Ice-coated runways formed by ice storm or freezing rain are dangerous during maneuvering while on the ground.

During contact flight the most probable type of ice formation is that which forms due to freezing rain. This would usually be a *glaze,* or *clear ice* formation, but it may also be mixed with snow or soft hail producing a rough and jagged appearance. The temperature will be below freezing, although due to calibration errors and expansional cooling, the wing strut thermometer or free air thermometer may read as high as 36° F.

During instrument flight all types of ice may occur when the free air temperature is 36° F or lower and the plane is flying through cloud or rain. Freezing rain and clouds composed of large droplets usually produce a glaze formation, while fog or clouds with small droplets give rime formation. Convective type clouds such as cumulus or active frontal clouds are normally composed of large droplets. Stable air clouds such as stratus or fog have small droplets.

A summary of certain precepts to be used in avoiding ice formation aloft are given by Minser.*

1. The regions of most severe icing are associated with frontal surfaces.

2. Vertical convection sustains large water droplets and thereby induces severe icing, provided temperatures are be-

* Minser, Edward J., Chief Meteorologist, Transcontinental & Western Air, Inc.

low freezing. Cloudiness associated with strong convection should therefore be avoided.

3. Temperature inversions to above freezing do not always exist above ice-forming regions, even when freezing rain occurs, and **escape from ice by climbing should not be attempted unless existence of above-freezing temperatures at higher levels is definitely known.**

4. Ice evaporates very slowly in clear, cold air, and an accumulation of ice induces rapid collection of more ice if descent is made through a cloud deck in which liquid droplets predominate and the temperature is 32° F or lower.

5. When uncertain of ice distribution in clouds, flight in clear air above the clouds is the safest flight path. If possible, the flight path on climb and descent should be through broken or thin clouds remote from the frontal surface.

6. A thorough study of the latest synoptic weather map to determine the position, slope, and tendency of fronts before flight is attempted is the only means by which ice-forming regions may be located and the probable intensity of icing determined.

7. The falling of precipitation (especially drizzle, snow, sleet, etc.) from a cloud is indicative of ice formation therein if the cloud is presumably or known to be at or below 32° F.

NOTE.—Since rime is more prevalent than glaze at temperatures below 15° F if flight must be made in stratiform clouds where subfreezing temperatures exist, it is generally preferable to fly at heights where the temperatures are below 15° F than at temperatures between 15° and 32° F.

Icing in cumuliform clouds. The vertical motions which give cumuliform clouds their characteristic appearance, support large droplets and make the formation of clear ice more frequent in this type of cloud. Cumuliform clouds form in unstable air. Therefore, clear ice is more apt to form in clouds in unstable air than in stable air. The instability may be due to steep lapse rates or mechanical turbulence caused by large vertical velocity gradients. Mountains may have some effect in producing instability within an air mass by causing the potentially unstable air to be lifted to its saturation level. *mT* air is often characterized by its potential instability, hence *the combination of temperatures near freezing, Tg air with its large water content, and mountains is almost sure to produce icing conditions.* This combination of factors occurs in winter particularly over the Appalachian Mountains. In winter, *mP* air contains considerable moisture in its lower levels by the time it reaches our Pacific coast and is also unstable in the lower levels. *When mP air crosses the Cascade, Sierra Nevada, and Rocky Mountains, serious icing conditions frequently result.*

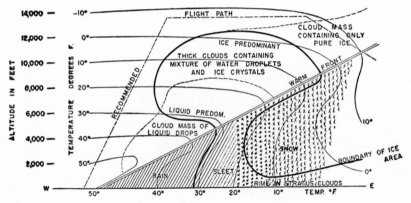

FIG. 11–2   A warm front icing situation.

Icing along fronts. About 85 per cent of the observed icing of aircraft has occurred in frontal zones. Typical *warm front clouds* (Fig. 11–2) are stratiform in character and rapid movement up the warm front may contain only a small vertical component, but the small lift of a great mass of warm air may produce thick cloud systems and heavy precipitation with larger drops than otherwise might be expected from stratiform clouds. The potential instability of the warm mass may be released to form cumuliform clouds. Clear ice or a combination of clear ice and rime may result. Warm front cloud systems are often of great extent, thereby causing flights in them to be of long duration with a subsequent increased danger of severe icing.

The overrunning warm air may be above 32° F in the lower levels and thus prevent icing in that region. If clouds in the warm air are thick and the temperature just above the frontal surface is only a few degrees above zero, the upper portion of this cloud system may well be considerably below 32° F, thus *providing a transition zone within the cloud system that is conducive to icing.*

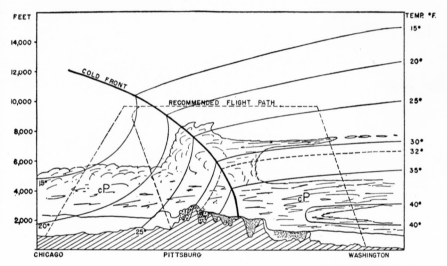

FIG. 11–3. Recommended flight path between Chicago or Pittsburgh and Washington with a cold front over the Appalachian Mountains.

Cold fronts are associated with cumuliform clouds, and hence are more apt to cause clear ice. The cold front cloud system is relatively narrow compared to the warm front system so that the period during which icing may take place on a flight across the frontal zone is shorter. However, the combination of clear ice and a higher rate of accumulation makes cold front icing zones extremely hazardous (Fig. 11–3).

Icing over mountains. Icing is more probable and more severe in mountainous areas. Mountain ranges cause upward motions on their windward side in air that is moving across them. Vertical motions over the ridges will support large droplets. The most severe icing will take place above the crests and to the windward side of the ridges (Fig. 11–4). The zone extends usually about 4000 feet above the tops of the mountains but in the case of unstable air may even be higher.

The movement of a front across mountains brings together two important factors that aid in the formation of icing zones. A study of icing in the Western United States has shown that almost all of the ice cases occurred where the air was blowing over a mountain slope or up a frontal surface or both.

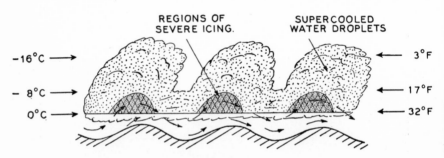

FIG. 11–4. Section across parallel ridges showing regions of severe icing.

EFFECTS OF ICE ON AIRCRAFT

The pilot should be thoroughly familiar with the weather and temperature conditions which may cause ice to form on his aircraft, but equally as important is an understanding of what is happening to the plane when an unexpected icing condition is encountered. A knowledge of the effect of ice formation on the flying characteristics of the plane will in most instances enable the pilot to quickly readjust his flight procedure to meet the increased demands which are placed upon the aircraft.

Remember it is always well to have an "out." Know which way to turn to get out of an icing condition. A study of the weather map and latest hourly weather sequence, together with a meteorologist's interpretation of the radiosonde data, is always desirable before any long flight is begun. This means cross-country as well as local flying when the flight remains aloft for extended periods and icing conditions are imminent.

It should, of course, be stated here that *light planes not equipped with full de-icing equipment are better off in the hangar when icing conditions are present.* Cases have been reported where ships without wing or propeller de-icers have been forced down out of control after less than 5 minutes' flight through an icing region.

When ice forms on an aircraft it can affect the flying characteristics in several ways.

1. *Ice on wings* and exposed surfaces produces the following:

   (*a*) **Loss of lift.**—This is caused by a deformation of the airfoil by ice which is frozen on the leading edges. The plane will stall at air speeds well above the normal stalling point.

   (*b*) **Added drag.**—This also produces an undesirable effect when rough ice forms back of leading edges and on protuberances.

   (*c*) **Added weight.**—This item is not usually as important as the first two but when weight is added and all of the other factors are at work it will be a contributing hazard.

2. *Propeller icing* is also one of the types of ice which according to some pilots is by far the most important. The propeller blades collect ice in the same way as the wings, with ice building out on the leading edge. Two important effects are observed.

   (*a*) **Loss of propeller efficiency.**—This immediately produces a hazard since a reduction in propeller efficiency produced by a distortion due to uneven ice formation on the blades and vibration means a loss of effective power. Under icing conditions all available power may be needed.

(*b*) **Vibration.**—This is caused when ice forms unevenly on propeller blades or when one blade throws off ice, producing an unbalanced condition. The vibration produced is harmful to the engines, engine mounts, and the whole structure.

3. *Freezing of controls* is important when the plane has been flying in rain and then enters a freezing zone or when the ship has been washed and removed from a warm hangar and outside air temperature is below freezing.

4. *Icing of pitot tubes* is important in that the airspeed indicator will fail when the pitot ices up. Turn indicator, rate of climb and other instruments connected to static side of pitot tube will also be affected.

5. *Frost* can be considered under the section on Ice on Wings, but since it is a type which collects on the top surfaces of the plane while it is on the ground, it has a slightly different category. The fine crystalline structure is often hardly visible but the increase in drag and air-flow distortion which it produces make the take-off characteristic very bad. The ship may not even be able to get off the ground and if it does the flight characteristics will be materially affected.

6. *Windshield icing* is dangerous since it restricts forward vision from the cockpit.

7. *Radio system icing.* In addition to unsatisfactory operation of range receivers and direction finders, due to precipitation static interference encountered during snowstorms and other icing conditions, ice can cause mechanical failure of the antennas. Severe ice accretion on radio antenna masts and wires produces heavy aerodynamic loads on these parts which may fail mechanically under such stresses.

8. *Fuel tank vents.* Fuel tank vents constitute a problem in military planes because their self-sealing fuel cells require a positive pressure inside to keep them from collapsing and from syphoning fuel through the vents. The pressure scoops must, therefore, be kept free from ice.

SAFETY SUMMARY

Some *DONT'S* for Safety Under Icing Conditions

ON THE GROUND:

1. Don't attempt take-off with any frost on wings or tail surfaces.
2. Don't attempt take-off with any loose snow on the wing or tail surfaces as it may be covering a hard ice formation caused by melted snow which has refrozen. Loose snow may also pack between the ailerons and the wings.
3. Don't taxi fast over pools of water when temperature is near freezing; splash may form ice on wings and stabilizer or the splash may ice up brakes or retracting mechanism of landing gear.
4. Don't take off without first testing all controls to insure that hinges have not frozen.
5. Don't warm up engine in a fog when temperature is near freezing. Ice may form on propeller and on wing and on stabilizer in back of propeller blast.
6. Don't attempt take-off with any ice on the airplane or propeller.
7. Don't take off into a known icing condition when plane is not equipped with all modern de-icing and anti-icing aids.
8. Don't plan flights through continuous icing zones even though ship is equipped with all de-icing and anti-icing aids.

9. Don't taxi fast on an ice-coated runway or taxi strip.
10. Don't apply brakes suddenly on an ice-coated runway after plane is on the ground.   Use full effective runway.   Radio for condition of runway before landing.
11. Don't take off during a wet snow condition.

Protection and removal while on the ground:

1. Keep plane in heated hangar if possible.
2. Filter gas through chamois or water separator.   Water particles may freeze in gas line when ship is taken out.
3. Wing covers and engine covers should be used if plane is kept in the open.
4. Cover pitot tube with loose rag to keep out snow during snow storm or blowing snow.   String from rag to block would insure removal before take-off.
5. Rubber scraper should be used to remove frost.   Waste rags may also be used.
6. Snow or frost may be removed by throwing a rope or strip of canvas over the wing and with a man on each end the snow may be "sawed off."
7. Removal of ice by application of hot water is not advised.   It will only freeze again and may produce a worse condition than before application.

IN THE AIR:

1. Don't continue flight into a region of known icing conditions.
2. Don't fly through rain showers or wet snow when temperature at flight level is near freezing.
3. Don't fly parallel to a front under icing conditions.
4. Don't fly into clouds at a low altitude above the crests of ridges or mountains.   Four or five thousand feet above ridges should be maintained when flying on

instruments through clouds at temperatures below 32° F.

5. Don't fly into cumulus clouds at low temperatures. Heavy glaze ice may be encountered.

6. Don't make steep turns with ice on the airplane.

7. Don't practice stalls or spins with ice on the airplane.

8. Don't land with power off when ice has formed on the wings and on exposed surfaces of the plane.

9. Don't try to climb too fast when ice has formed on plane, since stalling speed is higher than normal.

10. Don't forget when flying under icing conditions that gasoline consumption is greater, due to increased drag and the additional power required.

11. Don't attempt a cross-country flight in fall or winter without first consulting the nearest United States Weather Bureau Airway Forecast Center to obtain a forecast as to expected icing conditions.

Additional precautions while in the air:

1. Ice formation may be expected in the presence of any *visible* form of moisture such as:

   (*a*) Flying in any cloud at temperatures below 36° F.

   (*b*) Flying in temperatures below 36° F with rain and snow falling from above.

   (*c*) Going into clouds from air below 32° F.

   (*d*) Going into air below 32° F after having collected moisture in the clouds.

   (*e*) Going into clouds with small amounts of ice already on plane parts.

2. If necessary to fly in ice-forming conditions:

   (*a*) When approaching mountainous country with intent to go "on top," climb through *well in advance.* DO NOT WAIT until you are close to the mountains and then attempt to climb through overhanging clouds. If necessary, change (even reverse) your course so as to fly *away* from the mountains while climbing through.

(*b*) If you do not break through below 10,000 feet altitude the clouds will very likely extend well up to an altitude which will call for oxygen equipment for pilots and passengers, unless cockpit and cabin are "pressurized."

(*c*) If ice forms as you go up through clouds, expect a greater amount to form as you decend through them.

(*d*) Maintain an altitude of at least 1,000 feet above top of clouds while "on top."

(*e*) In letting down through an icing stratum, use rapid rate of descent with LOWEST AIR-SPEED PRACTICABLE. *Note,* however, that this procedure (with nearly closed throttle) is highly conducive to carburetor icing, and if ice forms on wings your stalling speed will be higher, so that *you must take suitable precautions on these two points also.*

SOME PILOT COMMENTS REGARDING ICE

On a trip from Newark to Chicago last winter we encountered a light icing condition near Chicago. We examined the leading edges with a flashlight and the amount of ice appeared negligible. Upon landing at Chicago, however, the plane stalled at about 90 mph. Fortunately, we came over the *edge* of the field with plenty of speed. Upon examination on the ground we found very little ice on the wing, but quite a bit on the stabilizer extending back on top. All the ice was rough as coarse gravel, accounting for the rapid loss of lift.

I do not think the matter of ice on propellers is sufficiently stressed.   Have had one or two occasions when wing de-icer equipment failed, only to find that with propeller anti-icer equipment working, the load of ice that could be carried was much heavier.   Loss of effective hp is of MAJOR importance compared to either wing distortion or weight.

When rime ice has formed on the wings in back of de-icers on the leading edge, I do not think you can stress enough the importance of increasing your gliding and landing speed. Ships with high wing loading are greatly affected with rime ice and it does not take very much to cause you to stall at slow speeds which would be all right under ordinary circumstances.

QUESTIONS

1. What factors, resulting from ice formation on aircraft, cause hazard to the aircraft?
2. To what is formation of ice on aircraft due?
3. What are the causes and effects of carburetor and intake-pipe icing?
4. Why should meteorologists be familiar with situations conducive to icing?
5. What is the usual cause of ice accretion on aircraft?
6. Under what condition may ice be formed on aircraft by direct sublimation of water vapor?
7. Between what ambient air temperatures does ice usually form on aircraft?   At what temperatures is it most frequent and most severe?
8. Name three types of ice formed on aircraft.   Describe (a) Rime ice. (b) Glaze ice.   (c) Frost.
9. What type of ice is the most usual?
10. Upon what does the rate of ice accretion usually depend?
11. Explain the freezing process which occurs after water droplets strike the airplane surface.
12. In what regions or areas is icing most common and most severe?
13. What altitude should be maintained in flying through a frontal zone under icing conditions?   What particular areas should be avoided?
14. When ice is forming rapidly, is it better to decrease or increase altitude? When impossible to reduce altitude, under such conditions, what action should be taken?
15. What types of ice formation can occur while aircraft are on the ground or taking off?
16. What is the most probable type of ice formation formed during contact flight?   During instrument flight?

17. What effect has vertical convection on ice formation?
18. Should escape from ice ever be attempted by climbing?
19. When uncertain of ice distribution in clouds, what is the safest flight path?
20. By what means may ice-forming regions be located, and the probable intensity of icing determined?
21. What combination of conditions is particularly conducive to icing in mT air? When and where is this particularly found?
22. When and where is icing in mP air particularly found?
23. Why should a pilot be thoroughly familiar with weather and temperature conditions which may cause ice to form on his aircraft?
24. What is the most advisable action regarding use of light planes under icing conditions?
25. What is the aerodynamic effect of ice on leading edges of wings, propellers, and control surfaces?

Chapter XII

PRESSURE–PATTERN FLIGHT OR AEROLOGATION

By Robert M. Mansfield

Since the beginning of aerial navigation, flight crews have been trained in the practices of surface navigation and have attempted to fit them to their three-dimensional problems. This modified surface type of navigation provides adequate safety, but does not allow the maximum efficiency of modern aircraft to be realized. Safety of operation is, of course, the first consideration of the navigator, but it should not be his only concern; commercial or military aviation requires efficiency as well as safety if it is to be successful.

To increase the efficiency of aerial navigation we must abandon several of the principles borrowed from surface navigation. If the navigator insists on flying a *fixed* route for every trip, the flight time can be shortened only by increasing the airspeed, resulting in a corresponding increase in operating costs. Probably the greatest fallacy of pioneer long-range flying was the continued use of the great circle route simply because it offered the shortest distance to destination. Operational records contain many proofs that this great circle flight required as much as four hours more time than other routes. This four-hour difference is an extreme case; however, even an apparently small interval cannot be disregarded.

To shorten the flight time without increasing the operating costs requires a careful and intelligent interpretation of flight level weather conditions. This weather analysis is just as important during the flight as it is during the planning stages. Before the introduction of the absolute (radio) altimeter as a part of the standard navigational equipment, this in-flight weather analysis was mainly guesswork; existing upper-air pressure distribution could only be generalized from information gathered by conventional navigation procedures. Now, the absolute altimeter used in conjunction with the pressure (aneroid) altimeter provides the means for measuring several important factors which facilitate weather analysis during flight. This altimetry * might well be the basis for development of a true air navigation.

Pressure-pattern navigation is an attempt toward the development of this true air navigation; it consists of the art of planning and navigating a long-range flight via the least-time route rather than the shortest-distance route. Basically, this is accomplished by careful investigation of synoptic and forecast upper-air pressure fields, and the determination of the least-time track by the direct use of flight level atmospheric pressures. The progress of a pressure-pattern flight is controlled by modification of the flight plan track to fit existing pressure fields when actual conditions are found to differ from the forecast pattern.

Most air carriers engaged in international operations use some form of pressure-pattern navigation, but there is no standard or common procedure in use at this time. Each airline has developed a technique for applying pressure-pattern principles to its individual operating requirements. Although these individual methods seem to be quite different, they are all based on common principles and can be understood by anyone having a working knowledge of pressure-pattern theory. The procedures explained in this chapter have been tested and proved on many hundreds of transatlantic flights and are designed to allow the maximum flexibility of flight operations. Pressure-pattern navigation can be used with equal success on over-land flights as well as on over-water flights; however, the procedures will vary. Since there are few long-range flights

---

* The use of comparative readings of two (or more) altimeters of different types (i.e., absolute and pressure) as an indication of pressure gradient.

operating over land areas at present, the explanations given in this text will be confined to over-water operations.

Conventional methods of flight planning require an accurate forecast of wind velocities at the desired flight level. These winds are usually obtained from a forecast upper-air weather map of the constant pressure type and are determined for each weather zone to be traversed. Ordinarily, the meteorologist will measure these winds with a geostrophic wind scale, adjusting the values thus found for cyclostrophic and isallobaric components when necessary. These forecast winds must then be translated by the navigator into drift correction and groundspeed factors before the flight plan can be completed. Pressure-pattern flight planning, on the other hand, uses pressure gradients directly for the determination of these components. Experience has shown that this flight planning by pressures is just as accurate as other methods.

A forecast upper-air weather map will show, with reasonable accuracy, the general pressure distribution and location of pressure area centers. By using the altimeters to determine flight level barometric pressures and other information supplied by conventional Dead Reckoning procedures, the navigator can revise this forecast map to show existing conditions. The analysis of existing weather is by no means the only purpose of altimetry; it is possible to determine the drift of the aircraft by making altimeter readings at regular intervals. This drift angle can be computed at any time and is extremely valuable to the navigator at those times when other navigational aids are not available.

The theories and procedures used in this problem are not based on "Black Magic," but are a result of the application of measured values to recognized laws of meteorology. We are indebted to Professor John C. Bellamy of the University of Chicago for the basic procedure used in this work; without Professor Bellamy's contribution, the greater part of this pressure-pattern navigation would be impossible.

Bellamy's drift formula is derived from the geostrophic wind equation, which is based on the following rules:

(*a*) Direction of the geostrophic wind is parallel to the isobars at levels above the surface friction layer.

(*b*) Force of the geostrophic wind is directly proportional to the pressure gradient (slope of the isobaric surface).

(*c*) Buys-Ballot's Law: In the Northern Hemisphere, the low-pressure area is to the left of an observer facing downwind. The low-pressure area would be to the right in the Southern Hemisphere.

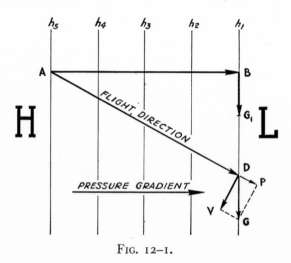

FIG. 12–1.

From the foregoing rules, it can be shown that wind direction will be at right angles to the pressure gradient, and by expanding this reasoning further it can be shown that it is possible to determine the cross-wind component affecting the aircraft by measuring the pressure gradient in the direction of the flight. Figure 12–1 shows the relationship of this "crosswind" component to the total geostrophic wind.

This cross-wind component, normal to the true heading of the aircraft, when combined with a parallel component which does not materially affect the drift angle, constitutes the total geostrophic wind. In the illustration, h_1, h_2, h_3, h_4, and h_5

represent isobars in an idealized pressure system. The pressure gradient is from high toward low, or to the right. By applying Buys-Ballot's Law, and assuming that we are in the Northern Hemisphere, the wind directon is determined to be from north. *AB* represents the actual pressure gradient, and BG_1 represents the total geostrophic wind. *AD* represents the direction of the flight and is the *measured* pressure gradient. By applying the formula for geostrophic wind to this measured gradient, we arrive at the cross-wind component, *DV*, which determines the amount of drift experienced by the aircraft. *DP* is the component parallel to the heading of the aircraft, while *DG* is the total geostrophic wind.

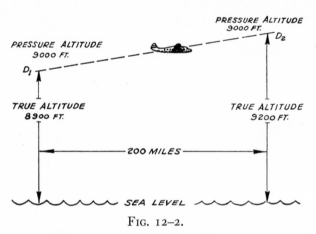

FIG. 12–2.

Figure 12–2 shows how pressure gradient, in the direction of the flight, is measured by altimetry. The aircraft altitude is being maintained by reference to the pressure altimeter, and the pressure altitude remains constant during the observation "run"; therefore, the aircraft is moving along an isobaric surface. The true altitude has increased, which indicates the flight is moving toward areas of higher pressure. The illustration shows an isobaric slope of 300 ft per 200 nautical miles.

It is true that the actual wind is seldom geostrophic and, for that reason, the drift formula based on the geostrophic wind formula is apparently inaccurate. Computation of the geostrophic wind assumes that the isobars are straight, parallel, and equally spaced; curvature of the isobars introduces a cyclostrophic wind component which varies proportionately with the radii of curvature. In the case of pressure systems of small diameter, or low-pressure trough and high-pressure ridge points where the curvature is of small radius, this component can be large enough to cause an error of several degrees in the computed drift angle. Pressure change over a fixed point, because of the movement of pressure systems, contributes an isallobaric wind component which can also be large enough to affect the accuracy of the computed drift angle. Temperature differences, horizontally, cause the third error: wind shear, or thermal wind component. All of these components, when combined with geostrophic wind, equal the total or actual wind at levels above the surface friction layer. Fortunately, it is seldom that these components become large enough to affect seriously the computed drift angle. We are limited at present by the fact that it is almost impossible to steer a desired heading any closer than two degrees, which makes the consideration of fractional adjustments impractical.

The Bellamy drift formula is as follows:

$$V_n = K \frac{(D_2 - D_1)}{X} \qquad (1)$$

in which

$V_n =$ The geostrophic wind component perpendicular to the true heading, expressed in knots. *This is a one-hour value.*

$K =$ A latitude constant, equal to $\frac{21.47}{\sin \text{lat}}$.

$D_1 =$ True altitude, measured by absolute altimeter, *minus* the pressure altitude at the start of the observation run.

$D_2 =$ True altitude *minus* pressure altitude at the end of the observation run.

$X =$ The air (no-wind) distance between the D_1 and D_2 observations.

In the Northern Hemisphere, the algebraic sign of $(D_2 - D_1)$ is the sign of the drift *correction*. By reviewing the rules for circulation of air around high- and low-pressure areas, the navigator will have a check on the direction of the drift. In the Northern Hemisphere, when headed toward areas of higher pressure, the wind is from the right, and when headed toward areas of lower pressure the wind will be from the left. This pressure trend is indicated by the altimeters; if the true height is increasing while the pressure altitude remains constant, the aircraft is headed toward areas of higher pressure.

The suggested procedures for determining D_1 and D_2 values are as follows:

(*a*) The time interval between D_1 and D_2 observations should be at least twenty minutes. The slope of the isobaric surface cannot be determined with the required accuracy at shorter intervals because of the possibility of accumulative altimeter errors. Time intervals of one hour will provide the most accurate results.

(*b*) The pressure altitude at the time of the D_2 observation should not be more than 200 feet different from the pressure altitude at the time of the D_1 observation.

(*c*) The True Heading should be held within ten degrees during the observation run. If the heading is changed, by an amount less than ten degrees, during the run, the V_n component should be applied to the average heading flown.

(*d*) Check the adjustment of the altimeters before reading: pressure altimeter set to 29.92 inches, and the absolute altimeter properly "zeroed." Do not make readings at times when the altimeters indicate a climb or descent. Tap the pressure altimeter, lightly, to remove frictional lag. Read both altimeters at the same time, or as closely as is possible. Read altitudes to the nearest twenty feet.

(*e*) Subtract pressure altitude from true altitude, being careful to apply the proper sign to the D difference.

To complete the problem, solving for the cross-wind component, V_n:

(*a*) Subtract D_1 from D_2, algebraically.

(*b*) Obtain the latitude constant, K, for the mid-latitude between observations. A K graph will be found at the end of this chapter, on p. 294.

(*c*) Determine the X factor (no-wind distance) by multiplying True Airspeed by the time interval between observations.

(*d*) Solve for V_n.

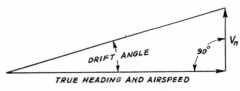

DRIFT ANGLE   90° V_n

TRUE HEADING AND AIRSPEED

Fig. 12–3.

The V_n component can be converted to a drift angle by plotting vectorially, as in Figure 12–3, or by the use of an E6-B or similar Dead Reckoning (D.R.) computer.

If the groundspeed is known, or can be estimated, the drift angle should be adjusted for the parallel component of the geostrophic wind. Figure 12–4 shows the difference between

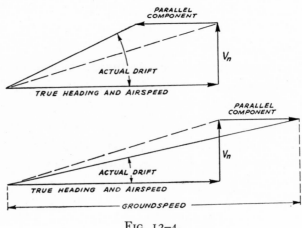

PARALLEL COMPONENT

ACTUAL DRIFT V_n

TRUE HEADING AND AIRSPEED

PARALLEL COMPONENT

ACTUAL DRIFT V_n

TRUE HEADING AND AIRSPEED

GROUNDSPEED

Fig. 12–4.

drift angles computed from airspeeds alone and those adjusted for groundspeed.

The tracking of the aircraft can be made more positive by the use of pressure lines of position. These lines are determined by computing the net effect of the wind up to the point in question. The theory behind computation of the net effect of the wind is the same as the theory from which the formula for the determination of V_n is derived. Figure 12–5 shows the

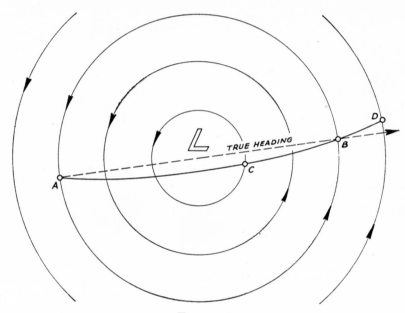

FIG. 12–5.

effect of the wind on an aircraft flying through an idealized pressure system.

If the flight is made from A to B, and the true heading is used as shown, it is obvious that the aircraft would arrive back on the heading line at point B, because the pressure at B is the same as the pressure at A, and the effect of the wind has been cancelled out; the net isobaric slope is zero. In this case the pressure system has been considered as being stationary. If the pressure area had been moving in the same direction as the

aircraft, the point at which the aircraft would arrive back on
the heading line would be some distance beyond B, depending
on the speed of movement of the pressure system.   Whenever
the aircraft arrived back on the heading line, the pressure at
that point would be the same as that of the point of departure;
only if the pressure is the same will the aircraft return to the
heading line.   In the Northern Hemisphere, if the pressure
is less than the pressure at the departure point, the aircraft will
have to be to the right of the heading line, as in the case of the
flight from A to C.   If the pressure is greater, the aircraft will
be to the left of the true heading line, as in the case of a flight
from A to D.

V_n, the one-hour component of wind at right angles to the
True Heading, multiplied by the time involved would be the
distance that the aircraft would drift from an air-plot (no-
wind) position.   It follows then that, if we denote the quantity, V_n times Time, as Z_n, this Z_n can be computed from the
same formula by substituting T.A.S. (True Airspeed) for X,
the air distance.   The mathematical derivation of Z_n is shown
below.

$$V_n = K \frac{(D_2 - D_1)}{X} \tag{2}$$

in which $X =$ True Airspeed times *Time,* or the air distance
travelled.   Then,

$$Time \text{ times } V_n = K \frac{(D_2 - D_1)}{\text{T.A.S.}} .$$

By stipulation, V_n times *Time* will be denoted as Z_n, and the
formula for determination of the net effect of the cross-wind is
written as follows:

$$Z_n = K \frac{(D_2 - D_1)}{\text{T.A.S.}} . \tag{3}$$

V_n is independent of the groundspeed because we are measuring the net change in height of an isobaric surface; thus, regardless of groundspeed, Z_n will be the distance, at right angles
to the air-plot course, that the aircraft has drifted between

the D_1 and D_2 observations. Z_n, plotted vectorially from an airplot position, indicates the distance the aircraft is from this airplot position. If a line is drawn through the end of this Z_n vector, parallel to the True Heading, the result is a "pressure line of position." The location of the aircraft along this line of position will depend on the net parallel component of wind for the period of observation. Figure 12–6 shows the pressure line of position (P.L.O.P.) and its relation to the air-plot.

The pressure line of position has been used with considerable success during the past several years. Experience has

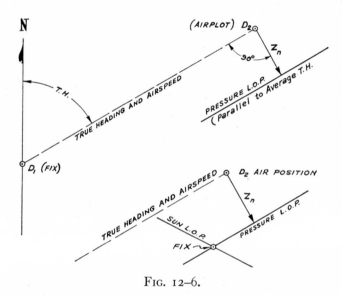

FIG. 12–6.

proved it to be accurate. Obviously, since we are basing the pressure line of position on an air-plot, the P.L.O.P. will only be accurate when the air-plot is accurate. The use of the Air Position Indicator (A.P.I.) will provide a more reliable L.O.P. at times when True Headings and Airspeeds are changed quite frequently. In any case, when constructing an air-plot from observed airspeeds and heading, or when the A.P.I. is used, the air-plot should not be continued for periods in excess of three hours; the accumulation of errors will seriously affect the accuracy of the pressure line of position if carried any further.

During daylight flights over routes where radio aids to navigation are limited, or are of poor quality, the navigator has a means of fixing the position of the aircraft at any time a sun observation is possible. The intersection of a sun L.O.P. and a pressure L.O.P. will provide a reasonably accurate fix.

The suggested procedure for determination of the P.L.O.P. is as follows:

(*a*) Use the altitude difference at some "fix" point as the D_1 value, and the altitude difference at the time of the desired P.L.O.P. as the D_2 value.

(*b*) Compute and plot the air-plot (no-wind) positions from the D_1 position to the time of the D_2 observation.

(*c*) Use the mid-latitude between the D_1 and D_2 observations as the latitude for the K constant.

(*d*) Compute Z_n and plot the Z_n vector at right angles to the True Heading, at the air-plot position, for the time of the D_2 observation. If the aircraft has been headed toward an area of lower pressures, the Z_n vector is to be plotted to the right (when in the Northern Hemisphere). The algebraic sign of $(D_2 - D_1)$ is used to verify this, a minus sign indicating right drift.

(*e*) Through the end of the Z_n vector, plot a line parallel to the mean True Heading from the start of the air-plot. This line is the pressure line of position.

Most short-range flight problems, such as search and patrol flights, require the maintenance of a fixed track, and the saving of flight time is not important. The absolute altimeter is a valuable aid to the navigator of these flights, but the value of the instrument in the problem of long-range aerial transport is immeasurable. The possible shortening of enroute flight time, with the resultant fuel and aircraft maintenance savings, is of prime importance in this type of operation.

Several methods have been devised in an attempt to shorten the flight time to destination, and all have had some success. They have been based on the pressure-pattern type of route selection, which consists of fitting the track of the flight around pressure areas to obtain the benefit of helping winds. The navigator studies the upper-air charts carefully, and selects a composite course which will keep the aircraft on the proper side of the pressure system for tail winds, or to minimize head winds if the added distance appears to be too great. The meteorologist then makes a wind forecast for the desired route, and a flight plan is computed in the conventional manner. This pressure-pattern method has been used with considerable success, but it still leaves a great deal to be desired. It is true that a navigator can steer "off-course" to find tail winds, but unless this is kept within reason, the added distance will offset the gain in groundspeed. Also, an inaccurate forecast might give the navigator considerable extra distance to fly against head winds instead of the expected tail winds. Finally, unless the navigator solves many flight plans, based on as many different combinations of routes, he will have no guarantee that the route he has selected is the most efficient.

The aerologation route, which is described here, seems to offer all of the advantages of the pressure-pattern route without the disadvantages outlined above. It is, in effect, an automatic pressure-pattern route which assures the best ratio of speed gain to added distance. While it is true that an aircraft on the great circle route might make a better groundspeed while in the same weather zone as the aircraft on the aerologation route, this aerologation route will ensure the better overall speed to destination. The use of the aerologation route will also provide a definite safety factor. The computation of the single drift correction, used for the entire flight, is not made from forecast winds; in fact the flight can be planned without any knowledge of wind direction and speed. This probably sounds like heresy to the many navigators who have had experience on the North Atlantic crossing, or other regions of intense weather and extremely high winds, but this is not just a theory; the methods have been tested and proved.

The maintenance of a fixed track, such as the great circle or rhumb line, often requires large corrections for drift with a resultant loss of groundspeed. If the navigator were to apply a single correction, which would be the average of all corrections required, the aircraft would then drift freely with the wind and better groundspeeds would be realized. It is true that the aircraft might drift one hundred or more miles from the normal track, but the minimum correction has been applied and the aircraft will drift back toward the destination. The feeling that the aircraft is lost if it is more than ten miles from a fixed path has no foundation in reasoning. Regardless of location, when making an ocean crossing, the aircraft is operating over the same kind of water, and the same navigational aids are usually available.

During the first years of scheduled over-ocean operation, several navigators used an average drift correction for the entire flight with fair success. These single drift corrections were determined by averaging the drift corrections computed for each weather zone. Since these drift corrections were computed from forecast winds, the flight would arrive at destination without further correction only if the forecast winds were accurate. In most cases the navigator had to make several revisions to the drift correction to make his desired landfall.

By applying what we now know of aerology and altimetry, the constant drift correction can be determined easily and accurately. If the drift over a past period can be computed from the slope of the isobaric surface, as measured in flight, it follows then that the drift ahead (drift correction) can be determined in the same manner if the net slope of the isobaric surface ahead can be found. The difference between the height of the slope at departure and destination points would be the $(D_2 - D_1)$ value used in the formula; the expected average True Airspeed would be used instead of the actual; and the Z_n thus found will be the net effect of the cross-wind for the entire flight. This Z_n can be converted into a drift correction angle by several different means.

The formula used is the same as used in the determination of pressure lines of position:

$$Z_n = K \frac{(D_2 - D_1)}{\text{T.A.S.}} \qquad (3)$$

in which

Z_n = The net effect of the cross-wind (geostrophic) for the entire flight, expressed in nautical miles.

K = Latitude constant for the mid-latitude of the flight.

D_1 = The absolute height of the selected pressure level (isobaric surface) over the departure point, at the time of departure.

D_2 = The absolute height of the same pressure level over the destination, forecast for the expected time of arrival.

T.A.S. = The average expected True Airspeed of the flight.

The Z_n value can be converted to drift correction angle graphically, by plotting the vectors involved, or mathematically by dividing the Z_n quantity by the great circle distance to destination which will provide the sine of the drift correction angle. The problem can be most easily solved on most types of D.R. navigation computers as an off-course problem. The drift correction angle found by use of the above methods will only be exact when the distance involved is less than 600 miles; at distances greater than this, a small error is introduced since we are using plane trigonometry to solve a spherical triangle. The error is negligible, however, since it is impossible to steer fractions of a degree with our present equipment.

The direction of the drift correction angle is determined in the same menner as for the pressure line of position. If the height of the isobaric surface is greater at destination that at departure, the net effect is that of approaching an area of higher pressures; in the northern hemisphere, the wind would be from the right and the drift correction would be *plus*. If the height at destination were lower than the height at the point of departure, the net effect would be a wind from the left, and the drift correction would be *minus*.

Here again, we are using forecast information for the determination of the single, average drift correction; however, the use of just two forecast values, the height of the isobaric surface at each end of the flight, instead of the many forecast winds enroute reduces the possibilities of error. Also, it is true that the height of this isobaric surface can be forecast with more accuracy than is possible, when attempting to forecast winds.

The $(D_2 - D_1)$ value, as determined by the above method requires the use of constant-pressure-type upper-air charts. This type of chart is in standard use throughout the world at present. If upper-air charts are not available, the navigator or the meteorologist will have to extrapolate surface pressures to the desired flight level and convert these pressures to heights. This can be done with reasonable accuracy by use of a pressure-height slide rule, or graph, but since it requires forecast upper-air temperatures, another source of error is encountered.

Ordinarily, the single drift correction is applied to the several chords of the great circle course, resulting in approximately five different True Headings for a flight of 2000 miles. However, this single correction can be applied to a rhumb line course with equal success, and the flight can be conducted with just one True Heading. The great circle is most desirable as the base for this planning since the distance saved will save a few more minutes of flight time than the use of the rhumb line.

Since the aircraft is to be allowed to drift off the fixed route, it is necessary for the navigator to compute and plot the expected track before flight, in order that it can be examined for possible adverse weather enroute. When this is found to be the case, it is often advisable to sacrifice some of the time savings and modify the route to avoid bad weather.

The problem of computing and plotting the expected track is not difficult and can be accomplished in a few minutes. All that is necessary is to compute and plot several pressure lines of position directly on the forecast upper-air chart. These pressure lines are computed for each 200-ft change in the height of the isobaric surface, since this is the contour interval of the chart. The lines are then plotted from the True Heading line, which is drawn on the chart, in such a manner that the P.L.O.P.'s will intersect the corresponding contour line.

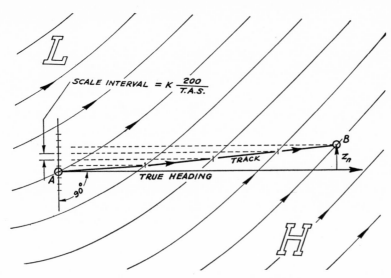

Fig. 12–7. Plotting the expected track on upper-air chart (200 ft contour interval).

By connecting these intersections, the expected track is plotted. Since we are using a constant of 200 ft for the $(D_2 - D_1)$ portion of the formula, it is only necessary to solve the problem once. The plotting can be simplified by constructing a scale of Z_n values (as at A, Figure 12–7) at right angles to the True Heading line. Figure 12–7 shows how this plotting for the expected track is done.

The problem illustrated in Figure 12–7 is based on the following factors:

(*a*) Flight from Gander, Newfoundland, to Shannon, Eire, which establishes 52° North as the mid-latitude of the flight. $K = 27.2$. (See "*K* Curve," p. 294.)

(*b*) Expected average True Airspeed of the flight is 240 knots.

(*c*) Flight altitude is 19,000 feet.

The Z_n value for each 200-ft change, using the factors given above, would be equal to:

$$\frac{27.2 \times 200}{240} = 22.7 \text{ miles.} \tag{4}$$

The 22.7 miles is the distance that the aircraft will drift for each 200-ft contour line crossed on the upper-air chart. If the flight is toward areas of lower pressure, the drift will be to the right of the True Heading line; and, conversely, when

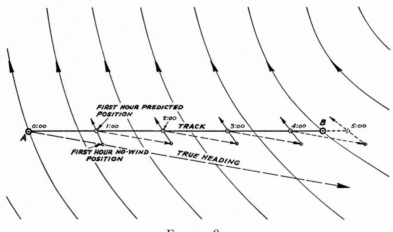

FIG. 12–8.

proceeding toward areas of higher pressure, the drift will be to the left.

The final and most important phase of the flight planning is the computation of flight time enroute. This can be done quickly and easily directly on the upper-air forecast chart, by the use of vector triangles. The standard dead reckoning wind triangle is used in this case, although not in the same manner as in usual problems. Figure 12–8 illustrates the plotting of the vector triangles for the determination of flight time enroute.

The procedure for this plotting is as follows:

(*a*) Allowing one-half minute adjustment for each thousand feet of climb to flight altitude, compute and plot the first-hour no-wind position along the True Heading line. If this flight altitude is 19,000 ft, the no-wind position would be found 50½ minutes of the True Airspeed along the True Heading line from destination, or at a distance of 202 miles.

(*b*) From this no-wind position, draw a line parallel to the average wind direction between departure and the first-hour air-plot. This average wind direction can usually be found by inspection, remembering that the wind direction at these altitudes will be parallel to the contour lines of the chart.

(*c*) The intersection of the wind line and the track line will give the expected position of the aircraft after the first hour of flight. It is not necessary to determine the wind speed for the solution of this problem, but a measurement of this wind line will provide the navigator with an estimated wind for the first hour of flight.

(*d*) Plot another True Heading line from this first-hour position, parallel to the original True Heading line, and measure one hour of True Airspeed along the line to establish the second-hour no-wind position. Draw a line from this air-plot position parallel to the average wind direction from the first-hour to the second-hour position. The intersection of this wind line with the expected track will show the expected position of the aircraft at the end of the second hour of flight.

(*e*) Continue plotting True Headings, True Airspeeds, and wind lines to the hourly position next beyond destination.

(*f*) The ratio of distance-remaining-to-go to the last hourly distance will give the fraction of an hour required to complete the flight plan time.

In those cases where the wind line and the True Heading are parallel, it is obvious that there is no drift, and that True Airspeed plus or minus wind speed will result in groundspeed. This case cannot be solved by plotting, but the navigator can measure the wind speed at the point in question. With dividers or scales, measure the distance between contour lines at this point; make certain that the measurement is made at right angles to the contours. Determine the K factor for the latitude and solve for wind using the following:

$$\text{Wind Speed } (V_n) = \frac{200}{\text{dist. between contours}} K.$$

Of course, the navigator's work is not done upon completion of the flight plan; he must now board the aircraft and lead it safely and efficiently to the desired destination. Although considerable effort has been expended in computing the flight plan, it would be extremely foolish to assume that it could be followed, blindly, without jeopardizing the safety of the flight. There are too many variables involved in meteorology to permit a completely accurate forecast of weather conditions all the way from departure to destination. Therefore, it is essential that the navigator employ every means at his command to check the progress of his flight.

In addition to the usual dead reckoning problems, and the determination of position, the navigator using a single drift correction route must maintain a continual watch of the altimeter values, and the trend of barometric pressures at destination. When it is apparent that the D_2 value, used in the computation of the single drift correction, is inaccurate, it will be necessary to determine a correct value and to revise the correction. The D_2 value over destination can be determined during flight by several methods; a D_1 value is measured at the position of the aircraft, and an entirely new problem is solved for the remainder of the flight.

Most of the North Atlantic flight terminals will furnish, upon request, the latest measured height of the standard pressure surface nearest the flight level, or they will report the D_2 value as a "*D* Factor" with the appropriate algebriac sign. If this service is not available, the navigator can extrapolate, to his own flight level, the reported sea level pressure at destination and obtain a D_2 value nearly as accurate as those reported by the local weather office. Procedures for using these different types of pressure values are given below.

HEIGHT OF STANDARD PRESSURE SURFACE HAS BEEN REPORTED BY DESTINATION

These Standard Pressures (850, 700, and 500 millibars) seldom coincide with the flight level barometric pressure of the aircraft. Therefore, it will be necessary for the navigator to extrapolate his measured flight level pressure to the standard pressure. This is done as follows:

(*a*) Check adjustments of pressure (aneroid) and absolute (radio) altimeters, pressure altimeter to be set to standard sea level pressure of 29.92 in. (1013.2 mb). Read altimeters carefully, and correct pressure altimeter reading for instrument and position errors. Note flight level temperature. *Do not correct altimeter readings for temperature.*

(*b*) Convert corrected pressure altitude to millibars, using table FEET TO MILLIBARS—U. S. STANDARD ATMOSPHERE (see p. 295). This is the flight level pressure at the True Altitude indicated on the absolute altimeter.

(*c*) Determine the height separation, in feet, between this flight level pressure and the standard pressure reported by the destination weather office. On the "PRESSURE–ALTITUDE GRAPH" (see p. 296) place one point of dividers at the intersection on flight level pressure and flight level temperature. Place the other divider point at the intersection of standard pressure and flight level temperature. Transfer dividers to the height scale at the left side of the graph and read the height separation. If the standard pressure is less than flight level pressure, the height separation should be added to the True

Altitude of the aircraft to obtain the height of this standard pressure at the position of the aircraft. This extrapolated value is then used as D_1 and the reported height over destination as D_2 in the formula for determining the net cross-wind component for the remainder of the flight.

This procedure of extrapolating flight level pressures to the standard pressures will also allow the navigator to check the accuracy of the forecast upper-air charts as the flight progresses. An example of this work follows:

(*a*) True Altitude (absolute altimeter) .... 8300 ft
(*b*) Indicated Pressure Altitude .... 8160 ft
    Instrument correction .... —20 ft
    Position correction .... +180 ft

    Corrected Pressure Altitude .... 8320 ft

(*c*) From conversion table, obtain pressure value for 8320 ft: 743 millibars. This is the flight level pressure at 8300 ft.

(*d*) Using PRESSURE-ALTITUDE GRAPH, determine height separation between 743 millibars and nearest standard pressure of 700 millibars. Assuming 0° centigrade for the flight level temperature in this problem, 700 millibars is found to be 1550 ft higher than aircraft True Altitude.

    8300 ft (True Altitude)
    1550 ft (Height Separation)

    9850 ft Height of 700 mb at aircraft.

"D" FACTOR HAS BEEN REPORTED BY DESTINATION

The *"D"* Factor, as reported by destination, is by far the easiest to use when checking the single drift correction. If the flight altitude is within 2000 ft of the height of the standard level given for the reported *"D"* Factor, it can be used directly without the need for time-consuming conversions. If the flight altitude is more than 2000 ft from the reported level, it will be necessary to interpolate from the *"D"* Factors reported at altitudes above and below the aircraft. To use the *"D"* Factor method of determining drift correction:

(*a*) Measure True and Pressure Altitudes; subtract Pressure Altitude from True Altitude to Obtain D_1.

(*b*) Consider the reported *"D"* Factor as D_2; subtract D_1 from D_2, algebraically.

(*c*) Proceed with solution for Z_n (cross-wind for remainder of flight) in usual manner.

EXTRAPOLATION OF SEA LEVEL PRESSURE AT DESTINATION

This method of obtaining the height of a given pressure surface is the least reliable of the three methods described here, but when other information is not available it can be a definite aid in the computation of drift correction for the remainder of the flight. The procedure for this extrapolation is as follows:

(*a*) Measure True Altitude and Pressure Altitude; correct Pressure Altitude for instrument and position errors. Note flight level temperature.

(*b*) Determine flight level pressure, as explained above.

(*c*) Compute mean temperature from surface to flight altitude. This can be the average of the reported surface temperature at destination, and flight level temperature.

(*d*) Determine height separation between reported sea level pressure and flight level pressure as found in (*b*) above.

(*e*) This height separation, or the difference between the height of flight level pressure at destination, and the True Altitude of the aircraft will be the $(D_2 - D_1)$ factor to be used in the formula for computing drift correction. If the height of the flight level pressure over destination is greater than the True Altitude of the aircraft, the effect will be that of flying into areas of higher pressures; in the Northern Hemisphere, the wind will be from the right and the drift correction will be *plus*.

An example of this type of problem is given here.

(a) Sea level pressure at destination 1020 millibars
    Surface temperature at destination +10° C
(b) True Altitude of aircraft ...... 8300 ft
    Corrected Pressure Altitude .... 8350 ft
    Flight level temperature .... —6° C
(c) Mean temperature, surface to
    flight altitude .... +2° C

(d) On PRESSURE-ALTITUDE GRAPH, place one divider point at intersection of sea level pressure (1020 mb) and mean temperature (+2°). Place other divider point at intersection of flight level pressure (743 mb) and mean temperature. Transfer dividers to altitude scale; read height of flight level pressure at destination: 8320 ft.

(e) Subtract True Altitude of aircraft from height found in (d) above.

$$\begin{array}{r} 8320 \\ -8300 \\ \hline +20 \ \ ft = (D_2 - D_1) \end{array}$$

SUMMARY

Aerologation, or Pressure-Pattern Navigation is not intended to replace conventional dead reckoning navigational practices; it is designed to supplement the work done by navigators on routine, fixed-track flights. As was mentioned at the beginning of this chapter, safety should always be the navigator's primary concern, and new procedures should not be accepted for use on over-water flights until they have been proved to be satisfactory. The techniques described in this text have been tested and proved, but the wise navigator will check them for himself under favorable flying conditions so that he will have confidence in his work during adverse conditions. *There is no device, or procedure, which can take the place of good judgment based on practical experience.*

The procedures explained here are used by many navigators today, but due to the continuing development of this art, they will probably be improved upon many times before a true aerial navigation is evolved. Many people are working at the problem of aerial navigation, along many different lines; however, there is one basic point on which there is no disagreement: *The safe and efficient navigator must have a sound working knowledge of meteorology.*

QUESTIONS

1. What instrument has greatly assisted the development of pressure pattern flight?
2. What is the essential difference between conventional methods of flight planning and those used in pressure pattern flight?
3. How does the navigator employ altimetry in pressure pattern flight?
4. With limited radio navigation aids, how can a navigator obtain a reasonably accurate fix of his position in pressure pattern flight?

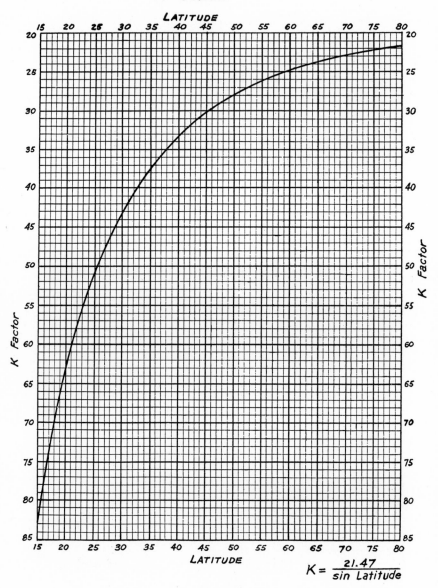

FIG. 12–9.

FEET TO MILLIBARS—U.S. STANDARD ATMOSPHERE
(PRESSURE ALTIMETER AT 29.92 IN.)

MILLIBARS	0	1	2	3	4	5	6	7	8	9	MILLIBARS
300	30050	29980	29900	29830	29750	29680	29610	29540	29420	29390	300
310	29320	29250	29180	29110	29040	28970	28900	28830	28760	28690	310
320	28620	28550	28480	28410	28340	28280	28210	28140	28070	28010	320
330	27940	27870	27810	27740	27670	27600	27540	27470	27400	27340	330
340	27270	27210	27140	27070	27010	26940	26870	26810	26750	26680	340
350	26610	26550	26490	26420	26360	26300	26230	26170	26110	26040	350
360	25980	25920	25850	25790	25730	25670	25600	25540	25490	25420	360
370	25350	25290	25230	25170	25110	25050	24990	24930	24860	24800	370
380	24740	24680	24620	24560	24500	24440	24380	24320	24260	24210	380
390	24150	24090	24030	23970	23910	23850	23790	23730	23670	23620	390
400	23560	23500	23450	23390	23330	23270	23210	23160	23100	23040	400
410	22990	22930	22870	22810	22760	22700	22650	22590	22540	22480	410
420	22420	22370	22310	22250	22200	22150	22090	22040	21980	21930	420
430	21870	21810	21760	21710	21660	21600	21550	21500	21440	21390	430
440	21330	21260	21230	21170	21120	21060	21010	20960	20910	20860	440
450	20800	20750	20690	20640	20590	20540	20490	20440	20380	20330	450
460	20280	20230	20180	20130	20080	20030	19970	19920	19870	19820	460
470	19770	19720	19660	19610	19560	19510	19460	19410	19360	19310	470
480	19260	19210	19160	19110	19060	19010	18970	18920	18870	18820	480
490	18770	18720	18670	18620	18570	18520	18470	18420	18370	18330	490
500	18280	18230	18180	18130	18090	18040	17990	17940	17900	17850	500
510	17800	17750	17700	17650	17610	17560	17510	17470	17420	17370	510
520	17330	17280	17230	17190	17140	17090	17050	17000	16960	16910	520
530	16860	16820	16770	16720	16680	16630	16580	16540	16490	16450	530
540	16400	16360	16310	16270	16220	16180	16130	16090	16040	16000	540
550	15950	15910	15860	15820	15770	15730	15680	15640	15590	15550	550
560	15510	15460	15420	15370	15330	15280	15240	15190	15150	15110	560
570	15070	15020	14980	14940	14900	14850	14810	14770	14720	14680	570
580	14640	14600	14550	14510	14470	14430	14380	14340	14300	14260	580
590	14220	14170	14130	14090	14040	14000	13960	13920	13880	13840	590
600	13790	13750	13710	13670	13620	13580	13540	13500	13460	13420	600
610	13380	13340	13300	13260	13210	13170	13130	13090	13050	13010	610
620	12970	12930	12890	12850	12810	12770	12730	12690	12650	12610	620
630	12570	12530	12490	12450	12410	12360	12320	12280	12240	12200	630
640	12160	12120	12090	12050	12010	11970	11930	11890	11850	11810	640
650	11770	11730	11690	11650	11610	11570	11540	11500	11460	11420	650
660	11380	11350	11310	11270	11230	11190	11150	11110	11080	11040	660
670	11000	10960	10930	10890	10850	10810	10770	10730	10700	10660	670
680	10620	10580	10550	10510	10470	10430	10400	10360	10320	10280	680
690	10250	10210	10170	10140	10100	10060	10030	9990	9950	9920	690
700	9880	9840	9800	9760	9730	9690	9650	9620	9580	9540	700
710	9510	9470	9440	9400	9360	9330	9290	9260	9220	9180	710
720	9150	9110	9070	9040	9000	8970	8930	8900	8860	8830	720
730	8790	8760	8720	8680	8650	8610	8570	8540	8510	8470	730
740	8440	8400	8370	8330	8300	8260	8230	8190	8150	8120	740
750	8080	8050	8010	7980	7950	7920	7880	7850	7810	7780	750
760	7740	7710	7670	7640	7600	7570	7530	7500	7460	7430	760
770	7400	7360	7330	7300	7260	7230	7200	7160	7130	7090	770
780	7060	7030	6990	6960	6930	6890	6860	6830	6790	6760	780
790	6720	6690	6660	6620	6590	6560	6530	6490	6460	6430	790
800	6390	6360	6330	6300	6260	6230	6200	6160	6130	6100	800
810	6060	6030	6000	5970	5940	5900	5870	5840	5800	5770	810
820	5740	5710	5670	5640	5610	5570	5540	5510	5480	5450	820
830	5420	5380	5350	5320	5290	5260	5220	5190	5160	5130	830
840	5100	5060	5030	5000	4970	4940	4910	4870	4840	4810	840
850	4780	4750	4720	4680	4650	4620	4590	4560	4530	4500	850
860	4460	4430	4400	4370	4340	4310	4280	4250	4220	4190	860
870	4150	4120	4090	4060	4030	4000	3970	3940	3910	3880	870
880	3850	3820	3790	3760	3730	3690	3660	3630	3600	3570	880
890	3540	3510	3480	3450	3420	3390	3360	3330	3300	3270	890
900	3240	3210	3180	3150	3120	3090	3060	3030	3000	2970	900
910	2940	2910	2880	2850	2820	2790	2760	2730	2700	2670	910
920	2650	2620	2590	2560	2530	2500	2470	2440	2410	2380	920
930	2350	2320	2300	2270	2240	2210	2180	2150	2120	2090	930
940	2060	2030	2000	1980	1950	1920	1890	1860	1840	1810	940
950	1780	1750	1720	1690	1660	1630	1600	1570	1550	1520	950
960	1490	1460	1430	1400	1380	1350	1320	1290	1260	1230	960
970	1210	1180	1150	1120	1100	1070	1040	1010	980	960	970
980	930	900	870	840	810	780	750	720	700	670	980
990	640	610	580	560	530	500	480	450	420	400	990
1000	370	340	310	290	260	230	200	170	150	120	1000
1010	90	60	40	10	-20	-50	-70	-100	-130	-150	1010
1020	-180	-210	-240	-260	-290	-320	-350	-380	-400	-430	1020
1030	-460	-480	-510	-540	-560	-590	-620	-650	-670	-700	1030

FIG. 12–10.

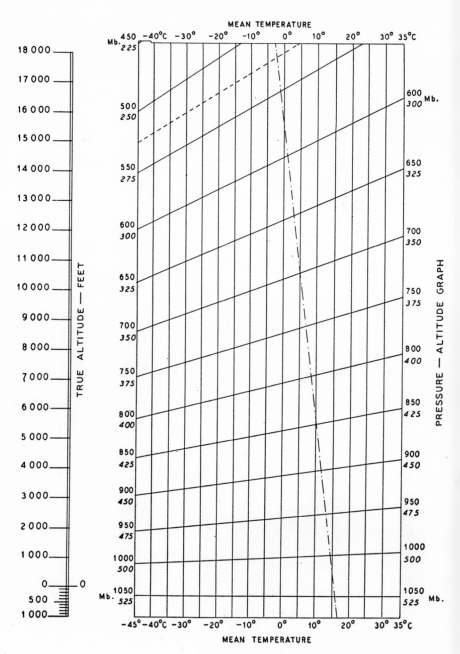

FIG. 12–11.

GLOSSARY

ABSOLUTE CENTIGRADE—A scale of temperature whereon 373° represents the boiling point of pure water at standard atmospheric pressure, and 273° represents the melting point of pure-water ice. It differs from the Centigrade Scale only by the constant 273°. For conversion of centigrade to absolute centigrade, see page 21. (See STANDARD ATMOSPHERE.)

ABSOLUTE ZERO—The temperature of a body from which all heat has been removed, and at which all molecular action ceases. For practical purposes, it is − 273° C and − 460° F. It is physically impossible to have any degree of temperature below "absolute zero" which, though impossible of practical attainment, marks a very real and practically useful basis of calculations involving the laws of gases.

ADIABAT—A curve or line on a chart showing the adiabatic lapse rate, —whether dry or moist, respectively.

ADIABATIC PROCESS—If a mass of air (or other gas) is compressed or expanded in volume without gaining or losing any heat to or from outside sources it is said to undergo an *adiabatic process*. Its temperature and volume will change in a manner peculiar to such circumstances only. In expansion it will undergo "adiabatic cooling," while in compression it will undergo "adiabatic heating," and its change in temperature will be an "adiabatic temperature change." When air is lifted it expands and cools adiabatically at a rate of 1° C for each 100 meters (or 1° F for each 180 ft) of altitude change, if the air is unsaturated; this is called the *dry-adiabatic lapse rate* of temperature change. If the air is saturated, the air cools at only (about) one half the above rate, and this is known as the *moist-adiabatic lapse rate*. The reason for the difference between these two lapse rates is found in the fact that, in the condensation of saturated air, the *latent heat of vaporization* is released back into the air again, tending to re-heat the air to a certain extent, thus slowing down the rate of cooling of the saturated air.

ADVECTION—Process of transfer by means of horizontal motion.

ADVECTION FOG—Advection fog is formed when warm moist air comes in contact with a colder surface; this contact with the cold surface cools the air to its dew point, thereby causing condensation and fog. It is a common phenomenon throughout the year over cold ocean currents (for example, the Labrador Current) when the air comes from warmer regions.

AEROLOGY—That branch of meteorology which treats of the free atmosphere, i.e., unaffected by surface effects.

AEROMETEOROGRAPH—An instrument made for carrying in an aircraft for the purpose of making an "air sounding," i.e., an investigation of the atmospheric conditions at various levels. The instrument makes a running record of atmospheric pressure, temperature and relative humidity at the various altitudes reached by the aircraft in flight.

AIR—A mechanical mixture of gases surrounding the earth and of which the earth's atmosphere is composed.

AIRFALL—A current of heavy air flowing down over the tops of ridges, buildings, etc.

AIR MASS—A term applied by meteorologists to an extensive body of air within which the conditions of temperature and moisture in a horizontal plane are essentially uniform.

AIR POCKETS—Areas in which descending currents of air cause an aircraft to drop rapidly toward the earth. They are found principally in clouds of the cumulus type, over small water or wooded areas, and on the lee side of hills, mountains, hangars and other obstacles.

ALTIMETER—An instrument based on the principle of the aneroid barometer and used for indicating altitude above or below a given datum point, usually the ground or sea level.

ALTIMETRY—In Pressure Pattern Flying, the use of comparative readings of two altimeters of different types (i.e., one of the radio absolute type, the other of barometric pressure type) to obtain an indication of horizontal pressure gradient while in flight.

ALTITUDE—Vertical distance measured above sea level. (See PRESSURE ALTITUDE.)

ANEMOGRAM—The record traced by a self-registering anemometer.

ANEMOGRAPH—An instrument which makes a running record of the velocity of the wind.

ANEMOMETER—An instrument which measures and indicates the momentary velocity of the wind.

ANEMOSCOPE—The direction of the wind velocity is indicated by a wind vane. When the vane is attached to an indicating instrument showing the direction on a calibrated scale, it is called an anemoscope.

ANEROID BAROMETER—An instrument for measuring the pressure of the atmosphere. Variation of the air pressure causes the expansion or contraction of a sealed thin, flat, metallic cylinder which in turn causes a pointer to move across a graduated dial. Temperature changes and mechanical friction within the instrument require that it be checked frequently with a mercurial barometer and corrections applied accordingly.

ANTICYCLOGENESIS—The term applied to the process which creates or develops a new anticyclone. The word is applied also to the process which produces an intensification of a pre-existing anticyclone.

ANTICYCLONE—(See EMINENCE).

ANTITRADES—Upper tropical winds blowing steadily in a direction opposite to the trade wind, beyond which, in the north temperate and the south temperate zones, it becomes a surface wind.

ANVIL—The characteristic fibrous, spreading top of a cumulo-nimbus cloud in full development.

AQUEOUS VAPOR—Water vapor.

ARCTIC AIR—Air of an air mass whose source lies in the frigid arctic or antarctic regions.

ARCTIC FRONT—The line of discontinuity between very cold air flowing directly from the Arctic regions and polar maritime air that has moved away from its source region in a more or less circuitous path and been warmed through contact with the ocean surface.

ARCTIC SMOKE—A form of fog caused by rapid evaporation from the surface of warmer water when very cold, dry air streams across it.

ATMOSPHERE—The whole mass of air surrounding the earth.

AURORA—A luminous phenomenon due to electrical discharges in the atmosphere; probably confined to the tenuous air of high altitudes. It is most commonly seen in sub-arctic and sub-antarctic latitudes. Called aurora borealis or aurora australis, according to the hemisphere in which it occurs. Observations with the spectroscope seem to indicate that a faint "permanent aurora" is a normal feature of the sky in all parts of the world.

BACKING—A shift of the wind in a counterclockwise direction, i.e., to the left of the direction from which it had been blowing. (See VEERING, opposite of BACKING.)

BAR—A unit of pressure equal to 1,000,000 dynes per square centimeter. A bar = 100 centibars = 1000 millibars. A barometric pressure of one bar is sometimes called a "C.G.S. atmosphere" and is equivalent to a pressure of 29.531 inches of mercury at 32° F and in latitude 45°.

BAROGRAM—The continuous record made by a self-registering barometer.

BAROGRAPH—An instrument based on the principle of an aneroid barometer which makes a continuous record of atmospheric pressure.

BAROMETER—An instrument which measures atmospheric pressure.

BAROMETRIC TENDENCY—The changes of barometic pressure within a specified time (usually 3 hours) before the observation, usually indicated by symbols at the right of the station as shown on the weather map.

BEAUFORT SCALE—The scale of wind force devised by Admiral Sir Francis Beaufort in 1805, beginning with dead calm indicated by 0 and ending with hurricane indicated by 17. The scale is based on the effect of wind on various ground objects such as smoke, leaves, trees etc. (Numbers above 12 are an extension of the original scale.)

BLIZZARD—A violent, intensely cold wind, laden with snow.

BUMPINESS—A condition of the air caused by thermal or mechanical turbulence, i.e., ascending and descending currents and eddies, which produces a sensation in flight comparable to riding along a rough road in an automobile. Such a condition close to the ground may be dangerous and requires great caution and alertness of the pilot.

BUYS–BALLOTT'S LAW—In the northern hemisphere, if you face the wind, the area of lower pressure is on your *right* and (generally) slightly behind you.   In the southern hemisphere, if you face the wind, the area of lower pressure is on your *left* and (generally) slightly behind you.

CALIBRATION—The name ordinarily given to the process of ascertaining the corrections to be applied to the indicated readings of an instrument in order to obtain true values.

CALM—A region where air movement is less than one mile per hour. Beaufort number zero.

CALMS OF CANCER: CALMS OF CAPRICORN—The belts of high pressure lying north of the northeast trade winds and south of the southeast trade winds, respectively.

CASCADE—The name applies to the mass of spray or dense vapor thrown outward from around the base of a water spout.   Also known as "bush," or "bon-fire."

CEILING—In general, the total distance from ground or water vertically to the base of lowest cloud layer that, in summation with all lower layers of clouds and obscuring phenomena, covers 0.6 or more of the sky. For detailed variations of the term, refer to the WBAN Manual of Surface Observations, "Circular N," U. S. Weather Bureau, Washington, D. C.

CENTER OF ACTION—Any one of several large areas of high and low barometric pressure, changing little in location, and persisting through a season or through the whole year; e.g., the Iceland low, the Siberian winter high, etc.   Changes in the intensity and positions of these pressure systems are associated with widespread weather changes.

CENTIGRADE—A scale of temperature whereon 100° represents the boiling point of pure water at standard atmospheric pressure, and 0° represents the melting point of pure-water ice.   For conversion of centigrade degrees to Fahrenheit degrees, see page 20.

CERAUNOGRAPH—An electronic instrument for recording the occurrence of lightning discharges whether close by or so far away as to be invisible and their thunder unheard.

CHINOOK, OR CHINOOK WIND—A Foehn blowing down the eastern slopes of the Rocky Mountains over the adjacent plains, in the United States and Canada.   In winter, this warm dry wind causes snow to disappear with remarkable rapidity, and hence it has been nicknamed the "snow-eater." The Santa Ana wind in Southern California is of the same type.

CHUBASCO—A violent squall on the west coast of tropical and subtropical North America.

CLIMATE—The prevalent or characteristic meteorological conditions of any place or region.

CLOUD—An accumulation of condensed water vapor, visible in the air. It may be composed of tiny water droplets in suspension, at low and medium altitudes, or of snow or fine ice crystals in the subfreezing temperatures of the upper altitudes.

CLOUD BANNER—A banner-like cloud streaming off from a mountain peak.

CLOUDBURST—A sudden, torrential downpour of rain usually from a thunderstorm (cumulonimbus) cloud.

CLOUD CAP—A cap-like cloud crowning (1) a mountain summit or (2) another cloud, especially a mass of cumulonimbus.

CLOUDINESS (Sky Cover)—Amount of sky covered, but not necessarily hidden, by clouds or obscuring phenomena aloft or concealed by obscuring phenomena on the ground or both. (Circular "N," U. S. Weather Bureau.)

COL—An area on the weather map between two depressions and two eminences, giving a "saddle back" shape to that part of the map.

COLD AIR MASS—An air mass that is colder than the surface over which it is moving.

COLD DOME—A moving mountain or mass of cold, dense air.

COLD FRONT—A narrow strip or zone (indicated by a special line on the weather map) marking the boundary between two air masses and where cold air replaces warm air.

COLD WAVE—A rapid and marked fall of temperature during the cold season of the year. The United States Weather Bureau applies this term to a fall of temperature in 24 hours equaling or exceeding a specified number of degrees and reaching a specified minimum temperature or lower, the specifications varying for different parts of the country and for different periods of the year.

CONDENSATION—The process whereby water vapor is re-formed into water, the reverse of the process of evaporation.

CONTINENTAL CLIMATE—The type of climate characteristic of the interior of a continent. As compared with a marine climate, a continental climate has a large annual and daily range of temperature.

CONVECTION—The process of transfer of heat in the atmosphere by ascending and descending currents, due to thermal instability.

CONVECTIONAL PRECIPITATION—Precipitation from clouds caused by thermal instability, i.e., clouds of the cumulus or cumulonimbus type.

CONVERGENCE—An inflowing of air into a region from more than one direction in such manner that more air flows in than flows out. So long as this continues it will tend to produce an increasing pressure and temperature with their consequent effects. If the air is sufficiently humid some of it, if forced upward, may cause a "convergent fog" or low stratus clouds.

CORIOLIS FORCE—A deflective force caused by the rotation of the earth on its axis. It causes moving bodies to be apparently deflected to the right of their course in the northern hemisphere and to the left in the southern hemisphere. The magnitude of this deflective force is basically dependent upon the velocity of the moving body and the latitude. (See FERREL'S LAW.)

CUMULIFORM—A general term applied to all clouds having dome-shaped upper surfaces which exhibit protuberances, the bases of such clouds being generally horizontal. Cumuliform clouds are characteristically distinct and separated from one another by clear spaces.

CYCLOGENESIS—The term applied to the process which creates or develops a new cyclone. The word is applied also to the process which produces an intensification of a pre-existing cyclone.

CYCLONE—This term, indicating in general a region of low atmospheric pressure, is now generally reserved to refer to violent disturbances originating in the tropics. In temperate and higher latitudes an area of low pressure is now usually designed as a *low* or a *depression*.

CYCLOSTROPHIC WIND—A wind which blows as a result of pressure gradient and centrifugal force, but in the absence of Coriolis Force. It is, of necessity, cyclonic and restricted to the equatorial zones—the only place where Coriolis Force is zero, or nearly so. Hurricanes are largely cyclostrophic until reaching latitudes high enough to be affected by Coriolis Force.

DEEPENING—The occurrence of decreasing pressure in the center of a moving pressure system.

DENSITY—The mass of a unit volume of any substance.

DEPRESSION—(See CYCLONE.)

DEVIATION OF THE WIND—The angle between the direction of the wind and the direction of the pressure gradient. (Cf. INCLINATION OF THE WIND.)

DEVIL—The name applied to a dust whirlwind in India. The term is also current in South Africa. (In Western U. S. the term is "dust devil.")

DEW—Condensed water vapor deposited on the surface of terrestrial objects.

DEW POINT—The temperature to which air must be cooled in order to become saturated, cooling below such temperature resulting in condensation.

DISCONTINUITY—The term applied in a special sense by meteorologists to a zone within which there is a comparatively rapid transition of the meteorological elements, particularly the boundary surface separating air masses of different temperatures.

DISTURBANCE—A local departure from the normal or average wind condition of any part of the world or, in other words, a feature of what is sometimes called the "secondary" circulation of the atmosphere, as distinguished from the general circulation. In every-day usage disturbance has come to be synonymous with *cyclone* and *depression*.

DIURNAL—Daily.

DIVERGENCE—The opposite of Convergence.

DOLDRUMS—The tropical regions of the Equatorial Belt characterized by calms and light, shifting winds with frequent thunderstorms, squalls and heavy showers.

DRIZZLE—Precipitation consisting of numerous tiny droplets. Drizzle originates from stratus clouds. The water droplets are so numerous the air seems full of them. "Drizzle" is essentially the same as mist in the U. S. weather code.

DROUGHT—A protracted period of dry weather.

DRY ADIABATIC LAPSE RATE—A rate of decrease of temperature with height approximately equal to 1° C per 100 meters (1° F per 180 ft). This is close to the rate at which an ascending body of unsaturated air will cool due to adiabatic expansion.

DRY BULB—A name given to an ordinary thermometer used to determine the temperature of the air, in order to distinguish it from the wet bulb.

DRY FOG—A haze due to the presence of dust or smoke in the air.

DYNAMIC COOLING—Decrease in temperature of air when caused by its adiabatic expansion in moving to a higher altitude or other region of lower pressure.

DYNAMIC METEOROLOGY—The branch of meteorology that treats of the motion of the atmosphere and its relations to other meteorological phenomena.

EDDY—A swirl in the air caused by flow over rough terrain, around terrestrial obstacles, or meeting with other air having different characteristics of density or motion.

EMINENCE—A region where the atmospheric pressure is higher than that of other surrounding regions. It is characterized by generally fair weather with a wind system of counterclockwise rotation. In the northern hemisphere rains, if existent therein, are usually found in the southern or southeastern sector. It is the counterpart of a *depression* or region of *low* pressure.

EQUATORIAL AIR—Air of an air mass whose source lies in the Equatorial Belt or *doldrums*.

EQUIVALENT POTENTIAL TEMPERATURE—The temperature that a given sample of air would have if it were brought adiabatically to to the top of the atmosphere (i.e., to zero pressure) so that along its route all the water vapor present were condensed and precipitated, the latent heat of condensation being given to the sample, and then the remaining dry air compressed adiabatically to a pressure of 1000 millibars. The equivalent potential temperature at any point is therefore determined by the values of absolute temperature, pressure, and humidity. It is one of the most conservative of air mass properties.

EVAPORIMETER—An instrument for measuring the rate of evaporation of water into the atmosphere.

EYE OF THE STORM—A calm region at the center of a tropical cyclone or a break in the clouds marking its location.

FAHRENHEIT—A scale of temperature whereon 212° represents the boiling point of pure water at standard atmospheric pressure, and 32° represents the melting point of pure-water ice. For conversion of Fahrenheit degrees to centigrade degrees, see page 21.

FALL–WIND—A wind blowing down a mountainside; or any wind

having a strong downward component. Fall-winds include the Foehn, mistral, bora, etc.

FALSE CIRRUS—Cirrus-like clouds at or somewhat below the summit of a thunder cloud; more appropriately called "thunder cirrus."

FERREL'S LAW—"When a mass of air starts to move over the earth's surface, it is deflected to the right in the Northern Hemisphere, and to the left in the Southern Hemisphere, and tends to move in a circle whose radius depends upon its velocity and its distance from the equator."

FESTOON CLOUD—Mammatocumulus.

FILLING—The occurrence of increasing pressure in the center of a moving pressure system. *Filling* is the opposite of *Deepening*.

FOEHN (or Föhn) **WIND**—A relatively warm, dry wind blowing along generally downward slopes. The air is heated in adiabatic compression as it flows to lower levels. Such winds are frequently caused by the subsidence of heavy, superior air from an upper air mass. In the United States they are found most frequently in the northwestern states and along the eastward slopes of the Rocky Mountain and Great Plains region.

FOG—Fog is formed when the air near the earth's surface is cooled below its dew point. Fog is, therefore, nothing but a cloud that touches the ground. By international agreement such a cloud is called *fog* when the visibility is less than 1 km; if the visibility is greater than this, it is called *mist,* or *thin fog.*

FRICTION LAYER—The lower layer of air, below the "free atmosphere," where friction with the earth's surface affects its flow. Depending upon conditions, its thickness is usually from 1500 to 3000 feet.

FRONT—A definite boundary or mixing zone (a few miles wide) which occurs between two dissimilar air masses, or a surface of discontinuity between two juxtaposed currents of air possessing different densities, or more simply, the boundary between two different air masses which have been brought together. The two air masses do not immediately mix and the denser, colder air always underlies or underrides the rarer (less dense) warm air in the form of a wedge. This condition of warm air overlying the colder air in the boundary or mixing zone, which is really the "front," is sometimes called a discontinuity surface and is generally inclined at a slight angle to the surface of the earth.

FRONTOGENESIS—The term used to describe the process which creates a front, i.e., produces a discontinuity in a continuous field of the meteorological elements; also applied to the process which increases the intensity of a pre-existing front. Frontogenesis is generally set up by the horizontal convergence of air currents possessing widely different properties.

FRONTOLYSIS—The term used to describe the process which tends to destroy a pre-existing front. "Frontolysis" is generally brought about by horizontal mixing and divergence of the air within the frontal zone.

FROST—A crystalline ice formation deposited on objects when the temperature is below 32° F. Sometimes caused by direct sublimation of the water vapor into ice crystals on an object whose temperature is below 32° F.

Will also form sometimes on an airplane when it passes from a cold layer of air into a stratum of air of much higher temperature and moist content. It is dangerous to attempt a take-off when the airplane is covered with frost as this greatly increases the drag by destroying the boundary layer of air next to the airfoil.

FROST SMOKE—(See ARCTIC SMOKE.)

GALE—Wind with an hourly velocity exceeding some specified value. In American practice a wind of force 7–10 on the Beaufort scale is counted a gale.

GENERAL CIRCULATION—The grand wind system of the entire earth, also called *Atmospheric Circulation*. (See Fig. 6–1.)

GEOSTROPHIC WIND—The velocity of the wind in the free atmosphere attained when blowing under the conditions of complete balance of forces, i.e., the "pressure force" due to the pressure gradient and the "anti-pressure component" of the Coriolis force. (See Fig. 6–3.)

GLAZE (or Glazed Frost)—A coating of clear ice formed on terrestrial objects by rain which freezes upon contact.

GLORY—A series of concentric colored rings around the shadow of the observer, or of his head only, cast upon a cloud or fog bank. It is due to the diffraction of reflected light.

GRADIENT—The increase or decrease of a meteorological element with respect to distance, either horizontal or vertical, e.g., a *barometric gradient* of plus 10 millibars per thousand miles, or a *vertical temperature gradient* of minus 4° C per thousand feet altitude, the latter being more commonly called the *lapse rate*. Temperature lapse rate is an indicator of atmospheric stability, while barometric gradient is an indicator of wind velocity. A steep barometric gradient indicates a rapid pressure drop with strong winds; a shallow one, the reverse.

GRADIENT WIND—The wind velocity necessary to balance the pressure gradient. The true wind above the friction layer is approximately equal to the gradient wind.

GRANULAR SNOW—Precipitation from stratus clouds (frozen drizzle) of small (1 mm or less in diameter) opaque grains of snow. Granular snow offers no appreciable icing conditions to aircraft in flight.

GREAT CIRCLE—A circle on the earth's surface, having the earth's diameter as its own diameter. A great circle can be drawn between any two points on the globe, and the arc between them is the shortest distance between the two points.

GUST—A sharp increase in wind velocity but of short duration.

HAIL—Hard ice globules falling from the clouds. *Soft hail* is milky white, pithy and soft.

HALO—A generic name for a large group of optical phenomena caused by ice crystals in the atmosphere. The commonest of these phenomena is the halo of 22° (i.e., of 22° radius), surrounding the sun or moon. The halo of 46° and the rare halo of 90°, or halo of Hevelius, also surround the luminary. Other forms of halo are the tangent arcs, parhelia (or paraselenae), parhelic (or paraselenic), circle, anthelion, etc.

HAZE—Very fine particles of moisture, smoke and dust suspended in the air. It decreases visibility.

HIGH—(See EMINENCE.)

HORSE LATITUDE—The regions of calms in the subtropical anticyclone belts.

HOT WAVE—A period of abnormally high temperatures. It has sometimes been defined, in the United States, as a period of three or more consecutive days during each of which the temperature is 90° F or over.

HUMIDITY—Water vapor content of the air. (See RELATIVE and SPECIFIC HUMIDITY.)

HURRICANE—Violent disturbance of tropical origin (see CYCLONE), any wind above 75 miles per hour.

HYDROMETEOR—A generic term for weather phenomena such as rain, cloud, fog, etc. which mostly depend upon modification in the condition of the water vapor in the atmosphere.

HYGROGRAPH—An instrument which makes a continuous record of humidity.

HYGROMETER—An indicator which indicates the momentary value of the humidity.

HYGROTHERMOGRAPH—An instrument which makes a continuous record of both humidity and temperature.

ICEBERG—A large mass of ice that breaks from the tongue of a glacier running into the sea and floats away.

ICE NEEDLES—Thin crystals or shafts of ice, so light that they seem to be suspended in the air.

INCLINATION OF THE WIND—The angle which the wind direction makes with the direction of the isobar at the place of observation. Over the ocean the angle is approximately 10°, while over-land it is usually between 20° and 30°. (Cf. DEVIATION OF THE WIND.)

INSOLATION—Solar radiation, as received by the earth or other planets; also, the rate of delivery of the same, per unit of horizontal surface.

INSTABILITY—That condition of saturated air when its lapse rate is greater than the moist adiabatic or of unsaturated air when its lapse rate is greater than the dry adiabatic. Instability is evidenced in ascending thermal currents, cumulus-type clouds and thunderstorms.

INTERTROPICAL FRONT—The boundary between the trade wind system of the northern and southern hemispheres. It manifests itself as a fairly broad zone of transition commonly known as the *doldrums*.

INVERSION—A stratum in the air where the lapse rate is such that the temperature increases (instead of decreases) with altitude.

IONOSPHERE—A layer of ionized air high above the earth's surface. It actually appears to be composed of at least three layers, E, F_1 and F_2, at heights varying from 40–50 to 175 or 200 miles.

ISALLOBARS—On a weather map, lines of equal barometric tendency.

ISOBARS—On a weather map, lines of equal barometric pressure.

ISOTHERMS—On a weather map, lines of equal temperature.

KNOT—A knot is a speed equal to one nautical mile (6080 ft) per hour. It is the standard unit of speed for marine and air navigation. (Its reference is to speed or velocity only, and is not used as a measure of distance.)

LAND AND SEA BREEZES—The breezes that, on certain coasts and under certain conditions, blow from the land by night and from the water by day.

LAPSE RATE—The rate of decrease of temperature in the atmosphere with height; usually the decrease in temperature with altitude is 3.5° F for each 1000 feet. (See ADIABATIC PROCESS.)

LENTICULAR CLOUD—A cloud having approximately the form of a double-convex lens. Clouds of this sort may be formed at the crests of standing waves of atmosphere such as are often induced by mountain ranges; usually they represent a traditional stage in the development or disintegration of one of the more well-known cloud types.

LID—A term often used to denote a temperature inversion in the atmosphere. Since the air in an inversion is stable, convectional currents cannot exist within it. For this reason an inversion is called a "lid," since it prevents the air below and above it from mixing. "Lids" may vary in thickness from a few feet to several hundred feet, according to the conditions.

LIGHTNING—The neutralizing electric flash between two oppositely-charged areas.

LINE SQUALL—A long cumulonimbus cloud (*cumulonimbus arcus*) extending along a cold front, with violent winds, rain, thunder and lightning, and, frequently, heavy hail. With a strong cold front, these squalls may extend from 100 to 400 miles in an almost unbroken line making it impracticable to fly around them. They may extend to such altitudes as to make it impracticable to fly over them, and the violent winds and torrential rain below them make it dangerous to attempt to fly in the area underneath them where may be found heavy downdrafts extending all the way to the ground. (See Fig. 7–4.)

LOW—See CYCLONE.

MACKEREL SKY—A sky covered with or containing large patches of cirro-cumulus or alto-cumulus clouds resembling the scales and stripes on the side of a mackerel.

MAMMATOCUMULUS—A form of cloud showing pendulous, sac-like protuberances.

MARINE CLIMATE—A type of climate characteristic of the ocean and oceanic islands. Its most prominent feature is equability of temperature.

MAXIMUM—The highest value of any element occurring during a given period.

MENISCUS—The curved upper surface of a liquid in a tube.

METEOROLOGY—The science of the atmosphere.

METEOROGRAPH—A self-recording instrument for recording pressure, temperature, and humidity in the free air.

MICROBAROGRAPH—An instrument designed for recording small and rapid variations of atmospheric pressure.

MILLIBAR—(See BAR.)

MINIMUM—The lowest value of any element occurring during a given period.

MIRAGE—An apparent displacement or distortion of observed objects by abnormal atmospheric refraction. Sometimes the images of objects are inverted, magnified, multiplied, raised, or brought nearer to the eye than the object. Refraction layers in the atmosphere often assume appearance of fog.

MIST—A very thin fog, in which the horizontal visibility is greater than 1 kilometer, or approximately 1100 yards. (This is the definition laid down by the International Meteorological Organization.) In North America the word is often used synonymously with drizzle or fine rain.

MONSOON—Seasonal winds which blow with great steadiness, reversing their direction with the change of season. In summer their direction is generally toward the large heated land areas, rushing in to displace the great volumes of air rising in convective currents. In winter they blow, with less force, outward from the great areas of ice and snow toward the tropics or out over the surface of the warmer ocean.

NEPHOSCOPE—An instrument used in observing the direction and velocity of cloud movement.

NEUTRAL POINT—The term applied in a special sense to any point at which the axis of a wedge of high pressure intersects the axis of a trough of low pressure. Also called "Saddle point." (See COL.)

NOCTILUCENT CLOUDS—Luminous, cirrus-like clouds sometimes visible throughout the short nights of summer; supposed to be clouds of dust at great altitudes shining with reflected sunlight. Such clouds were observed during several summers after the eruption of Krakatoa (1883) and are still occasionally reported.

NUCLEUS—A particle upon which condensation of water vapor occurs in the free atmosphere in the form of a water drop or an ice crystal.

OCCLUDED FRONT—(See OCCLUSION.)

OCCLUSION—When one front overtakes another, forcing one front upward from the surface of the earth, the front is said to be an *occluded front,* and the zone in which this condition exists is called the *occlusion.*

OROGRAPHIC LIFTING—The lifting of air caused by its flow up the slopes of hills or mountains.

OROGRAPHIC RAIN—Rain resulting from orographic lifting.

OROGRAPHY—The science which treats of mountains.

OZONE—A colorless gas (O_3) obtained as an allotropic form of oxygen. It is a strong oxidizer, and has a chlorine-like odor. It has an important absorbing effect on ultra-violet radiation. It exists in rather slight quantity near the earth's surface, increasing to a maximum at an average altitude of about 35,000 ft. It can often be smelled in the air near the surface immediately following a thunderstorm, particularly in the immediate vicinity of lightning flashes.

PARHELION (plural PARHELIA)—A mock sun, or sun dog; a form of halo consisting of a more or less distinctly colored image of the sun at the same altitude as the latter above the horizon, and hence lying on the parhelic circle, if present. The ordinary parhelia are 22° from the sun in azimuth, or a little more, according to the altitude of the luminary. Parhelia have occasionally been seen about 46° from the sun. Analogous phenomena seen in connection with the moon are called paraselenae, mock moons, or moon dogs. (See HALO.)

PILOT BALLOON—A small balloon inflated with hydrogen or helium until the buoyancy is sufficient to float the balloon in air with prescribed counterweights attached, thus giving it a known ascensional rate. When cast adrift it is employed in determining the direction and velocity of the wind at various levels. (See Fig. 3–10.)

POLAR AIR—Air of an air mass whose source lies in the region of the poles.

POLAR CONTINENTAL AIR—The term used to describe any air mass that originates over land or frozen ocean areas in the polar regions. Polar continental air is characterized by low temperatures, low specific humidity, and a high degree of vertical stability.

POLAR FRONT—The general frontal zone where air from the cold polar regions meets the warm tropical air from the subtropical anti-cyclone belts; more clearly defined over oceans than over continents.

POLAR MARITIME AIR—The term used to describe any air mass that originally came from the polar regions but has since been modified by reasons of its passage over a relative warm ocean surface. Polar maritime air is characterized by moderately low surface temperatures, moderately high surface specific humidity, and a considerable degree of vertical instability.

POTENTIAL TEMPERATURE. The resultant temperature attained by a sample of air when compressed adiabatically to standard pressure of 1000 millibars (i.e., approximately sea-level).

PRECIPITATION—The product of condensation of water vapor in the atmosphere.

PRESSURE—An elliptical expression, current in meteorological literature for atmospheric pressure, or barometric pressure.

PRESSURE ALTITUDE—The altitude indicated by an altimeter when the barometric scale thereof is adjusted to the standard sea level atmospheric pressure of 29.92 in. of mercury.

PRESSURE TENDENCY—Same as BAROMETRIC TENDENCY.

PRESSURE GRADIENT—The decrease in barometric pressure per unit horizontal distance in the direction in which the pressure decreases most rapidly.

PREVAILING WESTERLIES—Winds which blow toward the poles from the Horse Latitudes. Not so steady as the Trade Winds, but more constant in the Southern Hemisphere, due to oceans and lack of land interruptions. They are known as the "Roaring Forties" owing to the latitude at which they occur.

PSEUDO–ADIABATIC PROCESS—When saturated air is rising in the atmosphere and is losing its water vapor by condensation and precipitation, the process is called a pseudo-adiabatic process.

PSYCHROMETER—An instrument for measuring humidity. It is composed of two thermometers one of which has a water-saturated wick covering the thermometer bulb, called the "wet bulb." Evaporation from the wick cools the "wet bulb," making it read lower than the other ("dry bulb") thermometer. The drier (less humid) the air, the more rapid the evaporation and, consequently, the greater the difference in temperature between the wet and dry bulbs. With this difference in temperature and the dry bulb temperature as arguments, the relative humidity is obtained from a Humidity Table published by the U. S. Weather Bureau.—When the air is saturated, i.e., 100% relative humidity, evaporation ceases and the wet and dry bulbs read exactly the same.—In the "sling" type psychrometer (Fig. 3–4) the instrument is whirled around to produce the evaporation from the wet bulb.

PUMPING—Unsteadiness of the mercury in the barometer caused by fluctuations of the air pressure produced by a gusty wind, or due to the oscillation of a ship.

PYRHELIOMETER—An instrument that measures solar radiation by its heating effects.

QUASI–STATIONARY FRONT—The ideal stationary front is seldom found in nature, but it often occurs that the frontal movement is such that no appreciable displacement takes place. The front is then said to be quasi-stationary. Such a front constitutes the most intricate forecasting problem, for (1) as the velocity of the front is nil, its future movement will depent on the acceleration, which is exceedingly difficult to evaluate or even estimate, and (2) the lack of movement of the front is highly favorable for the formation of cyclonic disturbances.

RADIATION—Emission of energy in the form of waves, either light or heat or both.

RADIATION FOG—Fog characteristically resulting from the radiational cooling of air near the surface of the ground on calm clear nights.

RADIOMETEOROGRAPH—Same as RADIOSONDE.

RADIOSONDE—An instrument which fulfills the same functions as the AEROMETEOROGRAPH but to much greater altitudes. A small pilot balloon carries the instrument aloft; a small parachute lowers it to earth again when the balloon bursts in the upper atmosphere. By means of a small clockwork motor and very light weight radio transmitting set, the indications of instruments sensitive to pressure, temperature and humidity are automatically transmitted at regular intervals during the flight. The signals from the radiosonde are received and recorded on a special receiver on the ground and are then translated into readings of pressure, temperature and humidity at the various altitudes. Rewards, up to $20.00, are paid to persons who find and return radiosondes to the Weather Bureau. (See Fig. 3–12.)

RAIN—Water drops in the atmosphere, the result of precipitation.

RAINBOW—A luminous arc formed by the refraction and reflection of light in drops of water.

RAINFALL—The term sometimes synonymous with rain, but most frequently used in reference to amounts of precipitation (including snow, hail, etc.).

RAIN GAUGE—An instrument for measuring the amount of rainfall on the earth's surface.

RELATIVE HUMIDITY—The ratio of the actual moisture content of the air to the amount of moisture that the air could hold, saturated, at the same temperature. This is expressed as percentage.

REFRACTION—When light rays pass from a medium of one density into or through a medium of a different density, they are bent from the original direction of travel.

REPRESENTATIVE OBSERVATIONS—Those which give the true or typical meteorological conditions prevailing in an air mass; hence they must be relatively uninfluenced by local conditions.

RHUMB LINE—A line on the earth's surface which cuts all meridians at the same angle. Thus an aircraft flying a steady, true course is following a Rhumb Line, or loxodromic curve.

RIDGE—An elongated area of high pressure extending from an eminence, also called a WEDGE. (See Fig. 7–1.)

RIME ICE—White, opaque, granular ice which forms on various parts of aircraft in flight under certain conditions.

ROTATION OF THE EARTH (effect of)—(See CORIOLIS FORCE.)

SADDLE—(See COL.)

SANDSTORM—A storm wind filled with sand or dust particles.

ST. ELMO'S FIRE—A luminous brush discharge of electricity which appears on sharp points or edges of objects during the existence of strong electrical fields. It may appear as a general glow on the object or as numerous streamers. It is often seen on the wing tips and propellers of aircraft flying in or near thunder clouds.

SATURATED ADIABATIC LAPSE RATE—(See ADIABATIC PROCESS (Moist-adiabatic lapse rate).)

SATURATION—The condition that exists in the atmosphere when the partial pressure exerted by the water vapor present is equal to the maximum vapor pressure possible at the prevailing temperature. The condition of air which contains all the moisture it can hold.

SCARF–CLOUD—A thin cirrus-like cloud which often drapes the upper parts of tall cumulonimbus clouds.

SCUD—Low cloud fragments drifting below the main cloud layers, particularly following or during rainfall.

SEA BREEZES—(See LAND AND SEA BREEZES.)

SECONDARY FRONT—A second front of similar nature to and following fairly closely behind a primary front. A disturbance connected therewith is called a SECONDARY DISTURBANCE. Secondary disturbances frequently develop into much worse weather than, and have the effect of "killing," the primary disturbance.

SEMICIRCLE—The "dangerous semicircle" of a cyclone storm at sea is the half of the storm area in which rotary and progressive motions of the storm reinforce each other, and the winds are also directed in such a way as to drive a vessel running before the wind across the storm track ahead of the advancing center. The other half is called the "navigable" semicircle.

SHOWER—Precipitation of a rapidly varying intensity, falling from convective (cumulus type) clouds.

SKY COVER—(See "CLOUDINESS.")

SLEET—In the United States, sleet is another name for "freezing rain," i.e., rain which freezes on striking terrestrial objects. In Europe, sleet is defined as rain and snow falling simultaneously.

SMOG—A mixture of smoke and fog.

SMOKE—The products of incomplete combustion, suspended in the air.

SNOW—Condensed water vapor, congealed into white or transparent crystals or flakes in the air.

SOFT HAIL—White, opaque, round pellets of snow.

SOUNDING—An investigation of meteorological conditions at various altitudes above the earth's surface. Air soundings may be made by means of pilot (sounding) balloons for obtaining "winds aloft," or by aerometeorograph or radiosonde for obtaining pressure, temperature and humidity.

SOUNDING BALLOON—(See PILOT BALLOON.)

SOURCE REGION—An extensive area of the earth's surface characterized by essentially uniform surface conditions and so placed in respect to the general atmospheric circulation that air masses may remain over it long enough to acquire definite characteristic properties. Examples of source regions are the ice-covered polar regions and the broad expanses of uniformly warm tropical oceans.

SPECIFIC HUMIDITY—The number of grams of water vapor contained in one kilogram of air.

SQUALL—A sudden and violent wind often attended with rain or snow. A squall lasts for a matter of minutes as compared to a *gust* which usually passes in a matter of seconds.

STABILITY—Air is in a state of stability if, when displaced from its original level, it tends to return thereto. This holds true for saturated air when its lapse rate is less than the moist adiabatic, and for unsaturated air when its lapse rate is less than the dry adiabatic. (See INSTABILITY.)

STAGNATION POINT—The point on the leading edge of a body in the moving air stream which is the division point for the lines of airflow on either side of the body. The air is practically stationary at this point, and static pressure prevails, according to Bernoulli's Theory.

STANDARD ATMOSPHERE—A standard atmosphere is defined as one in which the sea-level temperature is $15°$ C; the sea-level pressure, 1013.2 millibars; and the lapse rate, $6.5°$ C per km up to 11 km (the stratosphere). In the ft-lb-sec system this amounts to very nearly a sea-level temperature of $59°$ F, a sea-level pressure of 29.92 in. of mercury, and a lapse rate of very nearly $3.5°$ F per 1000 ft of altitude. The real atmosphere duplicates the standard atmosphere only occasionally.

STATIC—In meteorology, a state in which the position or properties of an air mass or frontal zone are not changing or not moving, such as a "static front" or "static conditions." (See STATIONARY FRONT, QUASI-STATIONARY FRONT.)

STATIONARY FRONT—A stationary front is a front along which one air mass does not replace the other.

STORM—A violent disturbance of the atmosphere, either by wind or other undesirable meteorological conditions, such as rain, thunder and lightning, dust or sand, ice or sleet, etc.

STRATIFORM—A general term applied to all clouds which are arranged in unbroken horizontal layers or sheets.

STRATOSPHERE—The upper portion of the atmosphere lying above the tropopause. Motion of the air therein is mainly in horizontal, stratified flow with almost complete absence of vertical currents. (See Fig. 2–2.)

SUBLIMATION—At low temperatures the condensation nuclei become inactive and the sublimation nuclei become active. Under these conditions, water vapor present in the air changes directly from the vapor state to the solid state. An example of the sublimation process is the formation of frost, a condition wherein the vapor in the atmosphere sublimates, or changes directly into ice crystals without passing through the liquid state.

SUBSIDENCE—A slow downward "settling" of air from upper altitudes.

SUNSHINE RECORDER—An instrument for recording the duration of sunshine; certain types also record the intensity of sunshine.

SUPERIOR AIR—Superior air is believed to be developed by strong subsiding motions. Most frequently observed at higher and intermediate levels over the southwestern United States, it is found sometimes at the surface particularly in the South Central States. When aloft it is cold and dry, but when brought down by general subsidence, it is heated adiabatically in descent and produces the warm, dry Chinook or Foehn winds flowing down mountain sides and long downward slopes. Flying conditions in superior air are excellent.

SURGE—A general change in barometric pressure apparently superposed upon cyclonic and normal diurnal changes.

SYNOPTIC CHART—Technical name for a weather map, inasmuch as it depicts a synopsis of meteorological conditions over a large area at a given moment.

SYNOPTIC METEOROLOGY—The branch of meteorology that deals with the analysis of meteorological observations made simultaneously at a number points in the atmosphere (at the ground or aloft) over the whole or a part of the earth, and the application of the analysis to weather forecasting and other problems. ("Synoptic" comes from two Greek words meaning "general view.")

THERMOGRAM—The continuous record of temperature made by a thermograph.

THERMOGRAPH—An instrument used to make a continuous record of temperature.

THERMOMETER—An instrument used to measure temperature.

THUNDER—The sound following a discharge of lightning.

THUNDERSTORM—A storm attended by thunder and lightening. Thunderstorms are local disturbances, often occurring as episodes of cyclones, and, in common with squalls, are marked by abrupt variations in pressure, temperature, and wind.

TOPOGRAPHY—Descriptive features of any given portion of the earth's surface.

TORNADO—An extremely violent, rapidly whirling storm of great intensity, small diameter and steep pressure gradients. It is easily recognized by its dark funnel-shaped cloud. The most violent of all storms, it is highly destructive but fortunately short-lived.

TRADE WINDS—Steady seasonal winds which blow from the subtropical anticyclone belts toward the belt of lower pressure in the equatorial regions. They blow from the northeast in the northern hemisphere and from the southeast in the southern hemisphere.

TRAJECTORY—The path traced out by a small volume of air in its movement over the earth's surface.

TRANSITION ZONE—The relatively narrow region occupied by a front wherein the meteorological properties exhibit large variations over a short distance and possess values intermediate between those characteristic of the air masses on either side of the zone.

TRIPLE INDICATOR—In weather map analysis, a "discontinuity" or marked change in *temperature, dew point and wind direction* across a relatively narrow area on a synoptic chart constitutes a "triple indicator" of the existence of a frontal zone in that area. A change of two of the three items may or may not indicate a frontal zone, but a simultaneous change in all three is an almost positive indication. Similarly, when such a change occurs in a short period of time on the instruments at a weather station, it is an almost sure indication that a front has just passed the station.

TROPICAL AIR—Air of an air mass whose source lies in the equatorial belt or the subtropical eminences.

TROPICAL CYCLONE—Violent, whirling storms of destructive intensity originating in the tropics as small, concentrated and deep depressions. (See Figs. 7–11 and 7–12.)

TROPICAL DISTURANCE—The name used by the Weather Bureau for a cyclone wind system of the tropics that is not known to have sufficient force to justify the use of the words "storm" or "hurricane."

TROPICAL MARITIME AIR—The term used to describe any air mass that originates over an ocean area in the tropics. Tropical maritime air is characterized by high surface temperatures and high specific humidity.

TROPOPAUSE—The boundary between the troposphere and the stratosphere.

TROPOSPHERE—All the earth's atmosphere lying below the tropopause and the surface. All "weather" occurs in the troposphere, with its variable winds, currents, clouds, storms and other phenomena, whereas stratosphere conditions are clear, cloudless, steady and stable.

TROUGH—An elongated area of low pressure extending from a depression.

TURBULENCE—Irregular motion of the atmosphere produced when air flows over a comparatively uneven surface, such as the surface of the earth, or when two currents of air flow past or over each other in different direction or at different speeds. The existence of turbulence in the atmosphere is made apparent by the character of the trail of smoke from a ship's funnel and by gusts and lulls in the wind.

TWILIGHT—Astronomical twilight is the interval between sunrise or sunset and the total darkness of night. Civil twilight is the period of time before sunrise and after sunset during which there is enough daylight for ordinary outdoor occupations.

TYPHOON—A tropical cyclone common to the China Sea and caused almost entirely by convection.

U–SHAPED DEPRESSION—A trough with U-shaped isobars, in which fronts rarely form.

VANE—A device that shows which way the wind blows; also called weather vane or wind vane.

VAPOR PRESSURE—The partial pressure of the water vapor contained in the atmosphere.

V-SHAPED DEPRESSION—A trough with V-shaped isobars, in which fronts frequently exist or form.

VEERING—The reverse of *backing*. (See p. 141.) A shift to the right (i.e., clockwise) in wind direction.

VERNIER—An auxiliary scale for estimating fractions of a scale division when the reading to the nearest whole division on the main scale is not sufficiently accurate.

VISIBILITY—The horizontal transparency of the atmosphere at the surface:—The greatest distance at which an object can be recognized *as such* by the average unaided eye.

WARM AIR MASS—An air mass that is warmer than the surface over which it is moving.

WARM FRONT—A frontal surface (or zone) between two air masses wherein air of a lower temperature is being displaced by air of a higher temperature.

WARM SECTOR—That area in a depression in which relatively warm air is flowing toward the "center" of the disturbance. This warm air (usually of tropical origin) supplies the energy upon which the depression "feeds." When the supply of warm air is cut off, by the cold front overtaking the warm front and forming an occlusion, the depression "dies."

WATERSPOUT—A disturbance at sea very similar to a tornado over the land, but usually less violent.

WAVE—An undulation along the boundary between a cold and a warm air mass which usually results in the formation of a depression with a warm and a cold front, i.e., if the wave is of an *unstable* nature.

WEDGE—An elongated area of high pressure extending from an eminence. (See, also, RIDGE, and Fig. 7–1.)

WET BULB—(See PSYCHROMETER.)

WIND—Air in approximately horizontal motion. Streams of air moving vertically are called "air currents."

WIND ROSE—(1) A diagram showing the relative frequency and sometimes also the average strength of the wind blowing from different directions in a specified region. (2) A diagram showing the average relation between winds from different directions and the occurrence of other meteorological phenomena.

ZONDA—A chinook-type wind of Argentina.

COLLOQUIAL TERMS

BAGUIO—The name current in the Philippines for a tropical cyclone.

BORA—A cold wind of the northern Adriatic, blowing down from the high plateaus to the northward. Also, a similar wind on the northeastern coast of the Black Sea.

BRAVE WEST WINDS—The boisterous westerly winds blowing over the ocean between latitudes 40° and 50° S. This region is known as the "Roaring Forties."

BULL'S-EYE—(1) A patch of clear sky at the center of a cyclonic storm; the "eye of the storm." (2) A small, isolated cloud seen at the beginning of a bull's-eye squall, marking the top of the otherwise invisible vortex at the storm.

BULL'S-EYE SQUALL—A squall forming in fair weather, characteristic of the ocean off the coast of South Africa; so called on account of the peculiar appearance of a small isolated cloud that marks the top of the invisible vortex of the storm.

CALLINA—A Spanish name for dry fog.

CAT'S PAW—A slight and local breeze which shows itself by rippling the surface of the sea.

CHUBASCO—A violent squall on the west coast of tropical and subtropical North America.

CORDONAZO; in full, CORDONAZO DE SAN FRANCISCO ("last of St. Francis")—A hurricane wind blowing from a southerly quadrant on the west coast of Mexico as the result of the passing of a tropical cyclone off the coast.

DEVIL—The name applied to a dust whirlwind in India. The term is also current in South Africa.

INDIAN SUMMER—The period of mild, calm, hazy weather occurring in autumn or early winter, especially in the United States and Canada; popularly regarded as a definite event in the calendar, but weather of this type is really of irregular and intermittent occurrence.

MACKEREL SKY—An area of sky covered with cirrocumulus clouds; especially when the clouds resemble the pattern seen on the backs of mackerel.

MARE'S TAILS—CIRRUS in long slender streaks.

MISTRAL—Along the Mediterranean coast from the mouth of the Ebro to the Gulf of Genoa, a stormy cold northerly wind, blowing down from the mountains of the interior. (The name is sometimes applied to northerly winds on the Adriatic, in Greece and in Algeria.)

MOUNTAIN AND VALLEY BREEZES—The breezes that in mountainous regions normally blow up the slopes by day (valley breezes) and down the slopes by night.

NORTHER—A northerly wind, especially strong northerly winds of sudden onset, occurring during the colder half of the year over the region from Texas southward, including the Gulf of Mexico.

ROARING FORTIES—(See BRAVE WEST WINDS.)

SCUD—Shreds of small detached masses of cloud moving rapidly below a solid deck of higher clouds. Scud may be composed of either fractocumulus or fractostratus clouds.

SUN DOG—A mock sun or parhelion.

"SUN DRAWING WATER"—The sun is popularly said to be "drawing water" when crepuscular rays extend down from it toward the horizon. The sun's rays, passing through interstices in the cloud, are made visible through illumination of particles of dust in the atmosphere along their paths.

TABLECLOTH—A sheet of cloud that sometimes spreads over the flat top of Table Mountain, near Cape Town.

TEHUANTEPECER—A strong to violent northerly wind over Pacific waters off southern Mexico and northern Central America, confined mostly to the Gulf of Tehuantepec, and occurring during the colder months.

WOOLPACK—Cumulus.

APPENDICES

WB FORM 631-1
(Formerly 4061)
Eff. 6-1-51

UNITED STATES DEPARTMENT OF COMMERCE
WEATHER BUREAU

EXPLANATION OF TELETYPE SYMBOL WEATHER REPORTS

(BASED ON INSTRUCTIONS IN WEATHER BUREAU CIRCULAR N)

EXAMPLE OF A RECORD-SPECIAL OBSERVATION AS IT APPEARS IN A SEQUENCE COLLECTION OF REPORTS. ELEMENTS OF THE OBSERVATION ARE EXPLAINED BELOW.

PIT S7 3⊕M7V⊕25⊕11/2VL-FK 146/66/65→3/997/CIG 6V8 VSBY 1V2/ 808 6//6

Column labels (left to right): STATION IDENTIFICATION — TYPE OF REPORT — CEILING AND SKY — VISIBILITY — WEATHER — OBSTRUCTIONS TO VISION — SEA-LEVEL PRESSURE — TEMPERATURE — DEW POINT — WIND — ALTIMETER SETTING — REMARKS — ADDITIVE DATA

PIT — STATION IDENTIFICATION: Symbol for Pittsburgh.

S7 — TYPE OF REPORT: Special identified by letter "S". The "7" indicates the seventh special of the day. An out-of-sequence special report has a time group (24-hour clock, LST) following this designator, e.g., 0715E.

Record observations would appear on the sequence collection without the S7.

Local extra reports are indicated by "LCL" and a time group. (Local extras are transmitted on local teletype circuits only.)

3⊕M7V⊕25⊕ — CEILING AND SKY: Scattered 300 feet; ceiling measured 700 feet variable, broken; 2500 feet overcast. Heights are expressed in hundreds of feet, (e.g., 40 = 4000 feet), and are prefixed to the corresponding sky-condition symbol. The letter "V" immediately following a numerical value indicates that the ceiling is variable by an amount reported in "Remarks."

FK — OBSTRUCTIONS TO VISION: Fog and smoke. The following symbols indicate obstructions to vision in aviation reports:

BD	Blowing Dust	GF	Ground Fog
BN	Blowing Sand	H	Haze
BS	Blowing Snow	IF	Ice Fog
D	Dust	K	Smoke
F	Fog		

146 — SEA-LEVEL PRESSURE: 1014.6 millibars. Three figures, representing tens, units, and tenths of millibars, indicate the sea-level pressure.

66 — TEMPERATURE: 66°F. A minus(-) preceding the figures indicates a temperature below zero.

65 — DEW POINT: 65°F. A minus(-) preceding the figures indicates a dew point below zero.

A ceiling classification designator is prefixed to the ceiling layer only. Absence of a designator indicates an unlimited ceiling. Ceiling classification designators are:

A	aircraft	E	estimated	P	precipitation
B	balloon	M	measured	W	indefinite
●			

Sky condition symbols are:

X - Sky completely hidden by precipitation or obstructions to vision.
O - Clear - less than 0.1 sky cover.
⊖ - Scattered - 0.1 to less than 0.6 sky cover.
⊕ - Broken - 0.6 to 0.9 sky cover.
⊕ - Overcast - more than 0.9 sky cover.

Dark and thin layers are represented by the symbols plus(+) and minus(-), respectively, preceding the sky condition symbol to which they apply. A partial obscuration is represented by the minus(-) symbol preceding the "X."

In a combination of symbols, the phenomena coded in this portion of the report are reported in ascending order of height with respect to their distribution in space.

11/2V VISIBILITY: One and one-half miles variable. Prevailing visibility is reported in miles or fractions of miles. The letter "V" immediately following a visibility value indicates visibility is variable in an amount reported in "Remarks."

L- WEATHER: Light drizzle. Weather symbols are:

TORNADO. Not abbreviated. It is followed by a letter abbreviation showing the direction from the station.

T	Thunderstorm	R	Rain
T+	Heavy thunderstorm	RW	Rain showers
A	Hail	S	Snow
AP	Small hail	SG	Snow grains
E	Sleet	SP	Snow pellets
EW	Sleet showers	SW	Snow showers
IC	Ice crystals	ZL	Freezing drizzle
L	Drizzle	ZR	Freezing rain

A plus(+) following the symbols for precipitation indicates "heavy" intensity; a minus(-), "light"; a double minus(--), "very light"; the absence of a sign, "moderate" intensity.

→3 WIND: From the west, three miles per hour. Wind direction is indicated by arrows as follows:

N		S
NNE		SSW
NE		SW
ENE		WSW
E		W
ESE		WNW
SE		NW
SSE		NNW

Figures following the direction arrows indicate the speed in miles per hour. "C" indicates "calm"; the arrow and figures are omitted.

A plus(+) following the wind speed indicates gusts; the absence of a sign, a relatively steady wind. The peak speed of gusts follows the plus (+) symbol.

An arrow immediately following the current wind data indicates that the wind has shifted from the direction indicated by the arrow at the time indicated by a four-figure time group following the arrow. The time zone of the reporting station is shown by means of a letter. E.g., ↖1025E indicates a wind shift from the southeast at 1025 EST.

997 ALTIMETER SETTING: 29.97 inches. Three figures, representing units, tenths, and hundredths of inches, indicate the altimeter setting.

CIG 6V8
VSBY 1V2 REMARKS: Ceiling variable six to eight hundred, visibility variable one to two miles. Teletype symbols, contractions, or complete words are used to report significant meteorological phenomena that are not reportable elsewhere.

808 6//6 ADDITIVE DATA: Coded values relating to pressure and clouds. Precipitation data may also be included.

NON-METEOROLOGICAL DATA: Remarks concerning field conditions and the operation of radio facilities occasionally follow meteorological data.

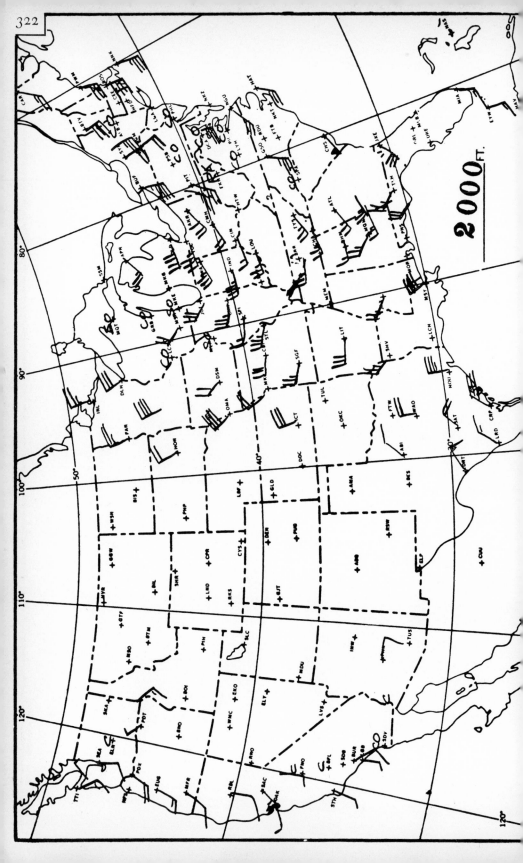

2000 FT.

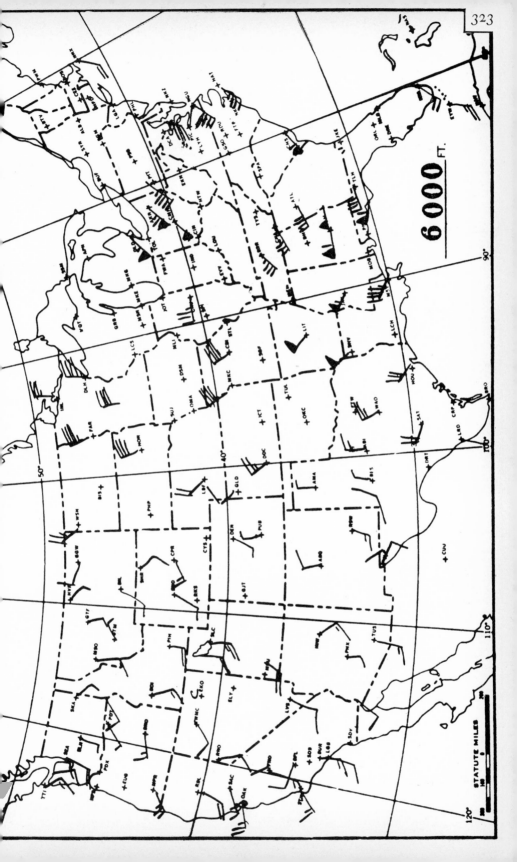

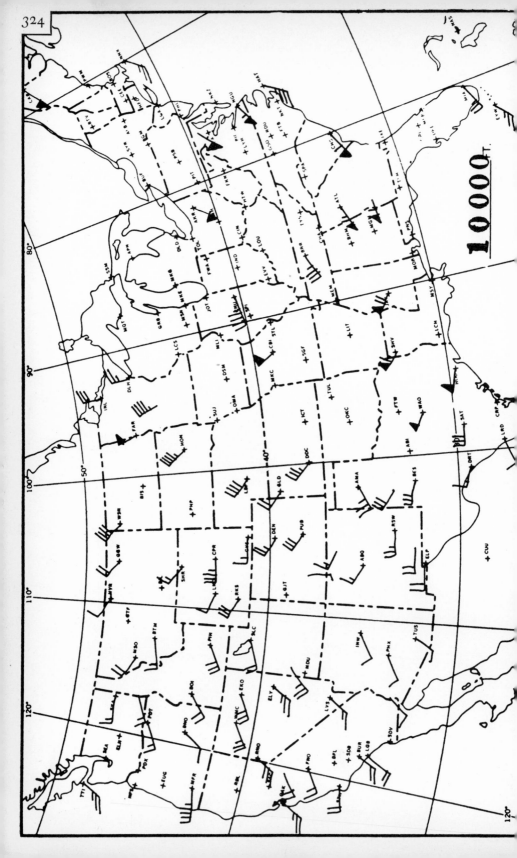

10000 T.

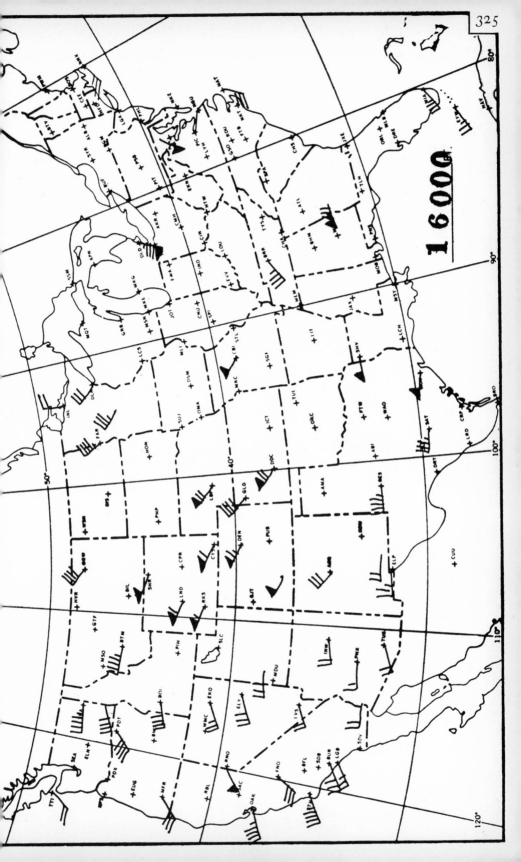

16000 FT.

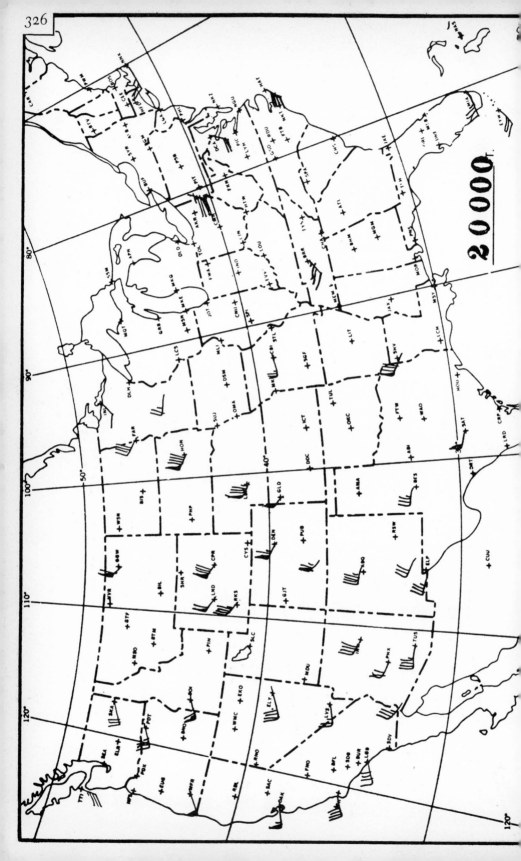

20000

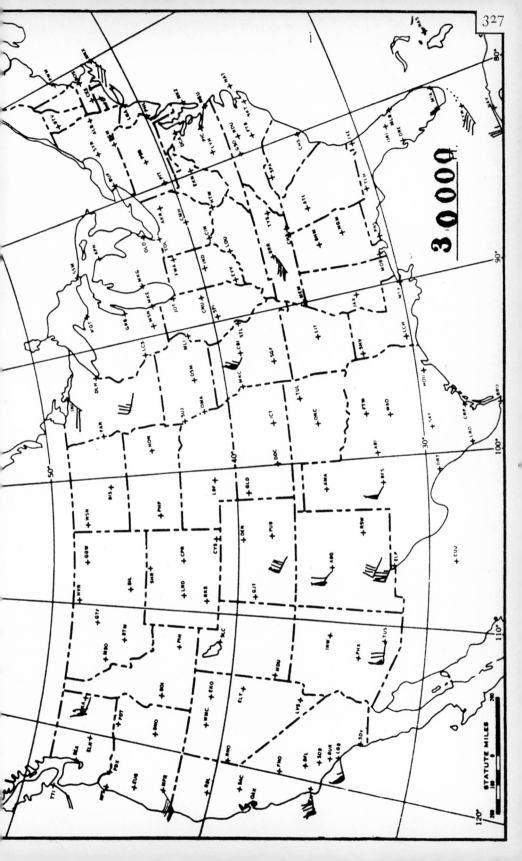

30,000 ft.

STATUTE MILES

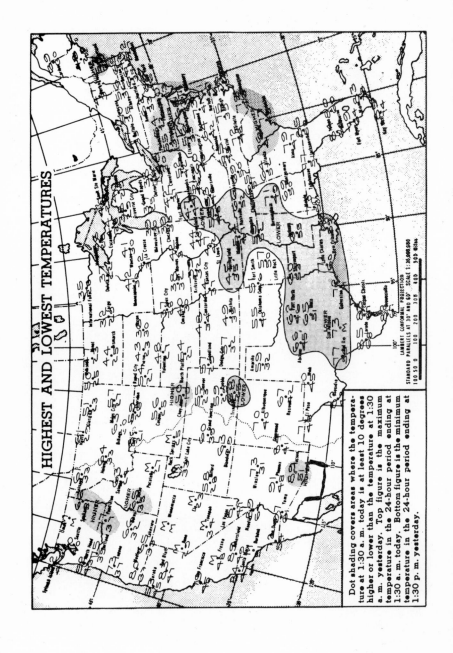

HIGHEST AND LOWEST TEMPERATURES

Dot shading covers areas where the temperature at 1:30 a. m. today is at least 10 degrees higher or lower than the temperature at 1:30 a. m. yesterday. Top figure is the maximum temperature in the 24-hour period ending at 1:30 a. m. today. Bottom figure is the minimum temperature in the 24-hour period ending at 1:30 p. m. yesterday.

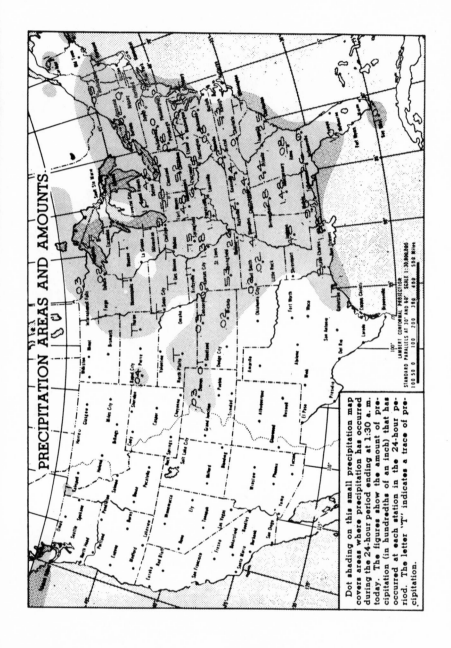

PRECIPITATION AREAS AND AMOUNTS

Dot shading on this small precipitation map covers areas where precipitation has occurred during the 24-hour period ending at 1:30 a. m. today. The figures show the amount of precipitation (in hundredths of an inch) that has occurred at each station in the 24-hour period. The letter "T" indicates a trace of precipitation.

329

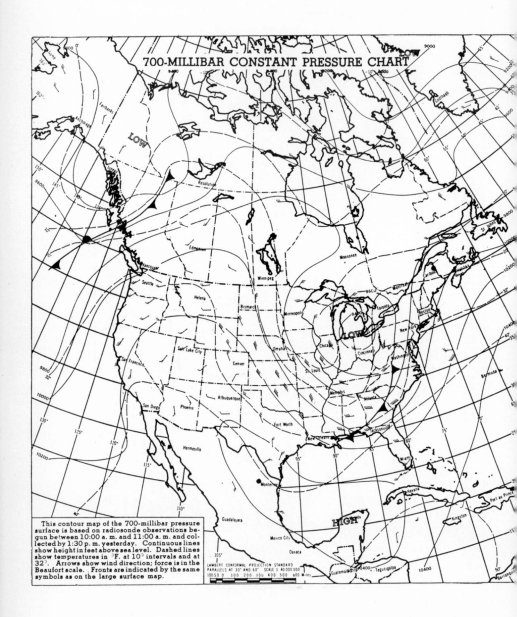

700-MILLIBAR CONSTANT PRESSURE CHART

This contour map of the 700-millibar pressure surface is based on radiosonde observations begun between 10:00 a. m. and 11:00 a. m. and collected by 1:30 p. m. yesterday. Continuous lines show height in feet above sea level. Dashed lines show temperatures in °F. at 10° intervals and at 32°. Arrows show wind direction; force is in the Beaufort scale. Fronts are indicated by the same symbols as on the large surface map.

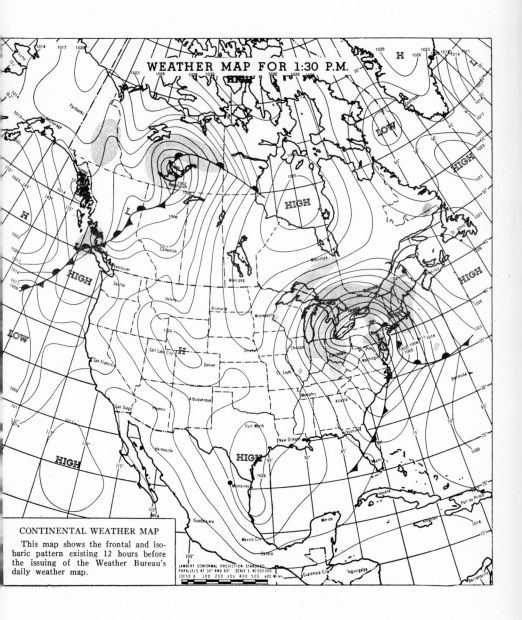

WEATHER MAP FOR 1:30 P.M.

CONTINENTAL WEATHER MAP

This map shows the frontal and isobaric pattern existing 12 hours before
the issuing of the Weather Bureau's
daily weather map.

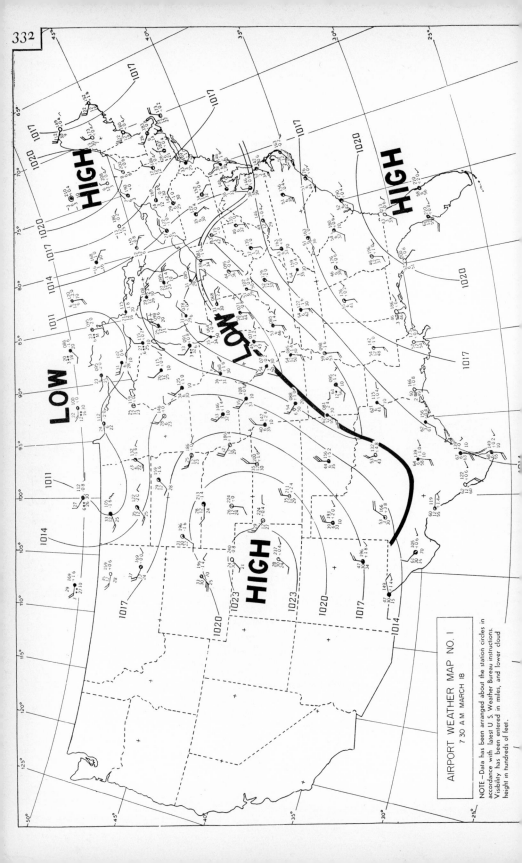

AIRPORT WEATHER MAP NO. 1

7 30 A M MARCH 18

NOTE – Data has been arranged about the station circles in accordance with latest U. S. Weather Bureau instructions. Visibility has been entered in miles, and lower cloud height in hundreds of feet.

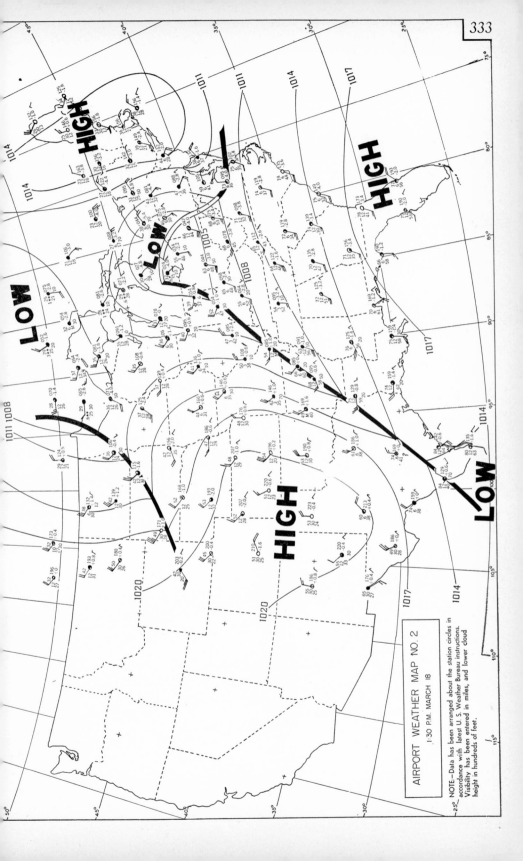

AIRPORT WEATHER MAP NO. 2

1:30 P.M. MARCH 18

NOTE.—Data has been arranged about the station circles in accordance with latest U. S. Weather Bureau instructions. Visibility has been entered in miles, and lower cloud height in hundreds of feet.

333

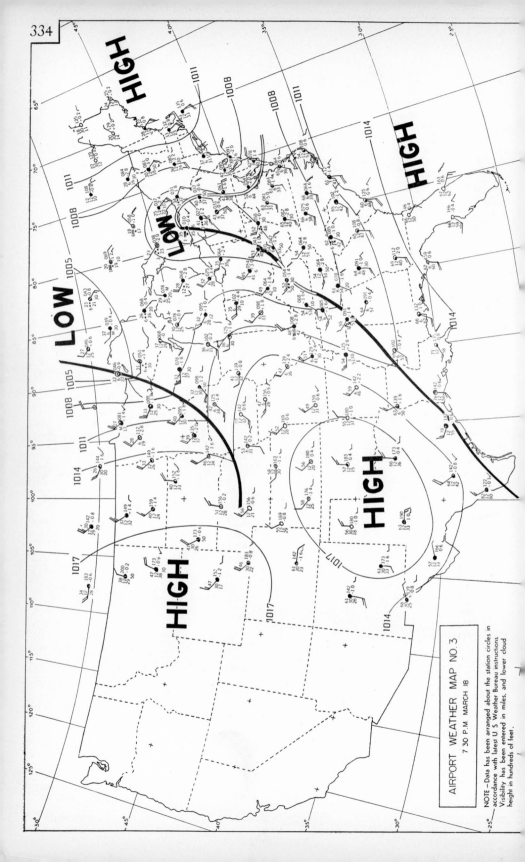

334

AIRPORT WEATHER MAP NO. 3

7 30 P.M. MARCH 18

NOTE – Data has been arranged about the station circles in
accordance with latest U S Weather Bureau instructions
Visibility has been entered in miles, and lower cloud
height in hundreds of feet.

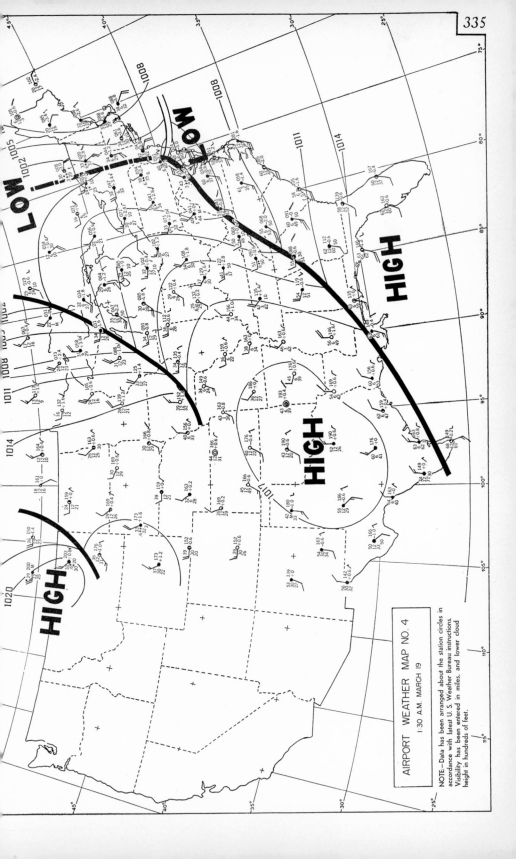

AIRPORT WEATHER MAP NO. 4

1:30 A.M. MARCH 19

NOTE—Data has been arranged about the station circles in accordance with latest U. S. Weather Bureau instructions. Visibility has been entered in miles, and lower cloud height in hundreds of feet.

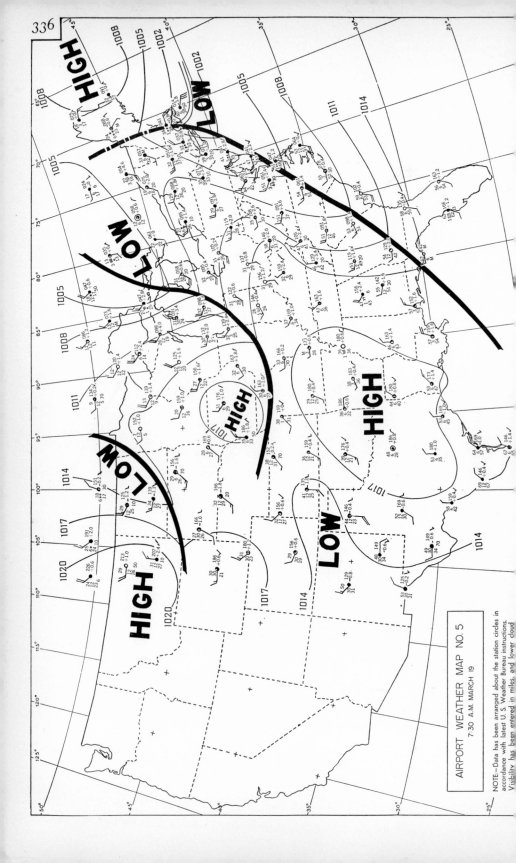

AIRPORT WEATHER MAP NO. 5

7:30 A.M. MARCH 19

NOTE.—Data has been arranged about the station circles in accordance with latest U. S. Weather Bureau instructions. Visibility has been entered in miles, and lower cloud

BEAUFORT SCALE

Beaufort number	M. P. H.	Knots	International description	Specifications
0	Less than 1	Less than 1	Calm	Calm; smoke rises vertically.
1	1–3	1–3	Light air	Direction of wind shown by smoke drift, but not by wind vanes.
2	4–7	4–6	Light breeze	Wind felt on face; leaves rustle; ordinary vane moved by wind.
3	8–12	7–10	Gentle breeze	Leaves and small twigs in constant motion; wind extends light flag.
4	13–18	11–16	Moderate breeze	Raises dust, loose paper; small branches are moved.
5	19–24	17–21	Fresh breeze	Small trees in leaf begin to sway; crested wavelets form on inland waters.
6	25–31	22–27	Strong breeze	Large branches in motion; whistling heard in telegraph wires; umbrellas used with difficulty.
7	32–38	28–33	Moderate gale	Whole trees in motion; inconvenience felt walking against wind.
8	39–46	34–40	Fresh gale	Breaks twigs off trees; generally impedes progress.
9	47–54	41–47	Strong gale	Slight structural damage occurs; (chimney pots, slates, removed).
10	55–63	48–55	Whole gale	Seldom experienced inland; trees uprooted; considerable structural damage occurs.
11	64–72	56–63	Storm	Very rarely experienced; accompanied by widespread damage.
12	73–82	64–71	Hurricane	
13	83–92	72–80		
14	93–103	81–89		
15	104–114	90–99		
16	115–125	100–108		
17	126–136	109–118		

INDEX

(For additional terms, see glossary, pp. 297–318.)

(Bold face numbers indicate pages on which illustrations appear.)

Absolute centigrade, 21
Absolute zero, 21
Adiabat, 77, 78, **78**
Adiabatic
  cooling, 69
  lapse rate, dry, 75
    moist (or saturated), 76
    pseudo, 76
Adiabatic process, 75
Advection fog, 67, 68, 69, 126
Aerologation (*see* Pressure-pattern
  flight)
Aerological soundings, 34, 36, 37
Aerometeorograph, 34–36, 37
Aeronautical Meteorology, 70
Air (*see also* Air currents, Air mass,
  and Atmosphere)
  characteristics, 4–6
  circulation, 96, 139, 164
    cyclonic theory of, 142
    general, **99**
  composition, 6–7
  density, **5**
  equatorial, 121
  free, 108
  heating, 90
  humidity, 11, 21, 34
  instability, 74
    conditional, 74
  maritime, 152
  mechanical lifting of, 69, 115, 138,
    147
  mixing, 70, 82, 94, 130
  mixing ratio, 22
  moist, 147
  pressure, 4
  saturated, 22

stable, 112
stability, **74**
  neutral, **74**
  surface, 96, 126
  temperature, 75, 85, 104
  upper air data, 153
  unsaturated, 22, 75, 76
  unstable, 86, 112, 127, 155
Air currents, 96 ff., 156
  ascending, 86, 112
  conventional, 82, 85, 86, **87**, 88, **89**
    90, 127
  cool, 58
  descending, 86
  "dust devil," 127
  effect on weather, 86
  importance of to glider pilots, 86
  uneven heating, 90
  vertical, 140, 147
  warm, 58, 62, 69
Aircraft flight analyzer, 14, **16**
Airfalls, 4
Air Force, 38
Air mass, 84, 118 ff., 228
  Arctic, 98, 121, 123, 124
  Atlantic, 124
  Bergeron, Classification, 121, 123
  boundaries of, 119, 135
  characteristics, 118, 122, 124
  classification of, 118
  cold, 122, 123, 124, 125
    properties of, 84, 124
  continental, 121, 123, 124
  development and effect, 118 ff.
  equatorial, 121
  fronts and disturbances, 120
  generation of, 118

Gulf, 124
itinerant, temperature changes in,
    84, 130
  equilibrium of, 85
latitude of source, 121
life history, 119
maritime, 121, 124
meeting of, effect, 135
Pacific, 121, 123, 124
physical properties, 119, 120, 121,
    122, 124
polar, 119, 121, 123, 152
rate of travel, 85, 119
Sahara, 122
source, 119, 122, 123
  region, 121, 123
  surface nature, 121, 123
subsidence, 128
superior, or high level, 122, 123,
    128, 153, 154
  source of, 128
surface layer, 122, 126
surface-temperature difference, 122
temperature changes in, 84
time en route, 119, 120
transitional, 122
traveling, 130
tropical, 121, 123, 124
warm, 126
  properties of, 127
Airway Code, 173
  elements, 173–187
    grouping of (table), 174
  sample messages, 187–188
Airway observations, 173
  classifications, 173
Airway reports
  altimeter setting, 183
    importance of, 185
  ceiling, 175
  dewpoint, 182
  gustiness, 183
  obstructions to vision, 181
  remarks, 179, 187
  sample reports, 187–188
  sea-level pressure, 181

sequence data in, 175
sky (sky cover), 176
  symbols, 177
temperature, 181
types, 174, 175
visibility, 180
weather, 180
wind, 182
  shifts, 183
Altimeter, 15, 18, 30, 271
  adjustment in flight, 134
  barometric scale, 134
  error in, 116, 159
  setting, National program (foot-
    note), 185
    importance of, 185
Altimetry, 270
Altitude, indicated, relation of isobars
    to, 134
Alto-cumulus (*see* Cloud types)
Alto-stratus (*see* Cloud types)
Anemograph, pitot static type, 25, 27
Anemometer, 25–29
  32-cup ("dines"), 28, 29
  triple-cup, 26
Anticyclone, 97, 160, 119, 121, 126,
    129, 135, 163 (*see also* Emi-
    nence)
  study of, 165
  subtropical, 97, 119, 121, 126, 129
Anvil, 47, 89
Aqueous vapor (*see* Water vapor)
Arctic smoke, 69
Arcus(*see* Cloud types cumulo-nim-
    bus)
Argon, 6
Atmosphere (*see also* Air)
  characteristic, 4
  composition of, 6
  defined, 17
  density, 5, 111
  diurnal changes, 79, 82
  energy of, 79, 130
  equilibrium, 74
  free, 112

instability, 74, 77
  conditional, 74
pressure, 96, 101, 104, 131, 132.
saturation, 75
stability, 74, 77
  neutral, 74
standard, 17, 18
stratification of, 75
structure, 7
temperature, 5, 6, **8**, 80
variation with altitude, 5, 6
Aurora, 10

Backing, 141
Balloon
  sounding, 30
  pilot, 34, **35**
Bar, defined, 17 (*see also* Millibar)
Barograph, 14
Barometer, 1, 97, 134
  aneroid, 14, **15**, 134
  mercurial, 12, 14, **15**
    vernier, 13
  wind-barometer indications, 222
Barometric pressure, 17, 116, 131,
  163
  tendency, 19, 202
  trough, 101
Beaufort scale, 29, **202, 337**
Bellamy, Prof. J. C., 271
  drift formula, 274
Bergeron, Table, 121, 123
Bjerknes, Prof. V., 142
Blocking effects, 224
Breeze(s) (*see* Winds)
Bumpiness, 62, 113 (*see also* Turbu-
  lence)
Buys-Ballot's law, 100, 163

Calm(s) (*see* Wind)
Carbon dioxide, 6
Cascade, 67
Ceiling, 11, 30, 171, 174, 175, 188
  classification, 176
  clinometer, 30

height of cloud base (*h*), 197
  Table, 199
Ceilometer, 30
Centigrade, 20
  absolute scale, 21
  absolute zero, 21
Charts (*see also* Weather maps)
  auxiliary, 215
  constant pressure, 190
  isobaric, 97
  synoptic, **193** ff.
  temperature, 215
  upper air, pilot, 116, 132
  wind roses, 116
Chinook (*see* Foehn winds)
Circulation of air, 96 ff., 139, 164
  cyclonic, theory of, 142
Cirro-cumulus (*see* Cloud types)
Cirro-stratus (*see* Cloud types)
Cirrus (*see* Cloud types)
Civil Aeronautics
  Administration, 169, 171
  Board, 171
Civil Air Regulations, 171
Climate, 34
Clinometer, 30
Cloud forms, 29, 43
  Manual of, 43
Cloudiness, 11, 29
Cloud(s), 11, 40, 41 ff., 229
  Arctic smoke, 69
  as aid in forecasting, 229
  Atlas of Clouds and of States of
    the Sky, International, 229
  causes of, 41
  development of, 59
    Manual of, 43
  forms, 29, 43
  halo, **48**, 49
  height of clouds, 40, 42
  high clouds, 42, 43
  Lenticular alto-cumulus, **53**, 54
  levels, 40, 42
  low clouds, 42, 55
  mackerel sky, **49**, 50
  mammato cumulus, 64, **65**

medium clouds, 42, 52
nuclei, 41, 91
parhelion, **48**, 49
rain cloud, 58 (*see also* nimbo-
    stratus)
scarf cloud, 64
scud, 58, **91** (*see also* fracto-
    stratus)
symbols, weather map, 198–199
tornado cloud, 65, **66**, 148
vertical development, clouds with,
    42, 59
waterspout, 66
Cloud types
alto-cumulus, **52**, 53, **54**, 56, 138,
    140
    castellatus, **52**, 54
    laminated, **54**
    lenticular, **53**, 54
alto-stratus, 43, 46, 50, **51**, 140,
    146
    "watery sky," 50
cirro-cumulus, **49**
cirro-stratus, 43, 46, **48**, 140
cirrus, 43, **44**, **45**, **46**, 47, 48, 49,
    140, 146
    band cirrus (cirrus vittatus), **45**,
        46
    false cirrus, same as scarf cloud
        and cirrus densus, 47, 64
    mare's tails, 45, 46
    windy, 46
cumulo-nimbus, 47, **61**, 62, 63, **65**,
    90, 91, 124, 138
    anvil, 47, 63, 64, 90
    cirrus densus, 64
    false cirrus, 47, 64
    ice crystals, 64
    rain, snow and hail, 64
    scarf cloud, 64
cumulo-nimbus arcus, "line squall,"
    65, 88, **143**
cumulo-nimbus mammatus (festoon
    cloud), 64, **65**
cumulus, **52**, 59, **60**, **61**, 62, 86, 124
    castellatus, **52**, 90

congestus ("cauliflower"), 62,
    88, 90
fracto-cumulus, **51**, 60
humilis, "fair weather," **59**, **60**,
    62, 88, 90
nimbo-stratus, **57**
    characteristics, 57
    rain cloud, 58
    scud, 58
    height, 58
strato-cumulus, **55**, 56
stratus, 58, **59**
    characteristics, 58
    indication of terrain below, 59
    fracto-stratus, **51**, 58
    scud, 58, **91**
    inversion accompanying, 59
    rain type produced, 58
    resulting from turblence, 230
Castellatus (*see* Cloud types, cumu-
    lus)
Col, "saddle back," gl., 135, 136, fig.
    7–2
Cold front, **152**, 155
    defined, 130
    "wind shift line," 156
Condensation, 23, 41, 47, 75, 122
    level, 61
        defined, 77
        temperature of, 77
Conduction, 90
Congestus (*see* Cloud types, cumulus)
Convection, 75, 85
    convectional currents, 60, 79, 82,
        106, 112
        effects of, 127
        on weather, 86
    precipitation from, 89, 90
Convectional precipitation (*see* Pre-
    cipitation)
Convergence, 70
Convergent fog (*see* Fog)
Coriolis force, 100, 104, 107, 108,
    110, 111, 132, 157
Ferrel's law, 107

Cumulo-nimbus (*see* Cloud types)
Cumulus (*see* Cloud types)
Currents, air (*see* Air currents)
Cyclone, 156, 158 (*see also* Depression)
  model, 139, fig. 7–3
  path of, 145
  tropical, 156, 159, 162
    characteristic track, Northern
      hemisphere, **160**
    characteristic track, Southern
      hemisphere, **162**
    development of, 157
    recurving, or inflection, 163
    semicircle, dangerous, 161
    semicircle, navigable, 162
    speed of travel along track, 163
  tropical vs. extratropical, compared,
    158
Cyclonic circulation, theory of, 142
Cyclostrophic wind, 274

Dangerous semicircle, 161
Density, **5,** 111
Depression, 43, 49, **131,** 135, 155, 163
  defined, 138
  development of, 120, 137, **148, 149**
  model, **139**
  occlusion, 137
  secondary, 241
  surface of discontinuity, 148
  traveling, 130, 135, 138
  trough, 155
  typical, 138, **139**
  U-shaped, 155
  unstable, 155
  V-shaped, 155
Devil, 127, 317
Dewpoint, 11, 23, 41, 61, 70, 97, 91,
    126, 182
  temperature, 77
Discontinuity, temperature, 130
Disturbances, 118 ff.
  anticyclone, 135
  col, 135
  depressions, 135

primary, 240
secondary, 240
traveling distrubances, 119, 135,
    138
tropical cyclones, 156–163, **160,**
    162
wave cyclone, or cyclone, or depression, 137
Diurnal variations, 93, 164, 235
  temperature, 93
Doldrums, 101–102
Drizzle, 58, 71, 151
  freezing, 71
Dust, 72, 94
Dust devil, or whirling dervish, 127
Dry bulb, **23,** 24

Earth's rotation (*see* Coriolis force)
Eddies, 112, **144**
  near obstacles, **113**
  stationary, 114
Eminence (High), **131,** 135, 163,
    164
  radiation weather in, 164
Equatorial belt, 97
Equivalent potential temperature (*see*
    Temperature)
Evaporation, 25, 75, 82
  temperature, 75
Eye of the storm, 160

Fahrenheit, scale of, 20
Fall wind, 128
False cirrus, 47, 64
Ferrel's Law, 107
Flight, planning, 3
Flight Analyzer, aircraft, 14, **16**
Flight rules, 171
Foehn wind, 128
Fog, 67, 116
  advection, 67, 68, 69, **126**
  Arctic smoke, 69
  convergent, 68, 70
  inversions, 94
  frontal, 68, 70
  land, 58, 94

mist (*see* Drizzle)
orographic lifting, 116
radiation (ground), 67, 68
sea, 68, 94
smog, 73
stratus, 67
study of, 67, 70
upslope, 67, 69
Force, deflecting, of the earth's rotation (*see* Coriolis Force)
Forecasts, airway, 142
Forecasting ice formation, 254
Fracto-stratus (*see* Cloud types)
Freezing process, 251
Freezing rain, 71, 256
Frequency tables, 34
Friction layer, 112
Front, 70, 129 ff., 136, 145, 150, 153, 195, 203, 206, 213, 228
Antarctic, 129
Arctic, 129
cold, 65, 147, gl.
defined, 129
delineating, 207
equatorial, 129
general source, 129
icing along, 259
indication on weather maps, 195, 203
movement of, 129
occluded, 137, 150, 213
polar, importance of, 129
polar maritime, 121, 123, 129
quasi-stationary, 130, 225
secondary cold, 241
triple indicator, 204, 207
upper, 152, 153
warm, 70
wind shifts, 156
Frontal fog, 68, 70
Frontal passage, 204
Frontal zones, 129, 255
Frontogenesis, 130, 136
defined, 130
Frontolysis, defined, 130

Frost, 248, 255, 262
Frost, smoke, 69

Gale, 98, 337
Garriott, Prof. E. B., 222
Gauge
rain, 33
snow, 33
Geostrophic wind, 111
relationship of cross wind component, 272
velocity, 112
Glaze, 248, 249, 257
Glider pilots, importance of currents to, 86
Gradient, pressure or barometric, 102, 105–109, 130, 132
altimetry, 273
decreasing, 109
equatorial, 104
force, 111
high, 99, 104
low, 99, 104
polar, 104
Gust, 91
resulting from turbulence, 112
Gustiness, 86, 182

Hail, 64, 71, 91, 92, 144
cloud (boiling), 92
soft, 71
Hair hygrometer, 24, 25, 36
Halo, 48, 49
Haze, 71, 72
Helium, 6
High, (*see also* Eminence), 132
defined, 131
movement of, 133
Horse latitudes, 102
Humidity, 11, 21, 34, 36, 38, 148
absolute, 23
low, 127, 128
relative, defined, 22, 25, 128, 145

specific, defined, 22, 25, 118, 124
vapor capacity, 21
Hurricane, 65, 156, 157 (*see also* Cyclone, tropical)
Humilis (*see* Cloud types, cumulus)
Hydrogen, 6
Hydrometeors, 71
Hygrograph, 24
Hygrometer (hair), 24, 25, 36
Hygrothermograph, 24

Ice crystals, 43, 89
  as nuclei, 42, 89
Ice formation on aircraft, 93, 234, 245 ff.
  along fronts, 258
  carburetor icing, 246
  cause of, 245
  contact flight, 256
  effects on aircraft, 260
  escape by climbing, 257
  factors causing hazard, 245
  factors in forecasting, 254
  freezing process, 251
  frost, 248
  glaze, 248, 249, 257, 258
  in cumuli-form clouds, 257
  instrument flight, 256
  over mountains, 259
  physics of icing, 247
  pilots' comments, 266
  precepts in avoiding, 256
  rate of accretion, 249
  rime, 248, 257, 258, gl.
  safety summary, 263
  synoptic considerations, 252
  windshields, 246
  zones, 255
Inflection (*see* Cyclone tropical)
Information of weather conditions, importance, 2
Insolation, 20,
Instability, 77, 78, 253
  conditional, 78
  totally unstable, 78
  wave, 137

Instrument Flight Rules, 171
  aircraft clearance, 172
International Atlas of Clouds and of the States of the Sky, 229
International Civil Aviation Organization (ICAO), 193
International Commission of Air Navigation, 34
International Meteorological Organization, 12, 17, 31, 32, 169, 193
International weather code, 194, 196, 197
Intertropical front (*see* Front)
Inversions (temperature), 59, 80, 93, 127
  accompanying stratus, 59
  effect on winds, 94
  importance to aviators, 94
  inversions and fogs, 94
  lid, 93
Ionosphere, 7, 9
  auroras in, 10
  reflects radio waves, 10
Isallobars, 133, 145, 206, 213
  defined, 133
  field of, 133
Isobars, 97, 109, 112, 131–132, 139, 158, 163, 164, 206
  defined, 131
  general rules, 208, 210
  geostrophic wind velocity, relation to, 112
  hills of air, 131, 132
  indicated altitude, relation to, 134
  tracing of, 208
  U-shaped, 155
  V-shaped, 155
  valley of air, 131
  wind direction, relation to, 132
Isobaric charts, 97
Isotherms, 133
Itinerant air masses, 84, 130

Knot, 27, 202, 337
Kraght, P. E., 118
Krypton, 6

Land breeze, 106
Lapse rate
  dry adiabatic, 75
  moist or saturated adiabatic, 76
  pseudo-adiabatic, 76
  temperature, 75, 76
Latitudes, horse, 102
Lenticular clouds, **53**, 54
Level, condensation, 61, 77, **78**
Lid, 93
Lightning, 92
  cause of, 92
Low, 131, 132, 155, 163
  Arctic, 98, **99**
  defined, 131
  movement of, 133
  trough, 155

Mackerel sky, 50
Mammatocumulus, 64, **65**
Map, weather (*see* Weather maps)
Maps, winds aloft, 214, **322–327**
  constant pressure chart, **190**
  continental, 216, **331**
  distribution, 217
  facsimile, weather, 217
  precipitation, 216, **329**
  temperature, 215, **328**
  700-millibar, 216, **330**
Mass, air (*see* Air mass)
Mercurial barometer (*see* Barometer)
Meteorology, 1, 11
  applied, 1
  dynamic, 1
  elements of, 11
  principles, 3
  synoptic, 1
Meteorological elements, 11 ff.
Meteorological factors of safety, 3
Meteorological terms, interchangeable, 163
Meteorological tropics, 97
Meteorograph, 34
Microbarograph, 14, **16**

Millibar, 17, 98, 133, 164
  defined, 17
Minser, Edward J., 256
Mist, 71
Moisture, content of air (*see* Humidity)
Monsoon, 104–105
Mountains, effect of, 113, 114, 219,
  227, 231, 254, 258, **259**, 260

National Altimeters Setting Program, 185
Navigable semicircle, 162
Neon, 6
Neutral point (*see* Col)
Neutral stability, 74
Nimbo-stratus (*see* Cloud types)
Nuclei, 41, 91

Observations, proper use of, 33
Obstacles and turbulence, 113
Occluded front (*see* Occlusion)
Occlusion, 70, 150, **151**
  cold front type, 70, **151**
  warm front type, **151**
Orographic lifting, 115, 231 (*see also*
  Effects of mountains)

Parhelion, 48, 49
Petterssen, Sverre, 121
Pilot balloon, 34, **35**
Pilot charts of the upper air, 116, 132
Polar air, 121
Polar continental air, 123, **152**
Polar front, 129
Polar maritime, 121, 123
Potential temperature, 118
Precipitation, 11, 32, 116, 138, 141,
  144, 158 (*see also* Rain)
  areas, 232
  forecast, 232
  from convection, 89, 90
  from cumulo-nimbus, 89, 138
  from cumulus, 60, 90
  from nimbo-stratus, 58, 141
  from stratus, 58

line squall, 143
nuclei, 41
occlusion, 151
tropical cyclones, 158
Pressure, atmospheric, 11, 12, 34, 36, 38, 96, 98
area of high, 98, 101, 119, 134
area of low, 101, 134
Arctic low, 98
center, 133, 158, 206, 213
track of, 206, 214
code for, 196, 197, 181
corrections to, 13, 14
differences, 134
distribution, 135
eminence (high), 131
equatorial belt, 97, 101
gradient, 104, 221
measured by altimetry, 273
horse latitudes, 102
line of position, 279
low (depression), 131, 136
normal distribution, 97, 99
rate of travel, 226, 227
region of high, 96, 104, 106, 110, 131
region of low, 96, 104, 110
sea level, 14, 96, 181
seasonal variations, 96
subtropical belts, 101
vapor, 24
Pressure gradient, 102
Pressure-pattern flight, 269 ff.
altimetry, 270
Bellamy drift formula, 274
conventional methods compared with, 271
cross wind component, 272
gradient measured by altimetry, 273
least-time route, 270
pressure line of position, 279
summary, 292
upper air weather maps and use of altimetry, 271

Pressure systems, 223
Pressure tendency, 11, 19, 202, 222
Prevailing westerlies, 99, 100, 103
Process, adiabatic (*see* Adiabatic)
Propellers, icing of, 245, 246, 256, 261, 263
Pseudo-adiabatic process, 76
Psychometer
dry bulb, 23, 24
swivel sling, 23, 24
wet bulb, 23, 24
Pumping (*see* Barometer)

Quasi-stationary fronts, 130, 225

Radiation, 79, 81, 82, 94
fog, 68
heat waves, 79, 122
long waves, 79
short waves, 79, 82
solar, 80, 82, 106
Radiation fog, 67, 68
Radiation weather, 164
Radiometeorograph, or radiosonde, 34, 37, 38
advantage of, 38
Radiosonde, radiometeorograph, 37, 38
advantages, 38
observations, 38, 189, 190
Rain, 71, 116, 232 (*see also* Precipitation)
anticyclones, 164
freezing, 71
from alto-stratus, 140
from cumulo-nimbus, 64, 90
from cumulus, 60, 90
from stratus, 58
gauge, 33
primary, 91
secondary, 91
tropical cyclones, 157
velocity of falling drops, 91
Rain drops, diameter and velocity, 71
frozen, 72
Rain gauge, 33

Regions, source of air masses, 119, 120, 121, 122
Relative humidity, 25
  defined, 22
  in superior air, 128
Ridge of high pressure, 132, 135
Rime, ice, 248, 257, 258
Rockets, high altitude, 190
Rotation of the earth (*see* Coriolis force)

Saddle (*see* Col)
Safety summary, icing, 263
Salt particles, as nuclei, 42
Sandstorm, 72
Saturation, 75 (*see also* Dewpoint)
Scarf-cloud, 64
Scud, 58, **91**
Sea breeze, 106
Sea level, 14, 96, 181
Secondary front, 241
Secondary storm center, 240
Semicircle, navigable, 162
Shower (*see* Cumulus)
Sky (sky-cover), 29, 176 (*see also* Cloudiness)
Sleet, 71
Smog, 73
Smoke, 71, 72, 94
  articles, 42
Snow, 58, 71
  gauge, **33**
  granular, 71
Soft hail, 71
Sounding, aerological 34, 36, 37
  balloon, **35**
Source region (*see* Region)
Specific humidity (*see* Humidity)
Squall, 141, 183
Squall line, **139**, 142
Stability, 74, 77, **78**
  over land, **80**, 81
  over water, **83**, 84
  total, 77
Stagnation point, 252
Standard atmosphere, defined, 17, 18

Stationary front (*see* Quasi-stationary)
Steering line, **139**, 142
Storm, 156, 159, 160
  center, 142, 161
  cyclone, 156, 159, 160
  dust, 72
  eye of, 160
  hurricane, 156, 157
  line squall, 65, **143**, 145, 147, 155
  sand storm, 72
  speed of travel, 161
  squall line, **142**
  steering line, **142**
  storm collar, **91**
  storm track, 162
  traveling depression, 130
  thunderstorm, 90, 92
  typhoon, 156
Strato-cumulus (*see* Cloud types)
Stratosphere, 7, 8, 9
  cloudless, 9
  temperature, 9
  varies in altitude, 8
Stratus (*see* Cloud types)
Subsidence, 128
Superior air, 122, 123, 128, 154
Symbols, meteorological, weather map, 196, 203, 205
Symbols, weather report, 187, 188, 196–202
Synoptic chart, (*see also* Weather maps)
Synoptic meteorology, 1

Taylor, George F., 70
Teletype circuits, 169, 170, 175, 187
Teletype symbols reports, explanation of, 320, 321
Temperature, 11, 19, 34, 36, 38, 74, 75, 158
  absolute centigrade, 21
  absolute zero, 21
  atmospheric, decrease with altitude, **5**, 6
  chart, 215

centigrade, 20
discontinuity, 130
fahrenheit, 20
itinerant air masses, 84
lapse rate, 124
low, 124
potential, 118
seasonal, 105
solar radiation, 80, 106
surface layer, 122
variations and effects, 74, 105
Temperature changes, 96, 105, 148
diurnal, 79, 81, 93
diurnal variations, 84, 93
itinerant air masses, 84
over land, 80
over water, 82
Temperature height curve, 77, 78, 79, 80, 83, 86, 87, 88, 89
Theodolite, 35
Thermograph, 20, 24
Thermometer
bimetalic, 36
dry bulb, 24
insolation, 20
maximum and minimum, 20
mercury, 19, 20
radiation cooling, 20
wet bulb, 24
Thunder, cause of, 92
Thunderstorm, 62, 86, 90, 92, 147, 153
avoiding in flight, 92, 93, 147
cold front type, 147
frontal, 145
hail, 91, 92
lightning, 92
line squall, 147
mechanical, 116, 146, 148
orographic, 115
storm collar, 91
thermal type, 90, 92
thunder, 92
thunderheads, 91
tornado, 148
upper-front, 147

vertical currents, 86
warm front type, 146
Topography, 59
effect on forecasting, 226, 227
influence of, 226
Tornado, 65, 148, 153
Tornado cloud, 65, 66
characteristics of, 65, 148
Trade winds, 99, 101
Transition zone (*see* Frontal zone)
Traveling disturbances, 119, 135, 138
anticyclone (eminence), 163, 164
col, 135
depression, 138
tropical cyclone, 156, 163
Triple indicator, 204, 207
Tropical air, 121, 124
Tropical cyclone (*see* Cyclone, tropical)
Tropical maritime air, 121, 123, 152
Tropics, meteorological, 97
Tropopause, 8, 76
Troposphere, 7, 122
Trough, low, 132, 136, 155
U-shaped, 155
V-shaped, 155
Turbulence, 62, 86, 112
bumpiness, 62
formation of stratus, 230
mechanical, 112, 126
thermal, 112
Turkey buzzard, 86
Typhoon, 105

Upper air data, 128, 189
constant pressure charts, 190
high altitude rockets, 190
radiosonde observations, 189–190
Upslope fog (*see* Fog)
U-shaped depression or trough, 155
U. S. Navy, 17, 38
U. S. Navy, Aviation Ground School Manual, 3
U. S. Navy Hydrographic Office, 116
U. S. Weather Bureau, 17, 170, 193

Vane, wind, 26, 27
Vapor pressure, 24
Veering, 141
Vernier, 13
Velocity, Beaufort scale of wind force,
    29, **202**, **337**
    of falling raindrops, 91
    wind, 9, 25, 111, 160
Visibility, 11, 31, 172, 180
    defined, 31
    recorded in U. S., 32
    table, 31
    within control areas, 172
    within control zones, 172
Vision, obstructions to, 71, 181
    dust, 72
    haze, 71
    sandstorm, 72
    smog, 73
    smoke, 72
Visual Flight Rules, VFR, 171
V-shaped depression, or trough, 155

Warm air mass (*see* Air mass)
Warm front, 130, 138, 142, 145, **146**,
    156
    defined, 130
Warm sector, **139**
Water droplets, 247
    supercooled, 247, 248
Waterspout, 66
Water vapor, 6, 43, 79
    condensation, 23, 41
    partial pressure, 24
    vapor pressure, 24
Wave (*see* Radiation)
    heat, 79
Wave theory, 136, 148, 149
    equilibrium, 137
    instability, 137
    occlusion, 137
    wave cyclone, 137, 149
WBAN, 173, 217
Weather, 11, 30, 129
    analysis, 1
    convectional currents, effects of, 86

data, arrangement about station cir-
    cle, 194, 196
elements, 11, 195, 196, 197
maps (*see* Weather maps)
minima, under flight rules, 171
past (W), 197, 202
present (ww), 197, 200, 201
radiation, 164
Weather Bureau, 38, 173
Weather code, 194
    sample message and explanation,
    196, 197
Weather forecasts, 219 ff.
    actual weather map series, 236–
    244, **332–336**
    air masses and fronts, 228
    airway forecast centers, 220
    airway forecast, when released, 220
    blocking effects, 224
    clouds, 229
    diurnal variations, 235
    ice accumulation, 234
    local topography, 219
    precipitation areas, 232
    pressure centers, rate of movement,
    226
    pressure gradient, effect of, 221
    pressure systems, 223
    seasonal topographical influence,
    226
    wind-barometer indications, 222
Weather maps, 132, 193 ff., **332–336**
    air mass designators, 204, 205, 213
    barometric tendency, 202
    cloud symbols, 198, 199
    drawing of, 206
    fronts, 195, 103, 213
        delineating, 207
        triple indicator, 204, 207
    isallobars, 213
    occluded front, 213
    precipitation, 199, 205, 213
    preparation of, 194
    pressure centers, 213
        tracks of, 213
    series of, 236–244, **332–336**

sky coverage, 199
station model, 194, 196
table of symbols, 196–202
winds aloft, 214, **322–327**
wind velocity (Beaufort scale), 29, **202, 337**
Weather panel, **28**
Weather reports, 128, 169
  classification of, 173
  collection and dissemination of, 169, 170
  from aircraft, 12
  from ships at sea, 12
  sample, airway report, 187, 188
  symbols, 196–202
  teletype, symbols, explanation of, 320, 321
Weather station, 140, 141
Wedge, 132, 135
Wet bulb (*see* Psychrometer)
Wind, 96, 97 (*see also* Wind direction and velocity)
  aloft, 35
  at ground level, 150
  calm, 202, **337**
  calms of Cancer and Capricorn, 102
  cyclostrophic, 274
  deflection of, 100
  direction, 11, 25, 100, 159
  doldrums, 101
  effect of inversions, 94
  geostrophic, 111

  gustiness, 86, 182
  higher latitudes, 99
  horse latitudes, 99
  in airway reports, 82
  land breezes, 106
  monsoon, 104, 105
  prevailing and general circulation, **99**
  prevailing westerlies, 100, 103
  Roaring Forties, 103
  sea breezes, 106
  source of energy, 150
  trade winds, 99, 101
  vane, **26**
  veering, 141
  velocity, 9, 11, 25, 111
  velocity in tropical cyclones, 160
Wind barometer indications, 222
Wind direction and velocity, 25, 36, 148, 158, 182
  backing, 141
  circulation of, 138
  direction of, 159, **160**, 182, 183
  direction by compass, 142
  effect of inversions, 94
  path of cyclone, 142
  relative to isobars, 132
  shifts, 156
  surface, 132
"Wind roses," 116 (*see also* Charts)
Wind vane, 25, **26**
Winds aloft maps, 214, **322–327**
Wright, Wilbur, 1